Middle School 2-1
중간고사 완벽대비

KB084798

적중100
영어 기출 문제집

중2
천재 | 이재영

Best Collection

구성과 특징

교과서의 주요 학습 내용을 중심으로 학습 영역별 특성에 맞춰 단계별로 다양한 학습 기회를 제공하여
단원별 학습능력 평가는 물론 중간 및 기말고사 시험 등에 완벽하게 대비할 수 있도록 내용을 구성

Words & Expressions

Step1	Key Words 단원별 핵심 단어 설명 및 풀이 Key Expression 단원별 핵심 숙어 및 관용어 설명 Word Power 반대 또는 비슷한 뜻 단어 배우기 English Dictionary 영어로 배우는 영어 단어
Step2	실력평가 단원별 수시평가 대비 주관식, 객관식 문제풀이
Step3	서술형 대비 학업성취도 및 수행능력평가 대비 서술형 문제풀이

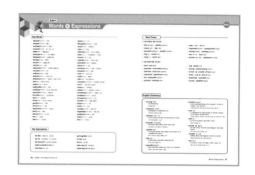

Conversation

Step1	핵심 의사소통 소통에 필요한 주요 표현 방법 요약 핵심 Check 기본적인 표현 방법 및 활용능력 확인
Step2	대화문 익히기 교과서 대화문 심층 분석 및 확인
Step3	교과서 확인학습 빈칸 채우기를 통한 문장 완성 능력 확인
Step4	기본평가 시험대비 기초 학습 능력 평가
Step5	실력평가 단원별 수시평가 대비 주관식, 객관식 문제풀이
Step6	서술형 대비 학업성취도 및 수행능력평가 대비 서술형 문제풀이

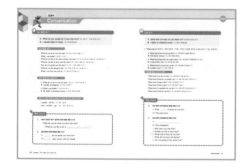

Grammar

Step1	주요 문법 단원별 주요 문법 사항과 예문을 알기 쉽게 설명 핵심 Check 기본 문법사항에 대한 이해 여부 확인
Step2	기본평가 시험대비 기초 학습 능력 평가
Step3	실력평가 단원별 수시평가 대비 주관식, 객관식 문제풀이
Step4	서술형 대비 학업성취도 및 수행능력평가 대비 서술형 문제풀이

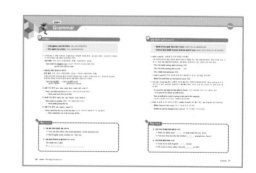

Reading

Step1	구문 분석 단원별로 제시된 문장에 대한 구문별 분석과 내용 설명 확인문제 문장에 대한 기본적인 이해와 인지능력 확인
Step2	확인학습A 빈칸 채우기를 통한 문장 완성 능력 확인
Step3	확인학습B 제시된 우리말을 영어로 완성하여 작문 능력 키우기
Step4	실력평가 단원별 수시평가 대비 주관식, 객관식 문제풀이
Step5	서술형 대비 학업성취도 및 수행능력평가 대비 서술형 문제풀이 교과서 구석구석 교과서에 나오는 기타 문장까지 완벽 학습

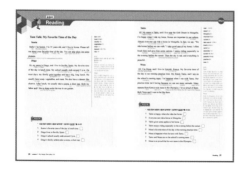

Composition

|영역별 핵심문제|

단어 및 어휘, 대화문, 문법, 독해 등 각 영역별 기출문제의 출제 유형을 분석하여 실전에 대비하고 연습할 수 있도록 문제를 배열

|단원별 예상문제|

기출문제를 분석한 후 새로운 시험 출제 경향을 더하여 새롭게 출제될 수 있는 문제를 포함하여 시험에 완벽하게 대비할 수 있도록 준비

|서술형 실전 및 창의사고력 문제|

학교 시험에서 점차 늘어나는 서술형 시험에 집중 대비하고 고득점을 취득하는데 만전을 기하기 위한 학습 코너

|단원별 모의고사|

영역별, 단계별 학습을 모두 마친 후 실전 연습을 위한 모의고사

교과서 파헤치기

- **단어Test1~3** 영어 단어 우리말 쓰기, 우리말을 영어 단어로 쓰기, 영영풀이에 해당하는 단어와 우리말 쓰기
- **대화문Test1~2** 대화문 빈칸 완성 및 전체 대화문 쓰기
- **본문Test1~5** 빈칸 완성, 우리말 쓰기, 문장 배열연습, 영어 작문하기 복습 등 단계별 반복 학습을 통해 교과서 지문에 대한 완벽한 습득
- **구석구석지문Test1~2** 지문 빈칸 완성 및 전문 영어로 쓰기

Contents

Off to a Good Start

🎤 의사소통 기능

- 의도나 계획 묻고 답하기

  A: What are you planning to do this weekend?

  B: I'm planning to see a movie.

- 충고하기

  A: I'm planning to go to the ballpark.

  B: Why don't you buy tickets first?

🎤 언어 형식

- 주격 관계대명사

  I want to have a friend **who** makes me happy.

- 접속사 if

  If it is sunny, I will go to the beach.

Words & Expressions

Key Words

- **achieve** [ətʃíːv] 동 달성하다, 성취하다
- **add** [æd] 동 추가하다
- **another** [ənʌ́ðər] 형 다른, 또 다른
- **app** [æp] 명 앱, 어플리케이션
- **beginning** [bigíniŋ] 명 초(반), 시작
- **behave** [bihéiv] 동 예의 바르게 행동하다
- **between** [bitwíːn] 전 ~ 사이에, ~ 중간에
- **birth** [bəːrθ] 명 탄생, 출생
- **bored** [bɔːrd] 형 지루한
- **carry** [kǽri] 동 들고 있다
- **change** [tʃeindʒ] 동 바꾸다, (옷을) 갈아입다
- **control** [kəntróul] 명 통제, 규제, 억제
- **death** [deθ] 명 죽음, 사망
- **dish** [diʃ] 명 요리
- **download** [dáunlòud] 동 다운로드하다, 내려받다
- **downtime** [dáuntàim] 명 한가한[휴식] 시간
- **easily** [íːzili] 부 쉽게
- **eco-friendly** [ékou-frɛndli] 형 친환경적인, 환경 친화적인
- **exercise** [éksərsàiz] 동 운동하다
- **even** [íːvən] 부 (비교급을 강조하여) 훨씬, 한층
- **free** [friː] 형 무료의, 자유로운
- **full** [ful] 형 배부른
- **goal** [goul] 명 목표
- **grade** [greid] 명 성적
- **habit** [hǽbit] 명 습관
- **hard** [hɑːrd] 형 어려운 부 열심히
- **heavy** [hévi] 형 무거운
- **historical** [histɔ́ːrikəl] 형 역사적인, 역사상의

- **however** [hauévər] 부 하지만, 그러나
- **hundred** [hʌ́ndrəd] 명 백, 100
- **late** [leit] 형 늦은
- **less** [les] 형 더 적은, 덜한 부 더 적게
- **light** [lait] 형 가벼운
- **list** [list] 명 목록, 명단
- **magazine** [mǽgəzìːn] 명 잡지
- **manage** [mǽnidʒ] 동 관리하다
- **messy** [mési] 형 지저분한
- **national** [nǽʃənl] 형 전국적인
- **pepper** [pépər] 명 고추, 후추
- **perfect** [pə́ːrfikt] 형 완벽한, 완전한
- **plant** [plænt] 동 심다 명 식물
- **popular** [pápjulər] 형 인기 있는
- **reader** [ríːdər] 명 독자
- **relax** [rilǽks] 동 휴식을 취하다
- **skill** [skil] 명 기술
- **someone** [sʌ́mwʌn] 대 어떤 사람, 누구
- **still** [stil] 부 여전히, 아직도
- **strange** [streindʒ] 형 이상한
- **stressful** [strésfəl] 형 스트레스가 많은
- **stuff** [stʌf] 명 물건
- **text** [tekst] 동 문자 메시지를 보내다
- **underpants** [ʌ́ndərpænts] 명 팬티
- **useful** [júːsfəl] 형 유용한
- **waste** [weist] 명 낭비 동 낭비하다
- **webtoon** [wébtuːn] 명 웹툰
- **weekly** [wíːkli] 형 매주의, 주간의

Key Expressions

- **because of** ~ 때문에
- **care for** ~를 돌보다, ~를 좋아하다
- **clean up** ~를 치우다[청소하다]
- **drive ~ crazy** ~을 미치게 하다
- **each other** 서로
- **focus on** ~에 집중하다, ~에 주력하다
- **for a minute** 잠깐, 잠시 동안
- **for an hour** 한 시간 동안
- **from now on** 이제부터, 지금부터는
- **get off to a start** 시작하다, 출발을 하다
- **get some rest** 약간의 휴식을 취하다
- **how to**+동사원형 ~하는 방법

- **in front of** ~의 앞쪽에[앞에]
- **jump rope** 줄넘기하다
- **keep one's room clean** 방을 깨끗이 하다
- **look down** 우울해 보이다
- **middle school** 중학교
- **once in a while** 가끔
- **on Wednesdays** 수요일마다
- **stand in line** 일렬로 서다
- **Pretty good.** 아주 좋아.
- **Same here.** 나도 그래.
- **So so.** 그저 그래.

Word Power

※ 명사에 -ful을 붙여 형용사가 되는 단어

- [ ] **use** (유용) → **useful** (유용한)
- [ ] **hope** (희망) → **hopeful** (희망적인)
- [ ] **color** (색깔) → **colorful** (다채로운)
- [ ] **thought** (생각) → **thoughtful** (사려 깊은)
- [ ] **help** (도움) → **helpful** (도움이 되는)

- [ ] **stress** (스트레스) → **stressful** (스트레스가 많은)
- [ ] **power** (힘) → **powerful** (힘센)
- [ ] **beauty** (아름다움) → **beautiful** (아름다운)
- [ ] **joy** (기쁨) → **joyful** (즐거운)
- [ ] **wonder** (놀라움) → **wonderful** (놀라운)

English Dictionary

- [ ] **achieve** 달성하다, 성취하다
  → to get or reach something by working hard
  열심히 일해 뭔가를 얻거나 이루다

- [ ] **beginning** 초(반), 시작
  → the time when something starts; the first part of an event, a story, etc.
  어떤 일이 시작되는 시간; 사건, 이야기 등의 첫 부분

- [ ] **behave** 예의 바르게 행동하다
  → to act in the way that people think is correct and proper
  사람들이 옳고 적절하다고 생각하는 방식으로 행동하다

- [ ] **death** 죽음, 사망
  → the end of the life of a person or animal
  사람이나 동물의 생애의 끝

- [ ] **downtime** 한가한[휴식] 시간
  → the time when someone stops working and is able to relax
  누군가 일을 멈추고 쉴 수 있는 시간

- [ ] **eco-friendly** 환경 친화적인
  → not harmful to the environment
  환경에 해가 되지 않는

- [ ] **goal** 목표
  → something that you are trying to do or achieve
  하려고 하거나 달성하려는 것

- [ ] **habit** 습관
  → something that a person does often in a regular and repeated way
  사람이 규칙적으로 또는 반복적으로 자주 하는 행동

- [ ] **messy** 지저분한
  → dirty and not neat
  더럽고 깨끗하지 않은

- [ ] **plant** 식물
  → a living thing that grows in the earth and has a stem, leaves and roots
  땅에서 자라며 줄기, 잎 그리고 뿌리를 가지고 있는 살아 있는 것

- [ ] **popular** 인기 있는
  → liked or enjoyed by many people
  많은 사람이 좋아하거나 즐기는

- [ ] **relax** 휴식을 취하다
  → to spend time resting or doing something enjoyable especially after work
  특히 일을 하고 난 후 쉬면서 시간을 보내다

- [ ] **strange** 이상한
  → different from what is usual, normal, or expected
  일반적인, 정상적인 또는 예상한 것과 다른

- [ ] **text** 문자 메시지를 보내다
  → to send someone a text message
  어떤 사람에게 문자 메시지를 보내다

- [ ] **useful** 유용한
  → helping to do or achieve something
  어떤 것을 수행하거나 달성하는 데 도움이 되는

- [ ] **waste** 낭비하다
  → to use more of something than is necessary or useful
  필요하거나 유용한 것보다 더 많은 것을 사용하다

01 다음 중 짝지어진 단어의 관계가 <u>다른</u> 것은?

① end – beginning
② heavy – light
③ full – hungry
④ popular – well-liked
⑤ easy – difficult

서답형

02 다음 우리말에 맞도록 빈칸에 알맞은 말을 쓰시오.

어떻게 하면 우리는 좋은 출발을 할 수 있을까?
➡ How can we _____ _____ to a good start?

[03~04] 다음 영영풀이에 해당하는 단어를 고르시오.

03

something that a person does often in a regular and repeated way

① list
② goal
③ skill
④ stuff
⑤ habit

중요

04

to get or reach something by working hard

① waste
② achieve
③ manage
④ exercise
⑤ behave

중요

05 다음 빈칸에 들어갈 말이 바르게 짝지어진 것은?

• You have to clean _____ your room.
• We need to help and care _____ each other.

① in – of
② for – about
③ up – for
④ on – with
⑤ out – over

서답형

06 다음 우리말에 맞도록 빈칸에 알맞은 말을 쓰시오.

나는 환경 친화적인 사람이 되고 싶다.
➡ I'd like to be an _____ person.

서답형

07 다음 영영풀이에 해당하는 단어를 주어진 철자로 시작하여 쓰시오.

different from what is usual, normal, or expected

➡ s_____

08 다음 중 밑줄 친 단어의 의미가 <u>다른</u> 하나는?

① What <u>grade</u> is Minsu in?
② I got a bad <u>grade</u> in art.
③ His <u>grade</u> was in the nineties.
④ My science <u>grade</u> was very low.
⑤ Sue got a high <u>grade</u> in English.

01 다음 짝지어진 두 단어의 관계가 같도록 빈칸에 알맞은 말을 쓰시오.

(1) fast : slow = death : _____

(2) wonder : wonderful = stress : _____

(3) end : beginning = _____ : heavy

02 다음 우리말에 맞게 빈칸에 알맞은 말을 쓰시오.

(1) 너는 가끔 휴식이 필요하다.

➡ You need to relax _____ _____

_____ _____.

(2) 나는 매일 한 시간씩 달릴 계획이다.

➡ I'm planning to run _____ _____ every day.

(3) 나는 매일 줄넘기를 할 것이다.

➡ I'm going to _____ _____ every day.

03 다음 빈칸에 공통으로 들어갈 말을 〈보기〉에서 골라 쓰시오.

┌─── 보기 ───┐

plant   hard   dish

(1) • He worked _____ on his farm.

• That question was really _____.

(2) • The _____ is in the sink.

• How do I eat this _____?

(3) • The man is watering the _____.

• We _____ trees on Arbor Day.

04 다음 빈칸에 들어갈 알맞은 말을 〈보기〉에서 골라 쓰시오.

┌─── 보기 ───┐

manage   weekly   goal   messy

(1) My home is a bit _____.

(2) I'm planning to make a _____ schedule.

(3) My _____ for the year is to pass the Korean History Test.

(4) I'd like to _____ my time better.

05 다음 빈칸에 알맞은 말을 〈보기〉에서 골라 쓰시오.

┌─── 보기 ───┐

get some rest / because of / in front of

(1) My room gets messy _____ my pet.

(2) Becky is standing in line _____ the cafeteria.

(3) She will stay home and _____.

06 다음 영영풀이에 해당하는 단어를 주어진 철자로 시작하여 쓰시오.

(1) b_____ : to act in the way that people think is correct and proper

(2) h_____ : something that a person does often in a regular and repeated way

(3) u_____ : helping to do or achieve something

(4) d_____ : the time when someone stops working and is able to relax

Conversation

1 의도나 계획 묻고 답하기

> **A** What are you planning to do this weekend? 이번 주말에 뭐 할 계획이니?
> **B** I'm planning to see a movie. 영화를 볼 계획이야.

■ I'm planning to ~.는 '나는 ~할 계획이다.'라는 의미로 미래의 계획이나 의도에 대해 이야기할 때 사용하는 표현으로, to 다음에 동사원형이 온다.

- A: What are you planning to do tonight? 오늘밤에 뭐 할 계획이니?
  B: I'm planning to watch Snow White. 백설 공주를 볼 계획이야.

의도나 계획 말하기 표현

- I have a plan to go to his office. 나는 그의 사무실로 갈 계획이야.
- I'm scheduled to leave this afternoon. 나는 오늘 오후에 떠날 예정이다.
- I'm going to watch a soccer game. 나는 축구 경기를 볼 예정이다.
- I'm planning to go camping with my family. 나는 가족과 함께 캠핑을 갈 계획이야.
- I'm thinking of reading some books. 나는 책을 몇 권 읽을까 생각 중이야.

의도나 계획 묻기 표현

- What are you planning[going] to do this weekend? 이번 주말에 무엇을 할 계획[예정]이니?
- What are your plans for this weekend? 이번 주말에 계획이 어떻게 되니?
- Do you have any plans for this weekend? 이번 주말에 무슨 계획 있어?
- What will you do this weekend? 이번 주말에 뭐 할 거니?

핵심 Check

1. 다음 우리말과 일치하도록 빈칸에 알맞은 말을 쓰시오.

   (1) **A:** What _____ you _____ _____ eat? (너는 무엇을 먹을 계획이니?)

      B: I'm _____ to eat rice and meat. (밥과 고기를 먹을 계획이야.)

   (2) **A:** _____ are _____ _____ for this weekend? (너는 이번 주말 계획이 뭐니?)

      B: _____ _____ _____ go camping with my family.
      (나는 가족과 함께 캠핑을 갈 계획이야.)

   (3) **A:** Do you _____ _____ _____ tonight? (너는 오늘밤에 계획이 있니?)

      B: I'm _____ _____ seeing a movie. (나는 영화를 볼까 생각 중이야.)

② 충고하기

> **A** I'm planning to go to the ballpark. 나는 야구장에 갈 계획이야.
>
> **B** Why don't you buy tickets first? 먼저 표를 사는 게 어때?

■ Why don't you+동사원형 ~?은 '~하는 게 어때?'라는 의미로, 상대방에게 충고를 할 때 사용하는 표현이다.

- A: Why don't you ride a bike? 자전거를 타는 게 어때?
  B: A bike? Let's go for a hike. 자전거? 하이킹하러 가자.

충고하기 표현

- How[What] about joining the volunteer club? 자원 봉사 동아리에 가입하는 게 어때?
- I think you should go to bed before 11 o'clock. 11시 전에 잠자리에 드는 게 좋겠다.
- You'd better take an umbrella with you. 우산을 가져가는 게 낫겠다.
- I advise you to go to the dentist. 치과에 가기를 충고한다.
- I suggest you to attend the party. 파티에 참석하는 게 좋겠다.

충고를 구하는 표현

- What should I do? 제가 어떻게 해야 하죠?
- Can you give me some advice? 제게 조언을 좀 해 주실 수 있나요?

핵심 Check

2. 다음 우리말과 일치하도록 빈칸에 알맞은 말을 쓰시오.

(1) **A**: I feel tired. (나는 피곤해.)

   B: You'd _____ rest. (너는 쉬는 게 좋겠다.)

(2) **A**: I broke my mom's favorite jar. (엄마가 가장 좋아하시는 단지를 깨뜨렸어.)

   B: _____ _____ _____ tell your mom you're sorry?

   (엄마에게 죄송하다고 말씀드리는 게 어때?)

(3) **A**: I can't focus when I study at home. _____ _____ _____ _____?

   (집에서 공부하면 집중할 수가 없어요. 어떻게 하면 좋을까요?)

   B: You _____ _____ at the library. (도서관에서 공부해야 해.)

A. Communicate: Listen - Listen and Answer Dialog 1

> G: Kevin, do you have a special goal for the year?
>
> B: Yeah, ❶I want to win a gold medal in the national swimming contest.
>
> G: ❷Cool!
>
> B: ❸What about you, Minsol?
>
> G: ❹I'd like to manage my time better.
>
> B: How would you achieve your goal?
>
> G: ❺I'm planning to make a daily and weekly schedule.
>
> B: ❻Sounds good.

G: Kevin, 올해의 특별한 목표가 있니?
B: 응, 전국 수영 대회에서 금메달을 따고 싶어.
G: 멋지네!
B: 민솔아, 너는?
G: 난 내 시간을 더 잘 관리하고 싶어.
B: 어떻게 네 목표를 달성할 거니?
G: 나는 일일 계획표와 주간 계획표를 만들 계획이야.
B: 좋은 생각이야.

❶ want to+동사원형: ~하고 싶다 / win a gold medal: 금메달을 획득하다 / national swimming contest: 전국 수영 대회
❷ '멋지네'라는 의미로 상대방을 칭찬할 때 사용하는 표현이다.
❸ What about you?는 '너는 어때?'라는 의미로 How about you?로 바꿔 쓸 수 있다.
❹ I'd like to+동사원형 ~: 나는 ~하고 싶다. / manage: 관리하다
❺ I'm planning to+동사원형 ~은 '나는 ~할 계획이다.'라는 의미로 의도나 계획을 나타내는 표현이다. / weekly: 주간의
❻ '좋은 생각이야.'라는 의미로 That's a good idea.로 바꿔 쓸 수 있다.

Check(√) True or False

(1) Kevin won a gold medal in the national swimming contest.　　T ☐ F ☐

(2) Minsol wants to manage her time better.　　T ☐ F ☐

B. Communicate: Listen - Listen and Answer Dialog 2

> G: ❶Can I talk with you for a minute, Minsu?
>
> B: Sure. ❷What is it?
>
> G: I'm working on my weekly schedule.
>
> B: Really? ❸Good for you, little sister.
>
> G: Here. ❹Have a look and give me some advice.
>
> B: Hmm, you have a lot of study time.
>
> G: Yeah, ❺I'm planning to study hard.
>
> B: ❻Why don't you add some downtime?
>
> G: Downtime?
>
> B: Yeah, ❼I mean you need to relax once in a while.

G: 민수 오빠, 잠깐 얘기 좀 할 수 있을까?
B: 물론. 뭔데?
G: 나는 주간 계획표를 작성하고 있어.
B: 정말? 잘했다. 동생아.
G: 여기 있어. 한번 보고 조언 좀 해 줘.
B: 음, 공부 시간이 많구나.
G: 응, 나는 열심히 공부할 계획이야.
B: '다운타임'을 조금 더 추가하는 게 어때?
G: '다운타임'?
B: 응, 내 말은 넌 가끔 쉬어야 한다는 거야.

❶ Can I+동사원형 ~?은 '~해도 되니?'라는 의미로 허락을 구하는 표현이다. / for a minute: 잠깐
❷ What is it?: 뭔데?
❸ Good for you.: 잘했어.(칭찬하는 표현)
❹ have a look: 한 번 보다 / give me some advice: 나에게 충고를 좀 해주다
❺ I'm planning to+ 동사원형 ~은 '나는 ~할 계획이다.'라는 의미로 의도나 계획을 나타내는 표현이다
❻ Why don't you+동사원형 ~?: ~하는 게 어때?(충고하기 표현) / downtime: 휴식 시간
❼ once in a while: 가끔

Check(√) True or False

(3) The girl is working on her's daily schedule.　　T ☐ F ☐

(4) The girl needs to relax from time to time.　　T ☐ F ☐

Communication: Listen - Listen more

(The phone rings.)

W: Hi, Jongha.

B: Hello, Grandma. ❶I'd like to visit you this Saturday.

W: That'll be great. ❷We can plant some vegetables together.

B: Really? ❸What kind of vegetables?

W: This time, ❹I'm planning to plant some tomatoes and peppers.

B: Wow! That'll be fun.

W: I heard it's going to be sunny this Saturday. ❺You should bring your cap.

B: Okay, I will.

W: ❻Why don't you put on sunscreen before you leave?

B: ❼No problem. I'll see you on Saturday.

W: Okay. Bye.

❶ I'd like to+동사원형 ~.: 나는 ~하고 싶다
❷ can+동사원형: ~할 수 있다 / plant: 심다
❸ what kind of: 어떤 종류의
❹ I'm planning to+동사원형 ~.: 나는 ~할 계획이다(의도나 계획 말하기)
❺ You should+동사원형 ~.: 너는 ~해야 한다(의무 표현)
❻ Why don't you+동사원형 ~?: ~하는 게 어때?(충고하기 표현) / put on: (얼굴·피부 등에) ~을 바르다
❼ No problem. 문제 없어.(충고 또는 제안에 대한 긍정의 응답)

 Communicate: Listen - Listen and Complete

M: 1. ❶How would you achieve your goal?
　　2. ❷I'd like to visit you this Saturday.

❶ achieve one's goal: 목표를 성취하다
❷ I'd: I would의 축약형

My Speaking Portfolio

1. G: Hello, I'm Nayeon. ❶I'd like to be an eco-friendly person. ❷I'm planning to walk to school every day.

2. B1: Hi, I'm Junho. ❸My goal for the year is to pass the Korean History Test. ❹I'm planning to take online classes. I'm also going to watch a lot of historical dramas on TV.

3. B2: Hi, I'm Hojin. I have a goal for the year. ❺I want to get good grades in math. ❻I'm planning to review math lessons regularly. I'm also going to solve 20 math problems every day.

❶ an eco-friendly person: 환경 친화적인 사람
❷ I'm planning to+동사원형 ~. = I'm going to+동사원형 ~. = I'm thinking of+동명사 ~. = I have a plan to+동사원형 ~.
❸ to pass: 보어로 쓰인 to부정사의 명사적 용법
❹ take an online class: 온라인 수업을 듣다
❺ get a good grade: 좋은 성적을 받다
❻ review a math lesson: 수학 수업을 복습하다

 Wrap Up - Listening ❸

B: ❶What are you going to do this weekend, Mina?

G: I'm planning to visit Yeosu with my aunt.

B: ❷That sounds great. ❸Do you have any plans in Yeosu?

G: Well, we'll visit Yeosu Expo Park and eat some seafood.

B: That'll be fun. Enjoy your weekend.

❶ What are you going to do ~?: 너는 ~에 무엇을 할 거니? (의도나 계획 묻기)
❷ That sounds great.: 상대방을 칭찬하는 표현
❸ Do you have any plans?: 너는 무슨 계획이 있니?(계획 묻기 표현)

 Wrap Up - Listening ❹

G: ❶You look down, Yunsu. ❷What's the problem?

B: I have a science project, and I don't have any ideas.

G: ❸Why don't you read science magazines in the library?

B: Science magazines?

G: Sure. ❹You can get some great ideas that way.

❶ look+형용사: ~하게 보이다 / look down: 우울해 보이다
❷ 좋지 않은 상태의 이유를 묻는 표현(= What's the problem?=What's the matter?, What happened (to you)?)
❸ Why don't you+동사원형 ~?: ~하는 게 어때?(충고 표현하기)
❹ that way: 그렇게 하면

● 다음 우리말과 일치하도록 빈칸에 알맞은 말을 쓰시오.

Communicate: Listen - Listen and Answer Dialog 1

G: Kevin, do you have a _____ _____ for the year?

B: Yeah, I want to _____ _____ _____ _____ in the national swimming contest.

G: Cool!

B: _____ _____ you, Minsol?

G: I'd like to _____ my time _____.

B: _____ would you _____ your goal?

G: I'm _____ _____ make a daily and _____ schedule.

B: _____ good.

Communicate: Listen - Listen and Answer Dialog 2

G: Can I talk with you _____ _____ _____, Minsu?

B: Sure. _____ is it?

G: I'm _____ _____ my weekly schedule.

B: Really? _____ _____ you, little sister.

G: Here. _____ a look and _____ me some _____.

B: Hmm, you have _____ _____ _____ study time.

G: Yeah, _____ _____ _____ study hard.

B: _____ _____ _____ add some downtime?

G: Downtime?

B: Yeah, I mean you need to relax _____ _____ _____ _____.

Communicate: Listen - Listen More

(The phone rings.)

W: Hi, Jongha.

B: Hello, Grandma. I'd _____ _____ visit you this Saturday.

W: That'll be _____. We _____ _____ some vegetables together.

B: Really? _____ _____ vegetables?

W: This time, I'm _____ _____ _____ some tomatoes and peppers.

B: Wow! That'll _____ fun.

W: I heard it's _____ _____ _____ sunny this Saturday. You _____ _____ your cap.

B: Okay, _____ _____.

W: _____ _____ you _____ sunscreen before you leave?

B: _____ _____. I'll see you _____ Saturday.

W: Okay. Bye.

G: Kevin, 올해의 특별한 목표가 있니?

B: 응. 전국 수영 대회에서 금메달을 따고 싶어.

G: 멋지네!

B: 민솔아, 너는?

G: 난 내 시간을 더 잘 관리하고 싶어.

B: 어떻게 네 목표를 달성할 거니?

G: 나는 일일 계획표와 주간 계획표를 만들 계획이야.

B: 좋은 생각이야.

G: 민수 오빠, 잠깐 얘기 좀 할 수 있을까?

B: 물론. 뭔데?

G: 나는 주간 계획표를 작성하고 있어.

B: 정말? 잘했다, 동생아.

G: 여기 있어. 한번 보고 조언 좀 해 줘.

B: 음, 공부 시간이 많구나.

G: 응, 나는 열심히 공부할 계획이야.

B: '다운타임'을 조금 더 추가하는 게 어때?

G: '다운타임'?

B: 응, 내 말은 넌 가끔 쉬어야 한다는 거야.

(전화기가 울린다.)

W: 안녕, 종하구나.

B: 안녕하세요, 할머니. 이번 주 토요일에 할머니를 방문하고 싶어요.

W: 그거 좋겠다. 우리는 함께 채소를 심을 수 있어.

B: 정말요? 어떤 종류의 채소죠?

W: 이번에는 토마토와 고추를 심을 계획이야.

B: 와! 재미있겠는데요.

W: 이번 토요일에 날씨가 맑을 거라고 들었어. 모자를 가져와야 해.

B: 알았어요, 그럴게요.

W: 떠나기 전에 자외선 차단제를 바르는 게 어때?

B: 그럼요. 토요일에 뵙겠습니다.

W: 알았어. 안녕.

Communicate: Listen - Listen and Complete

M: 1. _____ would you _____ your _____?

2. _____ _____ _____ visit you this Saturday.

M: 1. 너는 어떻게 목표를 달성할 거니?
   2. 난 이번 토요일에 너를 방문하고 싶어.

My Speaking Portfolio

1. G: Hello, I'm Nayeon. I'd like to be an _____ person. _____ _____ _____ walk to school every day.

2. B1: Hi, I'm Junho. My goal for the year is _____ _____ the Korean History Test. I'm planning to _____ online _____. I'm also _____ _____ _____ a lot of historical dramas _____ TV.

3. B2: Hi, I'm Hojin. I _____ _____ _____ for the year. I want to get good grades in math. I'm _____ _____ _____ math lessons regularly. I'm also going to _____ 20 math _____ every day.

1. G: 안녕, 나는 나연이야. 나는 환경 친화적인 사람이 되고 싶어. 나는 매일 걸어서 학교에 갈 계획이야.

2. B1: 안녕, 나는 준호야. 올해 나의 목표는 한국 역사 시험을 통과하는 거야. 나는 온라인 강의를 들을 계획이야. 나는 TV에서 역사 드라마도 많이 볼 거야.

3. B2: 안녕, 나는 호진이야. 나는 올해 목표가 있어. 나는 수학에서 좋은 성적을 받고 싶어. 나는 규칙적으로 수학 수업을 복습할 계획이야. 나는 또한 매일 20개의 수학 문제를 풀 거야.

Wrap Up - Listening ❸

B: What _____ you _____ _____ do this weekend, Mina?

G: I'm _____ to visit Yeosu _____ my aunt.

B: That _____ great. Do you _____ _____ _____ in Yeosu?

G: Well, we'll _____ Yeosu Expo Park and _____ some seafood.

B: That'll be _____. _____ your weekend.

B: 미나야, 이번 주말에 뭐 할 거야?
G: 나는 숙모와 함께 여수를 방문할 계획이야.
B: 그거 좋겠다. 여수에서 무슨 계획 있니?
G: 음, 우리는 여수 엑스포 공원에 가서 해산물을 먹을 거야.
B: 그거 재미있겠는데. 즐거운 주말 보내.

Wrap Up - Listening ❹

G: You _____ _____, Yunsu. What's the _____?

B: I have a science project, and I _____ _____ any ideas.

G: _____ _____ _____ read science magazines in the library?

B: Science magazines?

G: Sure. You can _____ some great _____ that way.

G: 윤수야, 우울해 보여. 무슨 문제 있니?
B: 나는 과학 프로젝트가 있는데, 아무 생각이 나질 않아.
G: 도서관에서 과학 잡지를 읽는 게 어때?
B: 과학 잡지?
G: 그럼. 그런 식으로 하면 좋은 아이디어를 얻을 수 있어.

01 다음 대화의 밑줄 친 부분의 의도로 알맞은 것은?

> A: What's the matter?
> B: I broke my arm.
> A: <u>You'd better see a doctor.</u>

① 비난하기   ② 원인 묻기
③ 변명하기   ④ 감정 표현하기
⑤ 충고하기

> break 부러지다

02 다음 대화의 밑줄 친 부분과 바꾸어 쓸 수 있는 것은?

> A: Do you have any plans for this weekend?
> B: <u>I'm planning to</u> go shopping with my sister.

① I can   ② I must
③ I would   ④ I used to
⑤ I'm going to

> plan 계획

03 다음 중 의도하는 바가 <u>다른</u> 하나는?

① You should wear a warm jacket.
② How about wearing a warm jacket?
③ You'd better wear a warm jacket.
④ Why did you wear a warm jacket?
⑤ Why don't you wear a warm jacket?

> wear (옷 등을) 입다
> warm 따뜻한

04 다음 대화의 빈칸에 알맞은 것은?

> A: _____
> B: We are planning to have a surprise party.

① Where are you going?
② What do you want to be?
③ What would you like to have?
④ What are you planning to do?
⑤ When are you having a surprising party?

> have a surprise party
> 깜짝 파티를 열다

[01~08] 다음 대화를 읽고, 물음에 답하시오.

> G: Can I talk with you for a minute, Minsu?
> B: Sure. What is it?
> G: I'm working on my ⓐweek schedule. (①)
> B: Really? _____ⓑ_____, little sister.
> G: Here. (②)
> B: Hmm, you have a lot of study time.
> G: Yeah, I'm ⓒplanning to study hard. (③)
> B: ⓓWhy don't you add some downtime?
> G: Downtime? (④)
> B: Yeah, I mean you need to relax once _____ⓔ_____ a while. (⑤)

01 위 대화의 ①~⑤ 중 주어진 문장이 들어갈 알맞은 곳은?

> Have a look and give me some advice.

①   ②   ③   ④   ⑤

02 위 대화의 밑줄 친 ⓐ를 알맞은 형태로 고쳐 쓰시오.

➡ _____

03 위 대화의 빈칸 ⓑ에 들어갈 말로 적절하지 <u>않은</u> 것은?

① Well done   ② You did well
③ Good for you   ④ That's terrible
⑤ You did a good job

04 위 대화의 밑줄 친 ⓒ와 바꿔 쓸 수 있는 단어를 쓰시오.

➡ _____

05 위 대화의 밑줄 친 ⓓ와 바꿔 쓸 수 없는 것은?

① How about adding some downtime?
② You never add some downtime.
③ You'd better add some downtime.
④ You should add some downtime.
⑤ What about adding some downtime?

06 위 대화의 빈칸 ⓔ에 알맞은 말을 쓰시오.

➡ _____

07 위 대화에서 다음 영영풀이에 해당하는 단어를 찾아 쓰시오.

> the time when someone stops working and is able to relax

➡ _____

08 위 대화를 읽고, 다음 질문에 영어로 답하시오.

> Q: What is Minsu's little sister planning to do?
> A: _____

[09~11] 다음 대화를 읽고, 물음에 답하시오.

> G: Kevin, do you have a special goal for the year?
> B: Yeah, I want to win a gold medal in the national swimming contest.
> G: Cool!
> B: ___ⓐ___ about you, Minsol?
> G: I'd like to manage my time better.
> B: ___ⓑ___ would you achieve your goal?
> G: ⓒI'm planning to make a daily and weekly schedule.
> B: Sounds good.

09 위 대화의 빈칸 ⓐ와 ⓑ에 알맞은 말이 바르게 짝지어진 것은?

① What – When　　② How – Why
③ How – What　　④ What – Where
⑤ What – How

10 위 대화의 밑줄 친 ⓒ 대신 쓸 수 있는 말을 모두 고르면? (정답 2개)

① I have a plan to make
② I made
③ I'm going to make
④ I was making
⑤ I should make

11 위 대화의 내용과 일치하지 <u>않는</u> 것은?

① Kevin은 올해의 목표가 있다.
② Kevin은 전국 수영 대회에서 금메달을 따고 싶어 한다.
③ 민솔은 Kevin을 칭찬해 주고 있다.
④ 민솔은 자기의 시간을 더 잘 관리하고 싶어 한다.
⑤ 민솔은 시간을 잘 관리하기 위해 월간 일정표를 만들 계획이다.

[12~15] 다음 대화를 읽고, 물음에 답하시오.

> G: You look down, Yunsu. ⓐWhat's the problem?
> B: I have a science project, and I don't have any ideas.
> G: ⓑWhy don't you read science magazines in the library?
> B: Science magazines?
> G: Sure. You can get some great ideas ⓒthat way.

12 위 대화의 밑줄 친 ⓐ와 바꿔 쓸 수 있는 것은?

① How come?　　② What about you?
③ How are you?　　④ What's wrong?
⑤ What's the answer?

13 위 대화의 밑줄 친 ⓑ의 의도로 알맞은 것은?

① 이유 묻기　　② 충고하기
③ 조언 구하기　　④ 비난하기
⑤ 금지하기

서답형

14 위 대화의 밑줄 친 ⓒ가 뜻하는 것을 우리말로 구체적으로 쓰시오.

➡ _____

서답형

15 위 대화를 읽고, 다음 질문에 대한 대답을 완성하시오.

| Q: Why does Yunsu look down? |
| A: Because _____ |
| _____. |

Conversation 서술형 시험대비

01 다음 대화의 밑줄 친 우리말을 괄호 안의 단어를 이용하여 영작하시오.

> **A:** 자전거 타는 게 어때? (why / ride)
> **B:** A bike? Let's go for a hike.

➡ _____

02 다음 대화의 빈칸에 알맞은 말을 〈보기〉에서 골라 쓰시오.

> ┤ 보기 ├
> • You'd better learn some Chinese words.
> • Thank you for your advice.
> • Why don't we study together?

(1) A: I think you should turn down the heat.

B: _____

(2) A: I'm worried about the math test next week.

B: _____

(3) A: I'm planning to visit Beijing next month.

B: _____

03 다음 우리말과 일치하도록 주어진 단어를 이용하여 빈칸을 채우시오.

(1) 이번 주말에 무슨 계획이 있니? (plan)

➡ Do you _____ _____ for this weekend?

(2) 나는 부모님을 위해 깜짝 파티를 열까 생각 중이야. (think)

➡ I'm _____ _____ having a surprise party for my parents.

(3) 나는 가족과 캠핑을 갈 계획이야. (plan)

➡ I'm _____ _____ _____ camping with my family.

[04~07] 다음 대화를 읽고, 물음에 답하시오.

> W: Hi, Jongha.
> B: Hello, Grandma. I'd like to visit you this Saturday.
> W: That'll be great. We can plant some vegetables together.
> B: Really? What ⓐ of vegetables?
> W: This time, I'm planning to plant some tomatoes and peppers.
> B: Wow! That'll be fun.
> W: I heard it's going to be sunny this Saturday. ⓑYou should bring your cap.
> B: Okay, I will.
> W: Why don't you put on sunscreen before you leave?
> B: No problem. I'll see you on Saturday.

04 위 대화의 빈칸 ⓐ에 다음 영영풀이에 해당하는 단어를 쓰시오.

> a particular variety or type

➡ _____

05 위 대화의 밑줄 친 ⓑ를 다음과 같이 바꿔 쓸 때 빈칸에 알맞은 말을 쓰시오.

> _____ _____ _____ bring your cap?

06 What is Jongha's grandma planning to do this Saturday? Answer the English.

➡ _____

07 What's the weather going to be like this Saturday? Answer the English.

➡ _____

Grammar
교과서

1 주격 관계대명사

> • I want to have a friend **who** makes me happy. 나는 나를 행복하게 만드는 친구를 가지고 싶다.
>
> • An orange is a fruit **which** has a lot of vitamin C.
> 오렌지는 비타민 C를 많이 가지고 있는 과일이다.
>
> • Hold the door open for someone **that** is behind you.
> 여러분 뒤에 있는 사람을 위하여 문을 열어 두세요.

■ 관계대명사는 선행사인 명사를 대신하는 일종의 대명사이면서 이 대명사가 이끄는 절을 접속시킨다는 점에서 「접속사+대명사」의 기능을 동시에 갖는다. 관계대명사가 이끄는 관계사절에 의하여 수식받는 명사 · 대명사를 선행사라 하며, 이때 관계사절은 선행사인 명사를 수식하므로 형용사절이다. 관계대명사는 선행사에 따라 which, who, that 등을 쓴다.

선행사	주격	소유격	목적격
사람	who	whose	whom / who
사물	which	whose / of which	which
사람, 동물, 사물	that	–	that

■ 주격 관계대명사는 관계대명사가 주어의 역할을 하는 경우에 쓰이며, 뒤따르는 동사는 선행사의 수에 일치시킨다.

- The boy **who** is wearing a blue shirt is my little brother. 파란색 셔츠를 입고 있는 소년은 내 남동생이다.

- This is a restaurant **which** is famous for pizza. 이것은 피자로 유명한 식당이다.

■ **주격 관계대명사 who, which, that**
관계대명사가 이끄는 문장에서 주어 역할을 한다. 사람을 설명할 때는 「사람+who+동사」의 형태이고, 사물이나 동물을 설명할 때는 「사물[동물]+which+동사」의 형태이다. that은 사람, 사물, 동물에 모두 쓰인다.

- Mr. Robinson is a teacher **who[that]** is from Australia. Robinson 씨는 호주에서 오신 선생님이다.

- Look at the robots **that[which]** are playing soccer. 축구를 하고 있는 로봇들을 봐.
  cf. 선행사 앞에 all, every, no, any, the same, the only, the+최상급/서수 등이 올 경우, 보통 that을 사용한다.

- She is the only student **that** can speak English. 그녀는 영어로 말할 수 있는 유일한 학생이다.

핵심 Check

1. 다음 괄호 안에서 알맞은 것을 고르시오.

(1) Do you know the boy (who / which) is sitting next to Kevin?

(2) This is the smart phone (who / which) was made in Korea.

(3) The girl (who / which) I met on the street is Jihun's sister.

(4) Mr. White is a teacher (who / which) teaches English.

2 조건을 나타내는 접속사 if

- **If** it is sunny, I will go to the beach. 내일 날씨가 맑으면 난 해변에 갈 것이다.
- **If** it rains tomorrow, I will stay at home. 내일 비가 오면 난 집에 있을 것이다.
- You can catch the train **if** you leave now. 너는 지금 떠나면 열차를 탈 수 있다.

■ 접속사 if는 두 개의 절을 하나로 연결하여 '만일 ~한다면'이라는 조건의 뜻을 나타낸다. 이때 if가 속한 절을 종속절이라 하고, 또 다른 절을 주절이라 한다. 「If+주어+현재시제, 주어+will[can/may]+동사원형」의 어순이다.

- **If** you speak slowly, I can understand you. 천천히 말하면 네 말을 이해할 수 있어.
  = I can understand you **if** you speak slowly.

■ if절에서는 실현 가능성이 있는 추측일 경우 현재형으로 미래를 나타낸다.

- **If** you run, you will get there in time. 뛰어가면 제시간에 거기에 도착할 것이다.
- **If** you are tired, we will go home. 네가 피곤하면 우린 집에 갈 거야.

  cf. if절이 명사절로 '~인지 아닌지'의 뜻을 나타낼 때는 미래 시제를 사용한다.

- Do you know **if** she will come to the party? 그녀가 파티에 올지 안 올지 너는 아니?

  cf. 명사절을 이끄는 if는 whether로 바꿔 쓸 수 있다.

- I don't know **if[whether]** he had breakfast. 그가 아침을 먹었는지 안 먹었는지 나는 모른다.

■ if ~ not은 '만약 ~하지 않으면'의 뜻으로, unless로 바꿔 쓸 수 있다.

- **If** you do**n't** follow the school rules, you will be in trouble. 교칙을 따르지 않으면 넌 난처해질 거야.
  = **Unless** you follow the school rules, you will be in trouble.

핵심 Check

2. 다음 괄호 안에서 알맞은 것을 고르시오.

(1) (If / Because) you arrive early, you will get a good seat.

(2) If she (takes / will take) the subway, she will be there on time.

(3) If I see her, I (give / will give) it to her.

(4) Unless you (drink / don't drink) water, you will feel very thirsty.

01 다음 두 문장을 한 문장으로 만들 때 빈칸에 알맞은 말을 쓰시오. (that은 쓸 수 없음.)

next to ~ 옆에
necklace 목걸이

(1) Do you know the girl? She is sitting next to Kevin.

➡ Do you know the girl _____ is sitting next to Kevin?

(2) This is the necklace. I got it from Jihun.

➡ This is the necklace _____ I got from Jihun.

(3) My uncle lives in a house. It has a beautiful garden.

➡ My uncle lives in a house _____ has a beautiful garden.

(4) The boy is wearing a blue shirt. He is my little brother.

➡ The boy _____ is wearing a blue shirt is my little brother.

(5) Turkey is a country. It has many interesting things.

➡ Turkey is a country _____ has many interesting things.

02 다음 두 문장을 if를 써서 한 문장으로 나타내시오. (단, 종속절이 주절의 앞에 오는 문장으로 바꿀 것.)

hurry up 서두르다
go on a picnic 소풍가다
finish 끝나다

(1) Hurry up. You will catch the bus.

➡ _____

(2) It will be fine tomorrow. We will go on a picnic.

➡ _____

(3) School finishes early today. Kate will read a book at home.

➡ _____

(4) You are tired. You can sit here.

➡ _____

03 다음 괄호 안에서 알맞은 것을 고르시오.

water 물을 주다
flow 흐르다

(1) There is a boy (who / which) is watering a flower.

(2) Those are the pictures (who / which) were taken by my sister.

(3) I have a friend (which / who) lives in China.

(4) Jane is the girl (that / which) is playing basketball.

(5) The Thames is the river (who / that) flows through London.

01 다음 빈칸에 들어갈 말이 바르게 짝지어진 것은?

> • I was late _____ the bus broke down.
> • I can finish that work _____ I have three days.

① when – how
② when – where
③ if – because
④ because – that
⑤ because – if

02 다음 대화의 빈칸 ⓐ, ⓑ에 들어갈 말이 순서대로 짝지어진 것은?

> A: Do you know the girl ___ⓐ___ is standing under the tree?
> B: Yes. She is Kevin's sister. Her hobby is ___ⓑ___ pretty dolls.

① who – collecting
② whom – collecting
③ which – to collect
④ whose – collecting
⑤ whose – to collect

03 다음 문장의 빈칸에 알맞은 것은?

> Why don't you cook some soup _____ you're hungry?

① and
② but
③ if
④ where
⑤ because

04 다음 밑줄 친 부분을 어법상 바르게 고쳐 쓰시오.

(1) He's the boy <u>which</u> broke the window.

➡ _____

(2) This is the biggest dog <u>whom</u> I have ever seen.

➡ _____

05 다음 밑줄 친 ①~⑤ 중 어법상 어색한 것은?

> My father ①will buy ②me a computer ③if I ④will get a perfect score ⑤in the final exam.

①　　②　　③　　④　　⑤

[06~07] 다음 문장의 빈칸에 알맞은 것을 고르시오.

06

> Do you know the man _____ is running after a dog?

① how
② who
③ whom
④ which
⑤ whose

07

> This is the building _____ was built in 1790.

① who
② how
③ what
④ which
⑤ where

서답형

08 다음 두 문장을 한 문장으로 바꿔 쓰시오.

> Susan does not get up now. She will miss the train.

➡ _____

_____

09 다음 빈칸에 알맞은 말이 순서대로 짝지어진 것은?

> • Susan is the girl _____ will go to Europe with me.
> • An orange is a fruit _____ has a lot of vitamin C.

① who – which
② whom – that
③ which – who
④ which – which
⑤ whose – that

중요

10 다음 빈칸에 들어갈 말이 나머지 넷과 다른 것은?

① Mike will stay at home _____ it is cold.
② You can stay at home _____ you're tired.
③ She'll watch TV _____ she finishes her work early.
④ He'll buy a necktie for his dad _____ he goes shopping.
⑤ I think _____ Anderson won't come back.

중요

11 다음 빈칸에 공통으로 알맞은 것은?

> • My dad bought me a bag _____ was black.
> • This is the smart phone _____ I bought last month.

① what
② who
③ whom
④ where
⑤ which

12 다음 두 문장의 의미가 같도록 빈칸에 알맞은 것은?

> I'll show you the picture. It was given to me by Ann.
> = I'll show you the picture _____ was given to me by Ann.

① who
② what
③ whom
④ which
⑤ whose

13 다음 우리말을 영어로 바르게 옮긴 것은?

> 나는 날씨가 좋으면 주말마다 낚시하러 간다.

① I go fishing on weekends because the weather is good.
② The weather is good, so I go fishing on weekends.
③ As the weather is good, I will go fishing on weekends.
④ If the weather will be good, I go fishing on weekends.
⑤ I go fishing on weekends if the weather is good.

서답형

14 다음 문장에서 어법상 어색한 부분을 찾아 바르게 고쳐 쓰시오.

> Look at the boy and his dog which are running in the park.

_____ ➡ _____

15 다음 빈칸에 공통으로 알맞은 것은?

> • You will get one free _____ you buy this.
> • I wonder _____ she is really a middle school student.

① as   ② if
③ that   ④ since
⑤ whether

16 다음 〈보기〉의 밑줄 친 부분과 쓰임이 같은 것은?

> ┤ 보기 ├
> Mr. Parker is a farmer that grows orange trees.

① They can't go that far.
② I'm afraid that he will not come.
③ The climate of Korea is similar to that of Germany.
④ There is a cat that is sleeping on the bench.
⑤ It was really nice weather that day.

서답형

17 다음 문장에서 어법상 어색한 부분을 바르게 고쳐서 문장을 다시 쓰시오

> What do you do if he visits your home tomorrow?

➡ _____

[18~19] 다음 중 어법상 어색한 것을 고르시오.

18 ① I'll phone you if I'll have time.
② If you don't have a ticket, you can't come in.
③ We can be in Seoul by 10 if we catch the first train.
④ If you don't give me my money, I'm going to the police.
⑤ If it is sunny tomorrow, we'll have the party outside.

19 ① Do you know the boy which is running in the park?
② The woman is the only person that loves me.
③ Look at the trees which stand in front of the house.
④ We remember the typhoon that hit the island last year.
⑤ The girl who danced with you is my sister.

20 다음 밑줄 친 부분의 쓰임이 〈보기〉와 같은 것은?

> ┤ 보기 ├
> I want to know if it will rain tomorrow.

① If he comes back, I will tell him about it.
② I won't go there if it is cold tomorrow.
③ If you turn right, you can see the building.
④ You may go home early if you don't feel well.
⑤ I doubt if the baby can understand your words.

01 다음 두 문장을 한 문장으로 만들 때 빈칸에 알맞은 말을 쓰시오.

> The dog has big ears. It is lying over there.
> ➡ The dog _____ is lying over there has big ears.

02 다음 문장에서 어법상 어색한 곳을 찾아 바르게 고쳐 쓰시오.

(1) If I won't be free tomorrow, I'll see you on Saturday.

_____ ➡ _____

(2) You'll be happy if you'll pass the exam.

_____ ➡ _____

03 다음 빈칸에 공통으로 알맞은 말을 쓰시오.

> • Look at the star _____ shines in the night sky.
> • I know the woman _____ is playing the vioin.

04 다음 문장에서 어법상 어색한 부분을 바르게 고쳐 문장을 다시 쓰시오.

(1) If it will rain tomorrow, we won't go hiking.

➡ _____

(2) Unless you don't hurry, you will miss the train.

➡ _____

05 다음 두 문장을 괄호 안의 관계대명사를 이용하여 한 문장으로 고쳐 쓰시오.

(1) The young lady is sitting on the bench. She is our music teacher. (who)

➡ _____

_____

(2) We found a dog. It was running toward us. (which)

➡ _____

(3) This is the firefighter. He saved the baby from the burning building. (that)

➡ _____

_____

(4) This is the only story. It is interesting to read. (that)

➡ _____

06 다음 빈칸에 알맞은 말을 〈보기〉에서 골라 쓰시오. (문장의 앞에 오는 경우 대문자로 쓰시오.)

> ┤ 보기 ├
> when   if   unless

(1) _____ you don't leave now, you will miss the last train.

(2) We had a big party _____ Sarah came home.

(3) _____ you start now, you'll be late for the meeting.

07 다음 두 문장을 관계대명사를 사용하여 한 문장으로 만드시오.

(1) I know the woman. She is standing by the car.

➡ _____

_____

(2) Did you see the car? It has only two doors.

➡ _____

(3) This is a restaurant. The restaurant is famous for its spaghetti.

➡ _____

(4) Mrs. Brown is my English teacher. She lives next door.

➡ _____

_____

08 다음 주어진 단어를 바르게 배열하여 문장을 완성하시오.

(she / will / if / get up / the train /, / she / miss / doesn't / early)

➡ _____

09 다음 우리말을 영어로 옮길 때 빈칸에 각각 알맞은 말을 쓰시오.

어제 발생한 교통사고는 끔찍했다.

➡ The traffic accident _____ happened yesterday _____ terrible.

10 접속사 if를 사용하여 다음 두 문장을 한 문장으로 바꿔 쓰시오. (단, 종속절이 주절의 앞에 오는 문장으로 바꿀 것)

(1) The weather is nice. I always walk to school.

➡ _____

(2) It rains on weekends. We watch TV.

➡ _____

(3) I am late for class. My teacher gets very angry.

➡ _____

11 다음 주어진 단어를 이용하여 우리말을 영어로 옮기시오.

나는 야구를 좋아하는 의사를 알고 있다.
(know)

➡ _____

12 다음 두 문장이 같은 뜻이 되도록 빈칸에 알맞은 말을 쓰시오.

(1) If you don't leave now, you will miss the school bus.

➡ _____ _____ _____ now, you will miss the school bus.

(2) Unless it rains tomorrow, I will go camping.

➡ _____ _____ _____ rain tomorrow, I will go camping

Beginning a New School Year

Beginning a new school year is stressful to many students. How can we get off to a good start? *Teen Today* asked Raccoon 97, a popular webtoon artist, for ideas.

Let's think about things that are hard to change or easy to change.

Things That Are Hard to Change

Your Messy Room_ You clean it up. Then you bring new stuff into it, and it soon gets messy again. But don't worry. Your room is much cleaner than mine.

Your Family_ There is always someone in your family who drives you crazy. Remember that he or she is still a member of your family. You just have to live together and care for each other.

Your Name on Your Teacher's List_ If you are late or do not behave, your teacher will put your name on his or her list. You cannot easily change the list.

be stressful to ~에게 스트레스가 되다

get off to a good start 좋은 출발을 하다

webtoon (컴퓨터) 웹툰

artist 예술가, 미술가

clean up 깨끗이 청소하다

messy 지저분한, 엉망인

stuff 것, 것들, 물건

bring A into B A를 B로 가져오다

someone 어떤 사람

drive ~하게 만들다[몰아가다]

crazy 미친 듯이 화가 난

still 여전히

member 일원, 구성원

care for ~을 돌보다, ~을 좋아하다

each other 서로

list 리스트, 목록

behave 예의 바르게 행동하다

easily 쉽게

확인문제

● 다음 문장이 본문의 내용과 일치하면 T, 일치하지 않으면 F를 쓰시오.

1 There are a lot of students who are worried about a new school year. ☐

2 Most things are easy to change. ☐

3 Your teacher's list is easy to change. ☐

Things That Are Easy to Change

Your Underpants_ If you change them every day, your mom will not
조건을 나타내는 접속사   = underpants   축약형 won't로 바꿀 수 있다.
tell you one hundred and one times.
백한번, 입이 닳도록
"Life is C between B and D." It means "Life is C□□□□ between
이다   B와 D 사이의   앞 문장을 받는 인칭대명사
Birth and Death."

Jean-Paul Sartre

Your Friends_ You can change your friends. Does it sound strange?
~하게 들리다   보어(형용사)
You may think that you have the perfect number of friends. If you add
추측을 나타내는 조동사   완벽한 수의
a new friend to the list, however, you will feel even better than before.
그러나(접속부사)   비교급 강조 부사   good의 비교급

Your Mind_ You thought one thing at first, and now you think another
think의 과거형   처음에(이때의 first는 명사)   또 다른
thing. That is okay. As someone said, "If you can change your mind,
앞 문장을 받는 지시대명사   ~한 것처럼   ~한다면
you can change your life."

"Focus on the things that are easy to change, and try to make
주격 관계대명사   to부정사의 부사적 용법   ~하기 위해 노력하다
today better than yesterday. Good luck!"
good의 비교급   행운을 빌어!

Top 5 Plans for the Year

We asked 200 *Teen Today* readers, "What are your plans for the year?"

---

underpants 팬티

hundred 100, 백

between A and B
A와 B 사이의

choice 선택

birth 탄생

death 죽음

perfect 완벽한, 완전한

add A to B B에 A를 더하다

however 그러나

at first 처음에는

focus on ~에 집중하다

luck 운, 행운

reader 독자

📎 **확인문제**

● 다음 문장이 본문의 내용과 일치하면 T, 일치하지 않으면 F를 쓰시오.

1   Your underpants are easy to change. ☐

2   A new friend is worse than an old friend. ☐

3   It is possible that your thought changes. ☐

4   You had better focus on the things that are hard to change. ☐

• 우리말을 참고하여 빈칸에 알맞은 말을 쓰시오.

1 _____ a new school year is stressful to many students.

2 _____ can we get off _____ a good start?

3 *Teen Today* _____ Raccoon 97, a popular webtoon artist, _____ ideas.

4 _____ *think about things that are* _____ *to change or* _____ *to change.*

5 Things _____ Are Hard to _____

6 Your Messy Room_ You clean _____ _____ .

7 Then you _____ new stuff _____ it, and it soon _____ messy again.

8 But don't _____ .

9 Your room is much _____ _____ mine.

10 Your Family_ There is always someone in your family who _____ you _____ .

11 _____ that he or she is still a _____ of your family.

12 You just _____ _____ live together and _____ _____ each other.

13 Your Name on Your Teacher's List_ If you are late or do not _____ , your teacher will _____ your name _____ his or her list.

---

1 새 학년을 시작하는 것은 많은 학생들에게 스트레스를 준다.

2 어떻게 하면 우리는 좋은 출발을 할 수 있을까?

3 Teen Today는 유명한 웹툰 작가인 Raccoon 97에게 아이디어를 물었다.

4 바꾸기 어렵거나 쉽게 바꿀 수 있는 것들에 대해 생각해 보자.

5 바꾸기 어려운 것들

6 너의 지저분한 방_ 너는 방을 깨끗이 치운다.

7 그런 다음 새로운 물건을 가져오면 곧 다시 지저분해진다.

8 하지만 걱정하지 마.

9 네 방은 내 방보다 훨씬 더 깨끗해.

10 너의 가족_ 너의 가족 중에는 항상 너를 미치게 하는 사람이 있다.

11 그나 그녀가 여전히 너의 가족 구성원이라는 것을 기억해라.

12 너는 함께 살아야 하고 서로 돌봐야 한다.

13 선생님의 명단에 있는 너의 이름_ 만약 네가 늦거나 예의 바르게 행동하지 않는다면, 너의 선생님은 너의 이름을 그나 그녀의 명단에 올릴 것이다.

14 You cannot easily _____ the _____.

15 Things _____ Are Easy _____ Change

16 Your Underpants_ If you _____ them every day, your mom will not _____ you one _____ and one times.

17 "Life is C _____ B _____ D."

18 It _____ "Life is Choice between _____ and _____."

19 Your Friends_ You can _____ your _____.

20 Does it _____ strange?

21 You _____ think that you have the _____ number of friends.

22 If you _____ a new friend _____ the list, however, you will feel _____ better than _____.

23 Your Mind_ You thought _____ thing at _____, and now you think _____ thing.

24 That is _____. As someone said, "If you can change your _____, you can change your _____."

25 "Focus _____ the things that are _____ to change, and try to make today _____ than yesterday. Good _____!"

26 Top 5 _____ for the Year

27 We _____ 200 *Teen Today* _____, "_____ are your plans _____ the year?"

14 너는 명단을 쉽게 바꿀 수 없다.

15 바꾸기 쉬운 것들

16 너의 팬티_ 만약 네가 매일 팬티를 갈아입으면, 너의 엄마는 너에게 입이 닳도록 말하지 않을 거야.

17 "인생은 B와 D 사이의 C이다."

18 그것은 "인생은 탄생과 죽음 사이의 선택이다."를 의미한다.

19 너의 친구들_ 너는 네 친구들을 바꿀 수 있다.

20 이상하게 들리는가?

21 너는 네가 완벽한 수의 친구들을 가지고 있다고 생각할지도 모른다.

22 하지만 새로운 친구를 목록에 추가하면 이전보다 훨씬 더 기분이 좋아질 것이다.

23 너의 마음_ 너는 처음에는 이런 것을 생각했고, 지금은 또 다른 것을 생각한다.

24 괜찮다. 누군가 말했듯이, "마음을 바꿀 수 있다면, 인생을 바꿀 수 있어."

25 "바꾸기 쉬운 일에 집중하고, 어제보다 오늘을 더 좋게 만들려고 노력해. 행운을 빌어!"

26 올해의 5대 계획

27 우리는 200명의 Teen Today 독자들에게 "올해의 계획은 무엇인가?"라고 물었다.

● 우리말을 참고하여 본문을 영작하시오.

1 새 학년을 시작하는 것은 많은 학생들에게 스트레스를 준다.

➡ _____

2 어떻게 하면 우리는 좋은 출발을 할 수 있을까?

➡ _____

3 Teen Today는 유명한 웹툰 작가인 Raccoon 97에게 아이디어를 물었다.

➡ _____

4 바꾸기 어렵거나 쉽게 바꿀 수 있는 것들에 대해 생각해 보자.

➡ _____

5 바꾸기 어려운 것들

➡ _____

6 너의 지저분한 방_ 너는 방을 깨끗이 치운다.

➡ _____

7 그런 다음 새로운 물건을 가져오면 곧 다시 지저분해진다.

➡ _____

8 하지만 걱정하지 마.

➡ _____

9 네 방은 내 방보다 훨씬 더 깨끗해.

➡ _____

10 너의 가족_ 너의 가족 중에는 항상 너를 미치게 하는 사람이 있다.

➡ _____

11 그나 그녀가 여전히 너의 가족 구성원이라는 것을 기억해라.

➡ _____

12 너는 함께 살아야 하고 서로 돌봐야 한다.

➡ _____

13 선생님의 명단에 있는 너의 이름_ 만약 네가 늦거나 예의 바르게 행동하지 않는다면, 너의 선생님은 너의 이름을 그나 그녀의 명단에 올릴 것이다.

➡ _____

_____

14 너는 명단을 쉽게 바꿀 수 없다.

➡ _____

15 바꾸기 쉬운 것들

➡ _____

16 너의 팬티_ 만약 네가 매일 팬티를 갈아입으면, 너의 엄마는 너에게 입이 닳도록 말하지 않을 거야.

➡ _____

17 "인생은 B와 D 사이의 C이다."

➡ _____

18 그것은 "인생은 탄생과 죽음 사이의 선택이다."를 의미한다.

➡ _____

19 너의 친구들_ 너는 네 친구들을 바꿀 수 있다.

➡ _____

20 이상하게 들리는가?

➡ _____

21 너는 네가 완벽한 수의 친구들을 가지고 있다고 생각할지도 모른다.

➡ _____

22 하지만 새로운 친구를 목록에 추가하면 이전보다 훨씬 더 기분이 좋아질 것이다.

➡ _____

23 너의 마음_ 너는 처음에는 이런 것을 생각했고, 지금은 또 다른 것을 생각한다.

➡ _____

24 괜찮다. 누군가 말했듯이, "마음을 바꿀 수 있다면, 인생을 바꿀 수 있어."

➡ _____

25 "바꾸기 쉬운 일에 집중하고, 어제보다 오늘을 더 좋게 만들려고 노력해. 행운을 빌어!"

➡ _____

26 올해의 5대 계획

➡ _____

27 우리는 200명의 Teen Today 독자들에게 "올해의 계획은 무엇인가?"라고 물었다.

➡ _____

[01~05] 다음 글을 읽고, 물음에 답하시오.

Beginning a new school year is stressful ___@___ many students. ⓑHow can we get off to a good start? *Teen Today* asked Raccoon 97, a popular webtoon artist, for ideas.

Let's think about things ⓒthat are hard to change or easy to change.

Things That Are Hard to Change

Your Messy Room_ You clean it up. Then you bring new stuff into it, and it soon gets messy again. But don't worry. Your room is ⓓmuch cleaner than mine.

01 위 글의 빈칸 @에 알맞은 것은?

① of   ② to

③ at   ④ for

⑤ with

서답형

02 위 글의 밑줄 친 ⓑ를 우리말로 옮기시오.

➡ _____

중요

03 위 글의 밑줄 친 ⓒ와 같은 용법으로 쓰인 것은?

① It is certain that he will be late.

② She said that she would help me.

③ Look at the house that stands on the hill.

④ It was yesterday that I met Ann.

⑤ The news that he married Ann is true.

04 위 글의 밑줄 친 ⓓ와 바꿔 쓸 수 있는 것은? (2개)

① far   ② many

③ lot   ④ very

⑤ a lot

05 위 글의 내용과 일치하지 <u>않는</u> 것은?

① 새 학기가 되면 많은 학생들이 스트레스를 느낀다.

② Raccoon 97은 인기 있는 웹툰 작가이다.

③ 바꾸기 어려운 일과 쉬운 일이 있다.

④ 새 물건을 방에 들여놓으면 방이 지저분해진다.

⑤ Raccoon 97의 방은 아주 깨끗하다.

[06~09] 다음 글을 읽고, 물음에 답하시오.

Your Family_ (①) There is always someone in your family who drives you crazy. (②) You just have to live together and care ___@___ each other. (③)

Your Name on Your Teacher's List_ If you are late or do not behave, your teacher will put your name on his or her list. (④) You cannot ⓑeasy change the list. (⑤)

06 위 글의 ①~⑤ 중 다음 주어진 문장이 들어갈 알맞은 곳은?

Remember that he or she is still a member of your family.

①   ②   ③   ④   ⑤

07 위 글의 빈칸 ⓐ에 알맞은 것은?

① from　　② to

③ for　　④ at

⑤ with

08 위 글의 밑줄 친 ⓑ를 알맞은 형으로 고치시오.

➡ _____

09 위 글을 읽고 여러분의 이름이 선생님의 리스트에 오를 수 있는 경우 두 가지를 우리말로 쓰시오.

① _____

② _____

[10~14] 다음 글을 읽고, 물음에 답하시오.

Things That Are Easy to Change

Your Underpants_ ___ⓐ___ you change them every day, your mom will not tell you one hundred and one times.

Your Friends_ You can change your friends. Does ⓑit sound strange? You ⓒmay think that you have the perfect number of friends. If you ___ⓓ___ a new friend to the list, however, you will feel ⓔeven better than before.

10 위 글의 빈칸 ⓐ에 알맞은 것은?

① If　　② As

③ When　　④ While

⑤ Though

11 위 글의 밑줄 친 ⓑ가 가리키는 것을 우리말로 쓰시오.

➡ _____

12 위 글의 밑줄 친 ⓒ와 같은 용법으로 쓰인 것은?

① You may come in if you wish.

② May she rest in peace!

③ The rumor may be false.

④ May I take a picture here?

⑤ You may stay at this hotel for a week.

13 위 글의 빈칸 ⓓ에 다음 정의에 해당하는 단어를 쓰시오.

to put one thing in or on the other thing, to increase, complete, or improve it

➡ _____

14 위 글의 밑줄 친 ⓔ와 바꿔 쓸 수 있는 것은? (2개)

① much　　② very

③ little　　④ a lot

⑤ many

[15~19] 다음 글을 읽고, 물음에 답하시오.

Your Mind_ You thought one thing at first, and now you think ____ⓐ____ thing. ⓑThat is okay. As someone said, "If you can change your mind, you can change your life."
"Focus on the things that are easy to change, and try ⓒto make today better than yesterday. Good luck!"
Top 5 Plans for the Year
We asked 200 *Teen Today* readers, "ⓓ올해의 계획은 무엇인가?"

15 위 글의 빈칸 ⓐ에 알맞은 것은?

① one   ② other
③ the other   ④ another
⑤ the others

서답형

16 위 글의 밑줄 친 ⓑ가 가리키는 것을 우리말로 쓰시오.

➡ _____

17 위 글의 밑줄 친 ⓒ와 같은 용법으로 쓰인 것은?

① We wished to reach the North Pole.
② I was sad to hear the music.
③ Please give me something to drink.
④ She has no house to live in.
⑤ He must study hard to pass the math exam.

서답형

18 위 글의 밑줄 친 ⓓ를 다음 주어진 말을 이용해서 영어로 옮기시오.

> (what, plans, the year)

➡ _____

19 위 글의 내용으로 보아 알 수 없는 것은?

① 사람의 생각은 바뀔 수 있다.
② 생각을 바꾸면 인생도 바꿀 수 있다.
③ 바꾸기 쉬운 일들에 초점을 맞추는 것이 좋다.
④ 바꾸기 어려운 일들에 도전할 필요가 있다.
⑤ 어제보다 더 낳은 오늘을 만들기 위해 노력해라.

[20~23] 다음 글을 읽고, 물음에 답하시오.

Let's think about things that are hard ⓐ*to change or easy to change.*
Things ⓑ**That Are Hard to Change**
Your Messy Room_ ⓒYou clean up it. Then you bring new stuff into it, and it soon gets messy again. But don't ____ⓓ____ . Your room is much cleaner than mine.

20 위 글의 밑줄 친 ⓐ와 용법이 같은 것은?

① We decided to visit the house.
② I need a baseball cap to wear.
③ Do you want to go skating now?
④ He made a promise to come again.
⑤ The house is comfortable to live in.

21 위 글의 밑줄 친 ⓑ 대신 쓸 수 있는 것은?

① Who   ② Whose

③ How   ④ What

⑤ Which

서답형

22 위 글의 밑줄 친 ⓒ를 어법상 <u>어색한</u> 것을 고쳐 다시 쓰시오.

➡ _____

중요

23 위 글의 빈칸 ⓓ에 문맥상 알맞은 것은?

① clean   ② worry

③ help   ④ keep

⑤ believe

[24~28] 다음 글을 읽고, 물음에 답하시오.

My Phone Habit

I want to change my phone habit. (①) I use my phone _____ⓐ_____ I feel bored. (②) I text my friends or play games on the phone. (③) ⓑ<u>From now on, I will do two things to break the habit.</u> (④) I will turn _____ⓒ_____ my phone after 10 p.m. (⑤) I will also download a phone control app to use my phone less often. If I feel bored, I will talk to my family or read comic books.

24 위 글의 ①~⑤ 중 다음 주어진 문장이 들어갈 알맞은 곳은?

> I know that it is a waste of time.

①   ②   ③   ④   ⑤

중요

25 위 글의 빈칸 ⓐ에 알맞은 것은?

① if   ② that

③ for   ④ when

⑤ though

서답형

26 위 글의 밑줄 친 ⓑ를 우리말로 옮기시오.

➡ _____

27 위 글의 빈칸 ⓒ에 알맞은 것은?

① on   ② off

③ to   ④ with

⑤ from

28 위 글의 내용으로 보아 대답할 수 <u>없는</u> 질문은?

① What does the writer want to do?

② What does the writer do with his or her phone?

③ What will the writer do to break his or her habit?

④ What apps does the writer usually download?

⑤ What will the writer do when he or she feels bored?

[01~04] 다음 글을 읽고, 물음에 답하시오.

Your Family_ There is always someone in your family ____ⓐ____ drives you crazy. Remember that he or she is still a member of your family. You just have to live together and ⓑcare for each other.

Your Name on Your Teacher's List_ ____ⓒ____ you are late or do not behave, your teacher will put your name on his or her list. You cannot easily change the list.

01 위 글의 빈칸 ⓐ에 알맞은 관계대명사를 쓰시오.

➡ _____

02 위 글의 밑줄 친 ⓑ와 같은 뜻이 되도록 빈칸에 알맞은 말을 쓰시오.

look _____

03 위 글의 빈칸 ⓒ에 알맞은 접속사를 쓰시오.

➡ _____

04 What can't you easily change? Answer in English.

➡ _____

[05~08] 다음 글을 읽고, 물음에 답하시오.

Things That Are Easy to Change
Your Underpants_ If you change ⓐthem every day, your mom will not tell you one hundred and one times.
Your Friends_ You can change your friends. ⓑDoes it sound strangely? You may think ____ⓒ____ you have the perfect number of friends. If you add a new friend to the list, however, you will feel even ⓓgood than before.

05 위 글의 밑줄 친 ⓐ가 가리키는 것을 우리말로 쓰시오.

➡ _____

06 위 글의 밑줄 친 ⓑ에서 어법상 틀린 것을 찾아 바르게 고쳐 쓰시오.

_____ ➡ _____

07 위 글의 빈칸 ⓒ에 알맞은 접속사를 쓰시오.

➡ _____

08 위 글의 밑줄 친 ⓓ를 알맞은 형으로 고치시오.

➡ _____

[09~13] 다음 글을 읽고, 물음에 답하시오.

Your Mind_ ⓐ You thought one thing at first, and now you think other thing. That is okay. As someone said, " ⓑ you can change your mind, you can change your life."

"Focus ⓒ the things that are easy to change, and try to make today better than yesterday. Good ⓓ !"

Top 5 Plans for the Year

We asked 200 *Teen Today* ⓔ read, "What are your plans for the year?"

09 위 글의 밑줄 친 ⓐ에서 어법상 어색한 것을 고치시오.

_____ ➡ _____

10 위 글의 빈칸 ⓑ에 알맞은 말을 쓰시오.

➡ _____

11 위 글의 빈칸 ⓒ에 알맞은 말을 쓰시오.

➡ _____

12 위 글의 빈칸 ⓓ에 다음 정의에 해당하는 단어를 쓰시오.

> success or good things that happen to you, that do not come from your own abilities or efforts

➡ _____

13 위 글의 밑줄 친 ⓔ를 알맞은 형으로 고치시오.

➡ _____

[14~18] 다음 글을 읽고, 물음에 답하시오.

ⓐ Minsol decided to have some downtime every weekends. She is planning to do some exercise ⓑ(like, alike) inline skating or bike riding. She is also going to see a movie ⓒ her friends. She will visit the art center to enjoy a free concert on the third Saturday of the month. On some weekends, she will stay home and ⓓ get some rest.

14 위 글의 밑줄 친 ⓐ에서 어법상 어색한 것을 고치시오.

_____ ➡ _____

15 위 글의 괄호 ⓑ에서 알맞은 것을 고르시오.

➡ _____

16 위 글의 빈칸 ⓒ에 알맞은 말을 쓰시오.

➡ _____

17 위 글의 밑줄 친 ⓓ와 바꿔 쓸 수 있는 말을 쓰시오.

➡ _____

18 What will Minsol do on the third Saturday of the month? Answer in English.

➡ _____

교과서

구석구석

My Speaking Portfolio - Step 3

"I have two goals for the year. First, I'd like to finish a 10km marathon. To

<u>I'd like to</u>+동사원형 ~: 나는 ~하고 싶다

achieve this goal, I'm planning to run for an hour every day. Also, I'm going to

to부정사의 부사적 용법(목적)   ~할 계획이다   매일   ~할 예정이다

jump rope every day. The other goal is ......"

줄넘기하다

구문해설 · goal: 목표 · finish: 끝내다 · achieve: 성취하다 · also: 또한 · other: 다른

해석

"나는 올해 두 가지 목표가 있다. 먼저 10킬로미터 마라톤을 완주하고 싶다. 이 목표를 달성하기 위해 나는 매일 한 시간씩 달릴 계획이다. 또한, 나는 매일 줄넘기를 할 것이다. 다른 목표는 ......"

My Writing Portfolio

My Phone Habit

I want to change my phone habit. I use my phone when I feel bored. I text my

<u>want to</u>+동사원형: ~하고 싶다   접 ~할 때   boring(×)

friends or play games on the phone. I know that it is a waste of time. From

전화로   접속사 that   이제부터

now on, I will do two things to break the habit. I will turn off my phone after

to부정사의 부사적 용법(목적)   ~을 끄다

10 p.m. I will also download a phone control app to use my phone less often.

to부정사의 부사적 용법(목적)   열등 비교급

If I feel bored, I will talk to my family or read comic books.

접 (만약) ~이라면 feel+형용사: ~하게 느끼다

구문해설 · habit: 습관 · change: 바꾸다 · text: 문자 메시지를 보내다 · waste: 낭비
· download: 다운로드하다[내려 받다] · control: 통제, 규제 · app: 앱, 어플리케이션
· less: 더 적게, 덜

내 전화 습관

나는 전화 습관을 바꾸고 싶다. 나는 지루할 때 전화기를 사용한다. 나는 전화로 친구들에게 문자를 보내거나 게임을 한다. 나는 그것이 시간 낭비라는 것을 안다. 이제부터 나는 그 습관을 없애기 위해 두 가지 일을 할 것이다. 나는 오후 10시 이후에 전화기를 끌 것이다. 나는 또한 내 전화를 덜 자주 사용하기 위해 전화 제어 앱을 다운로드할 것이다. 지루하면 가족과 이야기하거나 만화책을 읽을 것이다.

Wrap up - Reading

Minsol decided to have some downtime every weekend. She is planning to

decide to+동사원형: ~하기로 결정하다   주말마다   ~할 계획이다

do some exercise like inline skating or bike riding. She is also going to see a

~ 같은   be going to: ~할 셈이다

movie with her friends. She will visit the art center to enjoy a free concert on

to부정사의 부사적 용법(목적)   on+요일

the third Saturday of the month. On some weekends, she will stay home and

집에 머물다

get some rest.

휴식을 좀 취하다

구문해설 · downtime: 휴식 시간 · exercise: 운동 · free: 무료의 · third: 세 번째의

민솔은 주말마다 약간의 휴식 시간을 갖기로 결정했다. 그녀는 인라인 스케이트나 자전거 타기 같은 운동을 할 계획이다. 그녀는 또한 그녀의 친구들과 함께 영화를 볼 것이다. 그녀는 이달 셋째 주 토요일에 무료 콘서트를 즐기기 위해 예술 센터를 방문할 것이다. 어떤 주말에는, 그녀는 집에 머물면서 휴식을 취할 것이다.

영역별 핵심문제

01 다음 중 짝지어진 두 단어의 관계가 <u>다른</u> 것은?

① late – early ② full – hungry
③ fast – slow ④ relax – rest
⑤ useful – useless

02 다음 우리말에 맞게 빈칸에 알맞은 말을 쓰시오.

그들은 식료품점 앞에 차를 주차시키고 있다.
➡ They are parking _____ _____ of
the food store.

03 다음 영영풀이에 해당하는 단어는?

liked or enjoyed by many people

① useful ② popular
③ perfect ④ friendly
⑤ strange

04 다음 중 밑줄 친 부분의 의미가 나머지 넷과 <u>다른</u> 것은?

① How do I eat this <u>dish</u>?
② This <u>dish</u> is the only thing I can cook.
③ He cooked a chicken <u>dish</u> for dinner.
④ They helped themselves from a large <u>dish</u> of pasta.
⑤ This is a popular <u>dish</u> made of raw fish.

05 다음 빈칸에 알맞은 것은?

I want to focus _____ losing weight.

① in ② on
③ up ④ with
⑤ from

06 다음 빈칸에 들어갈 동사가 바르게 짝지어진 것은?

• We must _____ in line at a bus stop.
• There is always someone in your family who _____ you crazy.

① stand – puts ② take – takes
③ take – makes ④ stand – drives
⑤ stand – brings

07 다음 영영풀이에 해당하는 단어를 주어진 철자로 시작하여 쓰시오.

dirty and not neat

➡ m_____

08 다음 대화의 밑줄 친 부분의 의도로 알맞은 것은?

A: What's the matter?
B: I broke my arm.
A: <u>You'd better see a doctor.</u>

① 격려하기 ② 비난하기
③ 사과하기 ④ 금지하기
⑤ 충고하기

09 다음 대화의 빈칸에 알맞은 것은?

A: _____

B: We are thinking of having a surprise party.

① Where are you going?
② What do you want to be?
③ What would you like to have?
④ What are you planning to do?
⑤ When are you having a surprising party?

10 다음 대화의 밑줄 친 부분과 의미가 다른 것은?

A: I have a terrible cold.
B: You should see a doctor.

① I advise you to see a doctor.
② How about seeing a doctor?
③ Why don't you see a doctor?
④ You'd better see a doctor.
⑤ You want to see a doctor.

11 다음 짝지어진 대화 중 어색한 것은?

① A: What should I do?
   B: You should close the door.
② A: What are you going to do tomorrow?
   B: I'm thinking of going fishing.
③ A: Can you give me some advice?
   B: You'd better read it more closely.
④ A: What are you going to do next weekend?
   B: Nothing special. I'm looking forward to it.
⑤ A: Do you have any plans for next weekend?
   B: Yes. I'll go fishing with my brother.

[12~15] 다음 대화를 읽고, 물음에 답하시오.

G: Can I talk with you ⓐ a minute, Minsu?
B: Sure. What is it?
G: I'm working on my weekly schedule.
B: Really? Good ⓑ you, little sister.
G: Here. ⓒ a look and give me some advice.
B: Hmm, you have a lot of study time.
G: Yeah, ⓓ나는 열심히 공부할 계획이다.
B: ⓔWhy don't you add some downtime?
G: Downtime?
B: Yeah, I mean you need to relax once in a while.

12 위 대화의 빈칸 ⓐ와 ⓑ에 공통으로 알맞은 것은?

① in   ② of
③ for   ④ to
⑤ with

13 위 대화의 빈칸 ⓒ에 알맞은 것은?

① Get   ② Make
③ Hold   ④ Bring
⑤ Have

14 위 대화의 밑줄 친 ⓓ의 우리말을 주어진 단어를 이용하여 영어로 옮기시오.

(plan / hard)

➡ _____

15 위 대화의 밑줄 친 ⓔ와 같은 의미가 되도록 빈칸에 알맞은 말을 쓰시오.

You'd _____ add some downtime.

[16~17] 다음 문장의 빈칸에 알맞은 것을 고르시오.

16
Susan is the girl _____ comes from New Zealand.

① who   ② what
③ whom   ④ which
⑤ whose

17
If you _____, you will be late for the movie.

① hurry   ② will hurry
③ don't hurry ④ won't hurry
⑤ aren't

18 다음 빈칸에 공통으로 알맞은 것은?

• Look at the bird _____ is standing with one leg.
• Mike, _____ food do you like better, pizza or hamburgers?

① who   ② which
③ that   ④ where
⑤ what

19 다음 밑줄 친 부분을 어법에 맞게 고쳐 쓰시오.

Unless I <u>am not</u> busy, I'll go to Disney Land this Sunday.

➡ _____

20 다음 문장의 빈칸에 알맞지 <u>않은</u> 것은?

Everybody stopped to see _____ that were playing together.

① the boy   ② the tigers
③ the children   ④ a cat and a dog
⑤ a man and a monkey

21 다음 빈칸에 공통으로 알맞은 것은?

• I'm not going to work tomorrow _____ I don't feel well.
• I'm not sure _____ he will enter the speech contest.

① if   ② so
③ that   ④ since
⑤ whether

22 다음 중 밑줄 친 부분의 쓰임이 나머지 넷과 <u>다른</u> 것은?

① Please tell me <u>which</u> is your notebook.
② Can you see the bird <u>which</u> is flying over there?
③ Look at the castle <u>which</u> stands on the hill.
④ I will give him the vase <u>which</u> is very expensive.
⑤ This is the dictionary <u>which</u> gives me the meaning of words.

23 다음 우리말과 의미가 같도록 빈칸에 알맞은 말을 쓰시오.

> 너는 피곤하다면, 쉬어도 된다.
>
> ➡ _____ you _____ tired, you may take a rest.

[24~25] 다음 중 어법상 어색한 문장을 고르시오.

24 ① He is the only man that can solve the problems.
② Korea is a country which exports cars all over the world.
③ I have a dog which has long ears.
④ There is a man at the door who wants to see you.
⑤ The men who is in front of the house are my friends.

25 ① Unless it doesn't rain, we'll go hiking.
② As I'm sick, I can't go out.
③ While I was sleeping, he did the dishes.
④ Although he is usually brave, he is afraid of the dark.
⑤ I won't go to bed until they come back home.

26 다음 두 문장을 한 문장으로 바꿔 쓰시오.

> • What is the name of the tallest boy?
> • He just came in.

➡ _____

_____

Reading

[27~30] 다음 글을 읽고, 물음에 답하시오.

Beginning a new school year is stressful to many students. How can we get ___ⓐ___ to a good start? *Teen Today* asked Raccoon 97, a popular webtoon ⓑart, for ideas.
ⓒ*Let's think about things that are hard to change or easy to change.*
Things That Are Hard to Change
Your Messy Room_ You clean it up. Then you bring new stuff into it, and it soon gets messy again. ___ⓓ___ don't worry. Your room is much cleaner than mine.

27 위 글의 빈칸 ⓐ에 알맞은 것은?

① of
② off
③ for
④ with
⑤ from

28 위 글의 밑줄 친 ⓑ를 알맞은 형으로 고치시오.

➡ _____

29 위 글의 밑줄 친 ⓒ를 우리말로 옮기시오.

➡ _____

30 위 글의 빈칸 ⓓ에 알맞은 것은?

① And
② Or
③ But
④ For
⑤ Because

[31~34] 다음 글을 읽고, 물음에 답하시오.

My Phone Habit

I want to change my phone habit. I use my phone ①when I feel bored. ⓐ나는 전화기로 친구들에게 문자를 보내거나 게임을 한다. I know ②that it is a waste of time. From now on, I will do two things to ___ⓑ___ the habit. I will ③turn on my phone after 10 p.m. I will also download a phone control app ⓒto use my phone less often. ④If I feel bored, I will talk to my family ⑤or read comic books.

31 위 글의 밑줄 친 ①~⑤ 중 글의 흐름상 어색한 것은?

①   ②   ③   ④   ⑤

32 위 글의 밑줄 친 ⓐ를 주어진 어구를 이용해 영어로 옮기시오.

(text, play games, on the phone)

➡ _____

33 위 글의 빈칸 ⓑ에 알맞은 것은?

① stop   ② break
③ fix   ④ play
⑤ bring

34 위 글의 밑줄 친 ⓒ와 같은 용법으로 쓰인 것은?

① I have a baseball cap to wear.
② Love is to trust each other.
③ To live without air is impossible.
④ I went to a shopping mall to buy clothes.
⑤ I have some homework to do today.

[35~38] 다음 글을 읽고, 물음에 답하시오.

ⓐMinsol decided having some downtime every weekend. She is planning to do some exercise ⓑlike inline skating or bike riding. She is also going to see a movie with her friends. She will visit the art center to enjoy a ___ⓒ___ concert on the third Saturday of the month. On some weekends, she will stay home and get some rest.

35 위 글의 밑줄 친 ⓐ에서 어법상 어색한 것을 고치시오.

_____ ➡ _____

36 위 글의 밑줄 친 ⓑ와 같은 용법으로 쓰인 것은?

① Do you like apples?
② I like to watch baseball on TV.
③ How do you like this movie?
④ I like to walk in the park on Sundays.
⑤ I want to buy a hat like yours.

37 위 글의 빈칸 ⓒ에 다음 정의에 해당하는 단어를 쓰시오.

without paying for something

➡ _____

38 위 글의 내용과 일치하지 않는 것은?

① 민솔은 매주 한가한 시간을 즐겨 왔다.
② 민솔은 인라인 스케이트나 자전거를 탈 계획이다.
③ 민솔은 친구들과 영화를 보러 갈 것이다.
④ 민솔은 매달 세 번째 토요일은 콘서트를 보러 갈 것이다.
⑤ 민솔은 몇몇 주말에는 집에서 휴식을 취할 것이다.

01 출제율 95%

다음 짝지어진 두 단어의 관계가 같도록 빈칸에 알맞은 말을 쓰시오.

light : heavy = _____ : save

02 출제율 90%

다음 영영풀이에 해당하는 단어는?

to get or reach something by working hard

① behave   ② relax
③ search   ④ allow
⑤ achieve

03 출제율 100%

다음 빈칸에 공통으로 알맞은 것은?

- Everyone needs a break once _____ a while.
- People are standing _____ line to get tickets.

① to   ② of
③ in   ④ with
⑤ for

04 출제율 90%

다음 우리말에 맞게 빈칸에 알맞은 말을 쓰시오. (주어진 철자로 시작할 것)

민솔은 주말마다 약간의 휴식 시간을 갖기로 했다.
➡ Minsol decided to have some d_____ every weekend.

05 출제율 90%

다음 문장과 바꿔 쓸 수 없는 것을 모두 고르면?

I'm planning to buy second-hand books.

① I'm going to buy second-hand books.
② I'm thinking of buying second-hand books.
③ I used to buy second-hand books.
④ I should buy second-hand books.
⑤ I'll buy second-hand books.

06 출제율 100%

다음 대화의 밑줄 친 표현과 바꾸어 쓸 수 있는 것은?

A: I can't get up early in the morning. Can you give me some advice?
B: You'd better go to bed earlier at night.

① Shall we go to bed earlier at night?
② You may not go to bed earlier at night.
③ How about go to bed earlier at night?
④ Why don't you go to bed earlier at night?
⑤ You should not go to bed earlier at night.

07 출제율 95%

다음 대화의 순서를 바르게 배열하시오.

(A) You should jump rope every day.
(B) I want to grow taller. What should I do?
(C) All right. I'll give it a try.
(D) You look down. What's wrong?

➡ _____

[08~11] 다음 대화를 읽고, 물음에 답하시오.

> W: Hi, Jongha.
> B: Hello, Grandma. I'd like to visit you this Saturday.
> W: That'll be great. We can plant some vegetables together.
> B: Really? What kind of vegetables?
> W: This time, ⓐI'm planning to plant some tomatoes and peppers.
> B: Wow! That'll be fun.
> W: I heard it's going to be sunny this Saturday. ⓑYou should bring your cap.
> B: Okay, I will.
> W: ⓒWhy don't you put on sunscreen before you leave?
> B: No problem. I'll see you on Saturday.
> W: Okay. Bye.

08 위 대화의 밑줄 친 ⓐ와 바꿔 쓸 수 있는 것을 모두 고르면?

① I'll
② I must
③ I would
④ I hope to
⑤ I'm going to

09 위 대화의 밑줄 친 ⓑ와 바꿔 쓸 수 없는 것은?

① What about bringing your cap?
② I advise you to bring your cap.
③ How about bringing your cap?
④ You'd better bring your cap.
⑤ Why didn't you bring your cap?

10 위 대화의 밑줄 친 ⓒ의 의도로 알맞은 것은?

① to say hello
② to order some food
③ to give some advice
④ to agree with the boy
⑤ to give thanks

11 위 대화를 읽고, 답할 수 없는 질문은?

① When is Jongha going to visit Grandma?
② What is Grandma planning to do this Saturday?
③ What style of cap does Jongha have?
④ What's the weather going to be like this Saturday?
⑤ What should Jongha put on before he visits Grandma?

12 다음 문장의 빈칸에 알맞은 것을 고르시오.

> If it _____ tomorrow, we won't go fishing.

① rain
② rains
③ rained
④ will rain
⑤ would rain

13 다음 두 문장을 한 문장으로 연결할 때 빈칸에 알맞은 것은?

> There is a girl. She is sitting on the bench.
> ➡ There is a girl _____ is sitting on the bench.

① who
② what
③ whom
④ which
⑤ whose

14 출제율 90%

다음 세 문장의 뜻이 같도록 빈칸에 들어갈 말을 순서대로 짝지은 것은?

> Don't touch the button, or you'll be in danger.
> = _____ you touch the button, you'll be in danger.
> = _____ you touch the button, you won't be in danger.

① If − If
② If − Unless
③ Unless − If
④ As − If
⑤ Unless − As

15 출제율 100%

다음 중 밑줄 친 부분의 쓰임이 나머지 넷과 다른 것은?

① I want to know <u>who</u> she is.
② This is the boy <u>who</u> came from Africa.
③ The man <u>who</u> is in the room is my cousin.
④ Do you know the man <u>who</u> is wearing a blue jumper?
⑤ The teacher likes the students <u>who</u> ask many questions.

16 출제율 85%

다음 문장 중 어법상 어색한 것은?

① Unless he is late, we will start on time.
② Don't open the box until he says it's safe.
③ I'll go swimming if it will be sunny.
④ She will be happy when he sends her some flowers.
⑤ I'll wait here until the concert is over.

[17~21] 다음 글을 읽고, 물음에 답하시오.

Your Family_ There is always someone in your family ___ⓐ___ drives you crazy. Remember ⓑ<u>that</u> he or she is still a member of your family. You just have to live together and care ___ⓒ___ each other.

Your Name on Your Teacher's List_ ___ⓓ___ you are late or do not behave, your teacher will put your name on his or her list. You cannot easily change the list.

17 출제율 95%

위 글의 빈칸 ⓐ에 알맞은 것은? (2개)

① who
② whom
③ whose
④ that
⑤ what

18 출제율 85%

위 글의 밑줄 친 ⓑ와 용법이 같은 것은?

① It is strange <u>that</u> she doesn't come.
② I know <u>that</u> you don't like cats.
③ Look at the trees <u>that</u> stand on the hill.
④ It was here <u>that</u> she first met Mike.
⑤ This is the doll <u>that</u> my mother made for me.

19 출제율 90%

위 글의 빈칸 ⓒ에 알맞은 것은?

① to
② at
③ into
④ for
⑤ with

✏ 출제율 95%

20 위 글의 빈칸 @에 알맞은 것은?

① If   ② As
③ After   ④ Till
⑤ Because

✏ 출제율 90%

21 위 글의 내용으로 보아 알 수 없는 것은?

① 가족 중에는 여러분과 사이가 좋지 않은 사람이 있다.
② 가족은 함께 살아야 한다.
③ 가족은 서로 돌보아야 한다.
④ 학교에서는 예의 바르게 행동해야 한다.
⑤ 선생님은 학생들의 잘못에 관대하시다.

[22~27] 다음 글을 읽고, 물음에 답하시오.

Minsol decided @to have some downtime every weekend. She is planning to do some exercise ⓑsuch as inline skating or bike riding. She is also going to see a movie ⓒ with her friends. She will visit the art center to enjoy a free concert ___@___ the third Saturday of the month. On some weekends, she will stay home and ___ⓔ___ some rest.

✏ 출제율 100%

22 위 글의 밑줄 친 @와 같은 용법으로 쓰인 것은? (2개)

① He has made a promise to help me.
② We wanted to go fishing in the river.
③ They sent some people to live on the planet.
④ Where do you intend to spend your vacation?
⑤ I awoke to find myself lying on the floor.

✏ 출제율 90%

23 위 글의 밑줄 친 ⓑ와 같은 뜻의 한 단어로 바꿔 쓰시오.

➡ _____

✏ 출제율 85%

24 위 글의 밑줄 친 ⓒ와 같은 의미로 쓰인 것은?

① I often play with my classmates.
② Lucy is the girl with long hair.
③ Don't write with a pencil.
④ Do you agree with him?
⑤ Ben was pleased with the present.

✏ 출제율 90%

25 위 글의 빈칸 @에 알맞은 것은?

① at   ② on
③ in   ④ to
⑤ from

✏ 출제율 95%

26 위 글의 빈칸 ⓔ에 알맞은 것은? (3개)

① have   ② get
③ make   ④ take
⑤ hold

✏ 출제율 90%

27 위 글의 내용으로 보아 대답할 수 없는 질문은?

① What did Minsol decide to do?
② How busy was Minsol every weekend?
③ With whom is Minsol going to see a movie?
④ When will Minsol visit the art center?
⑤ Will Minsol stay home on some weekends?

01 다음 대화의 괄호 안에서 알맞은 것을 고르시오.

> A: What did you throw in the trash can?
> B: A juice bottle, Mom.
> A: You (would / should) put it in the recycling box.

02 다음 괄호 안의 단어들을 순서대로 배열하시오.

> A: I'm planning to go to the ballpark this Friday.
> B: (you / glove / why / your / baseball / don't / take)?

➡ _____

03 다음 대화의 빈칸에 공통으로 알맞은 단어를 쓰시오.

> A: I want to grow taller. What _____ I do?
> B: You _____ jump rope every day.

04 다음 밑줄 친 부분과 유사한 표현을 쓰시오. (3문장 이상)

> A: I often get up late.
> B: You'd better go to bed early.

➡ _____
_____
_____

05 다음 우리말과 같도록 빈칸에 알맞은 말을 넣어 대화를 완성하시오.

> A: (1) _____ this Saturday? (너는 이번 토요일에 뭐 할 계획이니?)
> B: (2) _____ baseball with Tim and Nick. (나는 Tim 그리고 Nick과 함께 야구를 할 생각이야.)

06 다음 두 문장을 관계대명사를 써서 한 문장으로 나타내시오.

(1) Dad cooks me a fried egg. It is my favorite.

➡ _____

(2) I have an uncle. He is a math teacher.

➡ _____

(3) She has a bird. It speaks English.

➡ _____

07 다음 우리말을 괄호 안의 단어를 이용하여 영어로 옮기시오.

(1) 열이 있으면 너는 의사의 진찰을 받아야 한다.
(have, you, fever, should, see, doctor)

➡ _____

(2) 내일 비가 오면 난 영화 보러 갈 거야.
(rain, tomorrow, it, go, a movie)

➡ _____

(3) 파란색에 노란색을 더하면 초록색이 된다.
(add, to, blue, green, yellow, you, it, become)

➡ _____

08 다음 문장에서 어법상 어색한 것을 찾아 바르게 고치시오. 중요

(1) The animals that is in cages are not happy.

_____ ➡ _____

(2) Where is the letter who came from Cathy this morning?

_____ ➡ _____

(3) The boy and the dog who fell into the river were saved.

_____ ➡ _____

[09~12] 다음 글을 읽고, 물음에 답하시오.

Your Friends_ You can change your friends. Does ⓐit sound strange? ⓑ여러분은 완벽한 수의 친구를 가지고 있다고 생각할지도 모른다. If you add a new friend ⓒ the list, however, ⓓyou will feel very better than before.

09 위 글의 밑줄 친 ⓐ가 가리키는 것을 우리말로 쓰시오. 중요

➡ _____

10 위 글의 밑줄 친 ⓑ를 주어진 말을 이용하여 영어로 옮기시오.

(may, that, have, perfect, number, friends)

➡ _____

_____

11 위 글의 빈칸 ⓒ에 알맞은 말을 쓰시오.

➡ _____

12 위 글의 밑줄 친 ⓓ에서 어법상 어색한 것을 고치시오. 중요

_____ ➡ _____

[13~15] 다음 글을 읽고, 물음에 답하시오.

Your Mind_ You thought one thing at first, and now you think another thing. ⓐThat is okay. As someone said, "If you can change your ___ⓑ___, you can change your ___ⓒ___." "Focus on the things ⓓthat are easy to change, and try to make today better than yesterday. Good luck!"

13 위 글의 밑줄 친 ⓐ가 가리키는 것을 우리말로 쓰시오.

➡ _____

14 위 글의 빈칸 ⓑ와 ⓒ에 알맞은 것을 다음 〈보기〉에서 골라 쓰시오.

┌─ 보기 ─────────────────────┐
live, mind, think, life
└───────────────────────────┘

ⓑ _____ ⓒ _____

15 다음은 위 글의 글쓴이가 주장하는 말이다. 빈칸에 알맞은 말을 넣어 문장을 완성하시오. 중요

┌──────────────────────────────┐
Your _____ can _____ . You should _____ to make _____ better than _____ .
└──────────────────────────────┘

01 다음 주어진 단어를 활용하여 예시와 같이 쓰시오.

Teacher	teach, students, school	ex) A teacher is someone who teaches students at a school.
Waiter	serve, food, restaurant	(1)
Zookeeper	look after, animals, zoo	(2)
Dessert	sweet food, serve, after meal	(3)

(1) _____

(2) _____

(3) _____

02 다음 (A)와 (B)에서 의미상 어울리는 것끼리 연결하여 〈보기〉와 같이 한 문장으로 쓰시오.

┌─ 보기 ─┐

If Mike proposes to her, she will marry him.

(A)	(B)
Andy is free next Sunday my brother doesn't get any better I win the first prize on the test	I take him to the hospital I go to a movie with him my mom buys me an i-Pad

(1) _____

(2) _____

(3) _____

03 다음과 같은 상황이 벌어진다면 어떨지 상상하여 〈보기〉와 같이 쓰시오.

• get an A on the math test	• go to China
• it is sunny tomorrow	• find an abandoned dog on the street

┌─ 보기 ─┐

If I get an A on the math test, I will be very happy.

(1) _____

(2) _____

(3) _____

단원별 모의고사

01 다음 중 짝지어진 단어의 관계가 <u>다른</u> 것은?

① full – hungry
② easy – difficult
③ messy – dirty
④ different – same
⑤ boring – interesting

02 다음 중 영영풀이가 <u>잘못된</u> 것은?

① free: not costing any money
② change: to put on different clothes
③ birth: the time when a baby is born
④ waste: to spend less money
⑤ goal: something that you are trying to do or achieve

03 다음 빈칸에 알맞은 말이 바르게 짝지어진 것은?

- Students should focus _____ studying.
- I don't really care _____ that kind of music.

① at – up
② in – of
③ with – in
④ on – for
⑤ for – about

04 다음 빈칸에 공통으로 알맞은 것은?

- The bag looks heavy, but it is _____.
- We're planning to leave as soon as it's _____.

① dark
② cool
③ bright
④ dull
⑤ light

05 다음 우리말에 맞도록 빈칸에 알맞은 말을 쓰시오.

이제부터 나는 물을 낭비하지 않을 거야.
➡ From now _____, I will not waste water.

06 다음 대화의 빈칸에 알맞은 것은?

A: I heard you're going to France. Do you have any special plans in mind?
B: _____ the Eiffel Tower.

① I saw
② I have seen
③ I'm planning to see
④ I have to climb
⑤ I want to stay

07 다음 대화의 밑줄 친 표현과 바꾸어 쓸 수 있는 것은?

A: You don't look well. What's wrong with you?
B: I got a terrible score on the English test.
A: <u>You should read some English books.</u>
B: All right. I'll give it a try.

① The English book is very funny.
② I like reading some English books.
③ You'd better buy some English books.
④ You can read some English books loudly.
⑤ How about reading some English books?

[08~11] 다음 대화를 읽고, 물음에 답하시오.

> G: Can I talk with you for a minute, Minsu?
> B: _____ ⓐ _____ What is it?
> G: I'm working on my weekly schedule.
> B: Really? Good for you, little sister.
> G: Here. Have a look and give me some advice.
> B: Hmm, you have a lot of study time.
> G: Yeah, I'm planning to study hard.
> B: ⓑ(some / don't / add / why / downtime / you)?
> G: Downtime?
> B: Yeah, I mean you need to relax ⓒ<u>once in a while</u>.

08 위 대화의 빈칸 ⓐ에 들어갈 말로 적절하지 <u>않은</u> 것은?

① Sure.　　　　　② Certainly.
③ Of course.　　④ No problem.
⑤ Not at all.

09 위 대화의 괄호 ⓑ 안의 단어를 순서대로 배열하시오.

➡ _____

10 위 대화의 밑줄 친 ⓒ와 바꿔 쓸 수 있는 것은?

① these days　　② before long
③ in no time　　④ in a moment
⑤ now and then

11 위 대화를 읽고, 답할 수 <u>없는</u> 질문은?

① What is the girl doing?
② What is the girl planning to do?
③ How many hours does the girl study?
④ What is Minsu's advice to the girl?
⑤ What does the girl need to do?

[12~13] 다음 문장의 빈칸에 알맞은 것을 고르시오.

12
> If it _____, we'll play soccer outside.

① won't rain　　② don't rain
③ doesn't rain　④ didn't rain
⑤ hadn't rained

13
> _____ she is sick, she won't be absent from school.

① If　　　　② Though
③ When　　④ Unless
⑤ Because

14 다음 문장에서 틀린 것을 고치시오.

> I have three books that tells us about China.

_____ ➡ _____

15 다음 빈칸에 알맞은 말이 순서대로 바르게 짝지어진 것은?

> • Jenny is the famous singer _____ appeared on TV last night.
> • I bought a chair _____ was made of wood.

① who – which　　② whom – that
③ which – who　　④ which – which
⑤ whose – that

16 다음 두 문장이 같은 뜻이 되도록 빈칸에 알맞은 말을 쓰시오.

> If you don't stop shouting, they will call the police.
> = Unless _____ _____ shouting, they will call the police.

[17~18] 다음 중 어법상 알맞지 <u>않은</u> 문장을 고르시오.

17 ① If he helps me, I can carry this easily.
② If you don't have breakfast, you will feel hungry soon.
③ If you will leave now, you can get there on time.
④ If she makes a lot of money, she will buy a car.
⑤ If school finishes early today, we'll go to the movies.

18 ① There's a house which has two chimneys.
② Can you see a boy who is running along the river?
③ I visited a town that is famous as a hot spring resort.
④ Mark is the cook who was on TV last night.
⑤ The man who is sitting on the box have a problem.

19 다음 두 문장의 의미가 같도록 빈칸에 알맞은 것은?

> If you don't eat breakfast, you can't focus on your studies.
> = _____ you eat breakfast, you can't focus on your studies.

① When   ② While
③ Because   ④ Unless
⑤ Although

[20~23] 다음 글을 읽고, 물음에 답하시오.

My Phone Habit
  I want to change my phone habit. I use my phone when I feel bored. I text my friends or play games ____ⓐ____ the phone. I know that it is a waste of time. From now ____ⓑ____, I will do two things to break the habit. I will turn ____ⓒ____ my phone after 10 p.m. I will also download a phone control app to use my phone ____ⓓ____ often. If I feel bored, I will talk to my family or read comic books.

20 위 글의 빈칸 ⓐ와 ⓑ에 공통으로 알맞은 것은?

① at   ② on
③ to   ④ till
⑤ after

21 위 글의 빈칸 ⓒ에 알맞은 것은?

① up   ② on
③ off   ④ from
⑤ over

22 위 글의 빈칸 ⓓ에 알맞은 것은?

① much   ② many
③ little   ④ more
⑤ less

23 위 글의 내용으로 보아 알 수 <u>없는</u> 것은?

① 글쓴이는 전화 습관을 바꾸기를 원한다.
② 글쓴이는 전화기로 친구들에게 문자를 보낸다.
③ 글쓴이는 전화기가 아주 유용하다고 생각한다.
④ 글쓴이는 오후 10시 이후에 전화기를 사용하지 않을 것이다.
⑤ 글쓴이는 심심하면 만화책을 읽을 것이다.

[24~26] 다음 글을 읽고, 물음에 답하시오.

(①) Minsol decided to have some downtime every weekend. (②) She is planning to do some exercise like inline skating or bike riding. (③) She is also going to see a movie with her friends. (④) She will visit the art center to enjoy a ⓐfree concert on the third Saturday of the month. (⑤)

24 위 글의 ①~⑤ 중 다음 주어진 문장이 들어갈 알맞은 곳은?

> On some weekends, she will stay home and get some rest.

①   ②   ③   ④   ⑤

25 위 글의 밑줄 친 ⓐ와 의미가 같은 것은?

① Are you free next Sunday?

② You are free to use my computer.

③ I have two free tickets for the musical.

④ The slaves finally became free.

⑤ I'm free all day today.

26 위 글을 읽고, 다음 질문에 완전한 문장으로 답하시오.

> When will Minsol visit the art center?

➡ _____

[27~30] 다음 글을 읽고, 물음에 답하시오.

Your Mind_ You thought one thing ⓐ first, and now you think another thing. That is okay. ⓑAs someone said, "If you can change your mind, you can change your ⓒlive." "Focus ⓓ the things that are easy to change, and try to make today better than yesterday. Good luck!"

27 위 글의 빈칸 ⓐ에 알맞은 것은?

① at   ② on

③ to   ④ till

⑤ after

28 위 글의 밑줄 친 ⓑ와 같은 의미로 쓰인 것은?

① They treated me as a friend.

② As it was fine, I went outside.

③ Do it as I asked.

④ As he grew older, he became wiser.

⑤ As you know, Julia is leaving soon.

29 위 글의 밑줄 친 ⓒ를 알맞은 형으로 고치시오.

➡ _____

30 위 글의 빈칸 ⓓ에 알맞은 것은?

① to   ② on

③ at   ④ in

⑤ for

Lesson 2

Connecting with the World

의사소통 기능

- 음식 권하고 답하기
  A: Would you like some *bibimbap*?
  B: Yes, please.

- 표현의 의미 묻고 답하기
  A: What do you mean by "landmarks"?
  B: I mean important places or special buildings.

언어 형식

- 목적격 관계대명사
  The woman **whom** I love most is my grandma.

- 의문사+ to부정사
  I can't decide **what to eat** first.

Words & Expressions

Key Words

- **admission fee** 입장료
- **appear** [əpíər] 동 나타나다
- **arrive** [əráiv] 동 도착하다
- **audition** [ɔ:díʃən] 명 오디션
- **carefully** [kɛ́ərfəli] 부 조심스럽게, 신중히
- **communicate** [kəmjú:nəkèit] 동 의사소통하다
- **country** [kʌ́ntri] 명 나라, 시골
- **culture** [kʌ́ltʃər] 명 문화
- **delicious** [dilíʃəs] 형 맛있는
- **different** [dífərənt] 형 다른
- **enough** [inʌf] 형 충분한
- **expression** [ikspréʃən] 명 표현
- **famous** [féiməs] 형 유명한
- **fantastic** [fæntǽstik] 형 환상적인
- **finally** [fáinəli] 부 마침내
- **follow** [fálou] 동 따라가다
- **fortune** [fɔ́:rtʃən] 명 운, 행운
- **growl** [graul] 동 꼬르륵거리다
- **hold** [hould] 동 ~을 들고 있다
- **however** [hauévər] 부 그러나
- **important** [impɔ́:rtənt] 형 중요한
- **information** [ìnfərméiʃən] 명 정보
- **kick** [kik] 동 (발로) 차다
- **knock** [nak] 명 노크[문 두드리는] 소리
- **landmark** [lǽndmà:rk] 명 주요 지형지물, 랜드마크
- **laugh** [læf] 동 웃다
- **mean** [mi:n] 동 ~을 뜻하다[의미하다]

- **meaning** [mí:niŋ] 명 의미
- **nervous** [nə́:rvəs] 형 긴장한
- **nothing** [nʌ́θiŋ] 대 아무것도 ~ 아니다
- **offer** [ɔ́:fər] 동 제의하다, 권하다
- **official language** 공용어
- **opening hour** 개장 시간
- **pass** [pæs] 동 합격하다
- **radio station** 라디오 방송국
- **remember** [rimémbək] 동 기억하다
- **repeat** [ripí:t] 동 반복하다
- **respond** [rispánd] 동 대답[응답]하다
- **save** [seiv] 동 남겨 두다, 저축하다
- **shout** [ʃaut] 동 외치다, 소리치다
- **special** [spéʃəl] 형 특별한
- **stick** [stik] 명 막대기
- **stomach** [stʌ́mək] 명 위
- **suddenly** [sʌ́dnli] 부 갑자기
- **theater** [θí:ətər] 명 극장
- **thumping** [θʌ́mpiŋ] 형 쿵쾅거리는
- **traditional** [trədíʃənl] 형 전통의, 전통적인
- **translation** [trænsléiʃən] 명 번역, 통역
- **translator** [trænsléitər] 명 번역가, 번역기
- **travel** [trǽvəl] 동 여행하다
- **traveler** [trǽvələr] 명 여행객
- **understand** [ʌ̀ndərstǽnd] 동 이해하다
- **way** [wei] 명 길, 방법
- **work** [wə́:rk] 동 효력이 있다

Key Expressions

- **be useful for** ~에 유용하다
- **Break a leg!** 행운을 빌어!
- **find out** ~에 대해 알아내다[알게 되다]
- **focus on** ~에 집중하다, ~에 중점을 두다
- **for a while** 잠깐, 잠시 동안
- **for example** 예를 들어
- **hurry up** 서두르다
- **in half an hour** 30분 후에
- **look around** ~을 둘러보다

- **point to** ~을 가리키다
- **right now** 지금 곧, 당장
- **stay behind** 뒤에 남다, 출발하지 않다
- **step onto** ~에 올라타다
- **sound like** ~처럼 들리다
- **sure enough** 아니나 다를까
- **try to** ~하려고 노력하다
- **walk in** ~ 안으로 들어가다
- **what kind of** 어떤 종류의

Words Power

※ 국가명 – 언어명

□ **Italy**(이탈리아) → **Italian**(이탈리아어)

□ **Russia** (러시아) → **Russian** (러시아어)

□ **China** (중국) → **Chinese** (중국어)

□ **Spain** (스페인) → **Spanish** (스페인어)

□ **Greece** (그리스) → **Greek** (그리스어)

□ **Turkey** (터키) → **Turkish** (터키어)

□ **France** (프랑스) → **French** (프랑스어)

□ **Vietnam** (베트남) → **Vietnamese** (베트남어)

□ **Germany** (독일) → **German** (독일어)

□ **Portugal** (포르투갈) → **Portuguese** (포르투갈어)

□ **Thailand** (태국) → **Thai** (태국어)

□ **Japan** (일본) → **Japanese** (일본어)

English Dictionary

□ **communicate** 의사소통하다
→ to make your ideas, feelings, thoughts, etc. known to other people so that they understand them
당신의 생각, 감정, 생각 등을 다른 사람들에게 알리고 그들이 그것들을 이해할 수 있도록 하다

□ **culture** 문화
→ the customs and beliefs, art, way of life, and social organization of a particular country or group
특정 국가 또는 집단의 관습과 신념, 예술, 생활 방식, 사회 조직

□ **enough** 충분한
→ as many or as much as someone needs or wants
누군가 필요하거나 원하는 만큼 또는 많이

□ **expression** 표현
→ things that people say, write, or do in order to show their feelings, opinions, and ideas
사람들이 자신의 감정, 의견, 생각을 보여주기 위해 말하거나, 글을 쓰거나 또는 하는 것들

□ **fortune** 운, 행운
→ chance or luck, especially in the way it affects people's lives
기회 또는 운, 특히 그것이 사람의 삶에 영향을 미치는 운[행운]

□ **information** 정보
→ facts or details about someone or something
누군가 또는 무언가에 대한 사실이나 세부사항

□ **landmark** 주요 지형물, 랜드마크
→ an object or structure on land that is easy to see and recognize
눈에 잘 띄고 알아보기 쉬운 지상의 물체나 구조물

□ **nervous** 긴장한
→ anxious about something or afraid of something
어떤 것을 걱정하거나 두려워하는

□ **pass** 합격하다
→ to achieve the required standard in an exam, a test, etc.
시험 등에서 요구되는 기준을 달성하다

□ **repeat** 반복하다
→ to say something again
어떤 것을 다시 말하다

□ **respond** 대답[응답]하다
→ to say or write something as an answer to a question or request
질문이나 요청에 대한 응답으로 어떤 것을 말하거나 쓰다

□ **save** 남겨 두다, 저축하다
→ to keep something available for use in the future
나중에 사용할 수 있도록 어떤 것을 가지고 있다

□ **shout** 외치다, 소리 지르다
→ to say something very loudly, usually because you want people a long distance away to hear you
보통 멀리 떨어져 있는 사람들이 너의 말을 듣기를 원하기 때문에 어떤 말을 아주 크게 말하다

□ **translation** 번역
→ words that have been changed from one language into a different language
한 언어에서 다른 언어로 옮겨진 글[말]

□ **work** 효력이 있다
→ to have the intended effect or result
의도하는 효과나 결과를 갖다

01 다음 중 짝지어진 단어의 관계가 <u>다른</u> 것은?

① cry – laugh
② full – hungry
③ arrive – depart
④ different – same
⑤ delicious – tasty

서답형

02 다음 우리말에 맞게 빈칸에 알맞은 말을 쓰시오.

입장료는 청소년과 아이들은 3,000원이다.
➡ The _____ fee is 3,000 won for teens and children.

 중요

03 다음 영영풀이에 해당하는 단어로 알맞은 것은?

things that people say, write, or do in order to show their feelings, opinions, and ideas

① habit
② meaning
③ information
④ expression
⑤ translation

서답형

04 다음 짝지어진 단어의 관계가 같도록 빈칸에 알맞은 말을 쓰시오.

Russia : Russian = Germany : _____

05 다음 빈칸에 들어갈 말로 적절하지 <u>않은</u> 것은?

• The cookies look _____ .
• Apples are my _____ fruit.
• Our app will be _____ for travelers.
• Kebab is a _____ Turkish food.

① useful
② delicious
③ favorite
④ official
⑤ traditional

서답형

06 다음 빈칸에 알맞은 말을 쓰시오.

그는 시내를 둘러볼 것이다.
➡ He's going to _____ _____ the city.

서답형

07 다음 영영풀이에 해당하는 단어를 주어진 철자로 시작하여 쓰시오.

as many or as much as someone needs or wants

➡ e_____

08 다음 빈칸에 들어갈 말이 바르게 짝지어진 것은?

• What kind _____ sports do you like?
• Students should focus _____ their classes.

① in – at
② of – on
③ on – for
④ for – with
⑤ about – over

01 다음 짝지어진 두 단어의 관계가 같도록 빈칸에 알맞은 말을 쓰시오.

(1) light : heavy = general : _____
(2) full : hungry = same : _____
(3) Thailand : Thai = Spain : _____
(4) Greece : Greek = Turkey : _____

02 다음 우리말에 맞게 빈칸에 알맞은 말을 쓰시오.

(1) 그 기차는 30분 후에 출발할 것이다.
➡ The train will leave in _____
_____ _____.

(2) 컴퓨터는 많은 일을 하는 데 유용하다.
➡ Computers are _____ _____
doing many things.

(3) 서둘러라, 그러면 제시간에 도착할 것이다.
➡ Hurry _____, and you will be in time.

(4) 너는 개장 시간에 대해 알 수 있다.
➡ You can find _____ about opening hours.

03 다음 빈칸에 들어갈 말을 〈보기〉에서 골라 쓰시오.

┌─ 보기 ─┐
landmark   meaning   audition
└──────┘

(1) I had an _____ for the school radio station.
(2) Each color has a different _____.
(3) The Opera House is a _____ in Sydney, Australia.

04 다음 빈칸에 공통으로 들어갈 말을 〈보기〉에서 골라 쓰시오. (필요하면 어형을 바꿀 것)

┌─ 보기 ─┐
work   save   way
└──────┘

(1) • The lady showed the _____ to us.
• What's the best _____ to cook corn?
(2) • His father _____ at a bank.
• The headache medicine didn't _____ at all.
(3) • I'll _____ money little by little.
• We should try to _____ water.

05 다음 빈칸에 알맞은 말을 〈보기〉에서 골라 쓰시오.

┌─ 보기 ─┐
mean by   right now   for example
└──────┘

(1) I'll clean up my room _____.
(2) In India, _____, some coins have square sides.
(3) What do you _____ "FYI"?

06 다음 영영풀이에 해당하는 단어를 주어진 철자로 시작하여 쓰시오.

(1) f_____ : chance or luck, especially in the way it affects people's lives
(2) n_____ : anxious about something or afraid of something
(3) t_____ : words that have been changed from one language into a different language

Conversation

교과서

1 음식 권하고 답하기

A Would you like some *bibimbap*? 비빔밥 좀 먹을래?
B Yes, please. 응. 부탁해.

- Would you like some ~?은 상대방에게 음식을 권할 때 쓰는 표현으로 '~ 좀 드시겠어요?'라고 해석한다.
  - A: Would you like some apple pie? 애플파이 좀 먹을래?
    B: Thanks, it looks delicious. 고마워. 맛있어 보이는구나.
- what을 사용하여 먹고 싶은 음식을 구체적으로 물어보는 표현을 나타낼 수도 있다.
  - A: What would you like to eat for lunch? 점심식사로 뭘 먹고 싶니?
    B: I'd like to eat hamburgers. 햄버거를 먹고 싶어.

음식을 권하는 표현

- Would you like some cookies? 쿠키 좀 드실래요?
- Why don't you have some pizza? 피자 좀 드실래요?
- Do you want some hamburgers? 햄버거 좀 먹을래요?
- Do you want to have[eat] some Chinese food? 중국 요리를 드시고 싶으세요?
- What will you have? 뭐 드실래요?
- How about some dessert? 디저트 좀 드시겠습니까?

음식 권하기에 답하기

(수락) • Yes, please / Yes, thank you. I'll try some. / Thanks, it looks delicious.

(거절) • No, thank you. I'm full. / No, thanks. I'm not hungry. / I've had enough.`

핵심 Check

1. 다음 우리말과 일치하도록 빈칸에 알맞은 말을 쓰시오.

(1) **A:** _____ you like some *bulgogi*? (불고기 좀 먹을래?)

　　B: Yes, _____. (응. 부탁해.)

(2) **A:** Would you _____ _____ apple pie? (애플파이 좀 드시겠어요?)

　　B: _____, _____. I'm not hungry. (아니요. 감사합니다. 배고프지 않아요.)

(3) **A:** _____ _____ _____ some more bread? (빵 좀 더 먹을래?)

　　B: No, thanks. I'm _____. (아니. 괜찮아. 나는 배불러.)

② 표현의 의미 묻고 답하기

> **A** What do you mean by "landmarks"? "landmarks"가 무슨 뜻이에요?
>
> **B** I mean important places or special buildings. 중요한 장소나 특별한 건물들을 말하는 거야.

■ What do you mean by that?은 '그게 무슨 뜻이니?'라는 뜻으로, 상대방의 말을 제대로 이해하지 못했을 때 무슨 뜻이냐고 물어볼 때 사용하는 표현이다.

- A: The math homework was a piece of cake. 수학 숙제는 누워서 떡먹기였어.
  B: What do you mean by that? 그게 무슨 뜻이니?
  A: It was very easy to do. 수학을 하기 매우 쉬웠단 말이야.

표현의 의미 묻기 표현

- What do you mean (by that)? 그게 무슨 뜻이니?
- What does that mean? 그게 무슨 뜻이니?
- I'm sorry, but could you explain that? 미안하지만 그것을 설명해 주겠니?
- What are you talking about? 무슨 말을 하는 거야?
- What is the meaning of that? 그것의 의미가 뭐니?

- A: What does G9 mean? G9은 무슨 뜻이니?
  B: It means "Good night." "잘 자."라는 뜻이야.

핵심 Check

2. 다음 우리말과 일치하도록 빈칸에 알맞은 말을 쓰시오.

(1) A: _____ _____, everyone. Hit the road! (서둘러, 모두들. Hit the road!)

B: I'm sorry, _____ what do you _____ by that? (미안하지만, 그게 무슨 뜻이니?)

A: _____ _____ it's time to start _____. (이제 움직이기 시작할 시간이라는 의미야.)

(2) A: What does THX _____? (THX가 무슨 뜻이야?)

B: _____ _____ " Thanks." (그건 "고마워."라는 뜻이야.)

(3) A: _____ _____ _____ mean by "Break a leg!"? ("Break a leg!"가 무슨 뜻이니?))

B: It means " _____ _____ !" ("행운을 빌어!"라는 뜻이야.)

A. Communicate: Listen - Listen and Answer Dialog 1

B: ❶It smells nice. What are you cooking, Uncle Abbas?

M: ❷I'm making kebab.

B: Kebab? What is it?

M: It's a traditional Turkish food. ❸We have small pieces of meat and vegetables on a stick.

B: Oh, ❹it sounds delicious.

M: ❺Would you like some?

B: Sure. I'd love some.

M: ❻Here you are.

B: ❼It tastes great. You should open your own restaurant!

M: Thanks. I'm glad you like it.

B: 냄새가 좋네요. Abbas 이모부, 무슨 요리를 하고 계세요?
M: 케밥을 만들고 있어.
B: 케밥이요? 그게 뭐죠?
M: 터키 전통 음식이야. 꼬치에 작은 고기와 채소 조각을 끼워서 먹는 거지.
B: 오, 맛있겠어요.
M: 좀 먹어 볼래?
B: 물론이죠. 좀 주세요.
M: 여기 있어.
B: 맛이 좋네요. 이모부는 직접 식당을 차려야 해요!
M: 고마워. 네가 마음에 든다니 기쁘다.

❶ smell+형용사: ~한 냄새가 나다 ❷ be동사의 현재형+-ing: ~하는 중이다 ❸ small pieces of: 작은 ~조각들 / meat: 고기 / stick: 막대기, 꼬치 ❹ sound+형용사: ~하게 들리다 / delicious: 맛있는(= tasty, yummy) ❺ Would you like some?: 좀 먹어 볼래?(음식을 권하는 표현) ❻ Here you are. 는 '여기 있어.'라는 의미로 Here it is.로 바꿔 쓸 수 있다. ❼ taste+형용사: ~한 맛이 나다

Check(√) True or False

(1) Kebab is a traditional Turkish food. T ☐ F ☐

(2) The boy's uncle opened a new restaurant. T ☐ F ☐

B. Communicate: Listen - Listen and Answer Dialog 2

W: ❶What are you going to do today, Kevin?

B: ❷I'm going to look around the city.

W: ❸Do you know how to find your way?

B: Sure. I have a map on my phone!

W: Okay. ❹Try to remember landmarks, too.

B: I'm sorry, but ❺what do you mean by "landmarks"?

W: ❻I mean important places or special buildings.

B: All right. ❼I will try to remember the places that I see.

W: Kevin, 오늘 뭐 할 거야?
B: 저는 시내를 둘러볼 거예요.
W: 길 찾는 방법을 아니?
B: 물론이죠. 전화기에 지도가 있어요!
W: 알았어. landmarks도 기억하도록 해라.
B: 죄송하지만, "landmarks"가 무슨 뜻이에요?
W: 중요한 장소나 특별한 건물들을 말하는 거야.
B: 알겠어요. 저는 제가 보는 장소들을 기억하도록 노력할게요.

❶ What are you going to + 동사원형 ~? 너는 ~할 거니?(의도나 계획 묻기) ❷ I'm going to+동사원형 ~.: 나는 ~할 것이다. / look around: 둘러보다 ❸ how to+동사원형: ~하는 방법 ❹ try to+동사원형: ~하려고 노력하다 / remember: 기억하다 / landmark: 주요 지형지물, 랜드마크 ❺ What do you mean by ~?: ~는 무슨 뜻이니?(표현의 의미 묻기) ❻ place: 장소 / special: 특별한 ❼ I will try to ~.: 나는 ~하려고 노력할게. / that: 관계대명사

Check(√) True or False

(3) Kevin knows how to find his way. T ☐ F ☐

(4) Kevin doesn't know what a "landmark" means. T ☐ F ☐

Communicate: Listen - Listen More

G: Hey, Jongha!

B: Hi, Claire. ❶Those cookies look delicious.

G: ❷Would you like some?

B: ❸No, thanks. I'm too nervous.

G: ❹Why are you so nervous?

B: ❺I have my audition for the school radio station in half an hour.

G: Oh, really? ❻Break a leg!

B: *Break a leg?* ❼What do you mean?

G: I mean "Good luck."

B: ❽That's a funny expression. Thanks! ❾Save some cookies for me, okay?

❶ look+형용사: ~하게 보이다 / delicious: 맛있는
❷ 음식 권하기 표현이다. (= Why don't you have ~? = Do you want some ~?)
❸ No, thanks.: 아니, 괜찮아. (음식 권하기에 사양하는 표현)
❹ Why are you ~?: 너는 왜 ~하니? / nervous: 긴장한
❺ station: 방송국 / in half an hour: 30분 후에
❻ break a leg: 행운을 빌다
❼ 표현의 의미를 묻는 표현이다.(=What does that mean?)
❽ expression: 표현
❾ save: 남겨 두다

Communicate: Listen - All Ears

M: 1. ❶The train will leave in half an hour.
2. ❷I have a busy schedule this week.

❶ in half an hour: 30분 후에 ❷ have a busy schedule: 일정이 바쁘다

Communicate: Speak 2

A: ❶Would you like some *bibimbap*?

B: ❷No, thanks. I don't like vegetables.

A: ❸Then how about pizza?

B: ❹Yes, please.

❶ 음식을 권하는 표현이다. (=Why don't you have some ~? = Do you want some ~? = Do you want to have[eat] some ~?)
❷ No, thanks.: 아니, 괜찮아.(음식 권유에 거절하는 표현)
❸ Then how about pizza?: 그러면 피자는 어때?(=Then what about pizza?)
❹ Yes, please.: 응, 부탁해.(음식 권유에 승낙하는 표현)

My Writing Portfolio - Step 1

G: Look. The name of our app is *Enjoy Paris*!

B: *Enjoy Paris*? ❶Sounds interesting!

G: ❷This app focuses on what to see in Paris.

B: ❸Does it give information on famous museums and theaters?

G: Yes. ❹You can find out about opening hours and admission fees.

B: Fantastic.

G: ❺It also tells you how to get there.

B: Oh, ❻I'll download it right now!

G: ❼I'm sure you'll like it.

❶ sound+형용사: ~하게 들리다
❷ focus on: ~에 중점을 두다 / what to+동사원형: 무엇을 ~할지
❸ it은 this app을 가리킨다. / give information: 정보를 제공하다 / famous: 유명한
❹ find out: ~에 대해 알아내다[알게 되다] / admission fee: 입장료
❺ how to+동사원형: ~하는 방법
❻ download: 다운로드하다 / right now: 지금 바로
❼ I'm sure you'll ~: 나는 네가 ~할 거라고 확신한다.

Wrap Up - Listening ❺

B: ❶Would you like some sandwiches?

G: ❷What kind of sandwich?

B: Ham and egg sandwich.

G: ❸No, thanks. I don't eat eggs.

B: Then, would you like some apple pie?

G: Okay. ❹Apples are my favorite fruit.

❶ 음식 권하기 표현이다.
❷ what kind of: 어떤 종류의
❸ No, thanks.: 아니, 괜찮아. (음식 권하기에 사양하는 표현)
❹ favorite: 아주 좋아하는

Wrap Up - Listening ❻

G: ❶Hurry up, everyone. Hit the road!

B: ❷I'm sorry, but what do you mean by that?

G: ❸I mean it's time to start moving.

B: Like, "❹It's time to go"?

G: Yes.

B: Great! ❺Let's hit the road.

❶ hurry up: 서두르다
❷ 표현의 의미를 묻는 표현이다. (=What does that mean? = I'm sorry, but could you explain that?)
❸ I mean (that) 주어 + 동사 ~. 내 말 뜻은 ~라는 거야.
❹ It은 비인칭 주어이다.
❺ Let's ~: ~하자 / hit the road: 출발하다

● 다음 우리말과 일치하도록 빈칸에 알맞은 말을 쓰시오.

Communicate: Listen - Listen and Answer Dialog 1

B: It _____ nice. What are you _____, Uncle Abbas?

M: I'm _____ kebab.

B: Kebab? _____ is it?

M: It's a _____ Turkish food. We have small _____ _____ meat and vegetables on a stick.

B: Oh, it _____ delicious.

M: _____ you _____ some?

B: Sure. I'd _____ some.

M: Here _____ are.

B: It _____ great. You _____ _____ your own restaurant!

M: Thanks. I'm glad you _____ it.

Communicate: Listen - Listen and Answer Dialog 2

W: What _____ you _____ _____ do today, Kevin?

B: I'm going to _____ _____ the city.

W: Do you know _____ _____ find your way?

B: Sure. I have a _____ on _____ phone!

W: Okay. _____ _____ remember landmarks, too.

B: I'm sorry, _____ what do you _____ _____ "landmarks"?

W: I mean _____ places or _____ buildings.

B: All right. I will _____ _____ remember the places _____ I see.

Communicate: Listen - Listen More

G: Hey, Jongha!

B: Hi, Claire. Those cookies _____ _____.

G: _____ you _____ some?

B: No, _____. I'm too _____.

G: _____ are you _____ nervous?

B: I have my _____ for the school radio station _____ _____ _____.

G: Oh, really? _____ a leg!

B: *Break a leg?* _____ do you _____?

G: I mean "_____ _____."

B: That's a funny _____. Thanks! _____ some cookies _____ me, okay?

해석

B: 냄새가 좋네요. Abbas 이모부, 무슨 요리를 하고 계세요?

M: 케밥을 만들고 있어.

B: 케밥이요? 그게 뭐죠?

M: 터키 전통 음식이야. 꼬치에 작은 고기와 채소 조각을 끼워서 먹는 거지.

B: 오, 맛있겠어요.

M: 좀 먹어 볼래?

B: 물론이죠. 좀 주세요.

M: 여기 있어.

B: 맛이 좋네요. 이모부는 직접 식당을 차려야 해요!

M: 고마워. 네가 마음에 든다니 기쁘다.

W: Kevin, 오늘 뭐 할 거야?

B: 저는 시내를 둘러볼 거예요.

W: 길 찾는 방법을 아니?

B: 물론이죠. 전화기에 지도가 있어요!

W: 알았어. landmarks도 기억하도록 해라.

B: 죄송하지만, "landmarks"가 무슨 뜻이에요?

W: 중요한 장소나 특별한 건물들을 말하는 거야.

B: 알겠어요. 저는 제가 보는 장소들을 기억하도록 노력할게요.

G: 이봐, 종하야!

B: 안녕, Claire. 저 쿠키들 맛있어 보인다.

G: 좀 먹어 볼래?

B: 아니, 괜찮아. 너무 긴장돼.

G: 왜 그렇게 긴장하니?

B: 30분 후에 학교 라디오 방송국 오디션이 있어.

G: 아, 정말? Break a leg!

B: Break a leg? 무슨 뜻이지?

G: "행운을 빌어."라는 뜻이야.

B: 그거 재미있는 표현이네. 고마워! 쿠키 좀 남겨줘, 알았지?

Communicate: Listen - All Ears

M: 1. The train will leave in _____ _____ _____.

2. I _____ a busy _____ this week.

Communicate: Speak 2

A: _____ _____ _____ some *bibimbap*?

B: _____, _____. I don't like vegetables.

A: Then _____ _____ pizza?

B: Yes, please.

My Writing Portfolio - Step 1

G: Look. The name of _____ _____ is *Enjoy Paris*!

B: *Enjoy Paris*? _____ interesting!

G: This app focuses on _____ _____ _____ in Paris.

B: Does it _____ _____ _____ famous museums and theaters?

G: Yes. You can _____ _____ about opening hours and _____ _____.

B: Fantastic.

G: It also tells you _____ _____ _____ there.

B: Oh, I'll download it _____ _____!

G: _____ _____ you'll like it.

Wrap Up - Listening ❺

B: _____ you _____ some sandwiches?

G: _____ _____ _____ sandwich?

B: Ham and _____ _____.

G: No, _____. I don't eat eggs.

B: Then, _____ _____ _____ some apple pie?

G: Okay. Apples are my _____ fruit.

Wrap Up - Listening ❻

G: _____ _____, everyone. Hit the road!

B: I'm sorry, but _____ do you _____ _____ that?

G: I mean it's _____ _____ _____ moving.

B: Like, "It's _____ _____ _____"?

G: Yes.

B: Great! _____ hit the road.

[01~02] 다음 대화의 빈칸에 알맞은 것을 고르시오.

01

> A: Would you _____ some sandwiches?
> B: Sure, I'd love some.

① want　　　　　② take
③ need　　　　　④ like
⑤ have

02

> A: What do you _____ by a "landmark"?
> B: I mean an important place like a park.

landmark 주요 지형지물, 랜드마크

① do　　　　　② want
③ like　　　　　④ look
⑤ mean

03 다음 대화의 밑줄 친 부분의 의도로 가장 알맞은 것은?

> A: Would you like some *bibimbap*?
> B: No, thanks. I don't like vegetables.

① 감사하기　　　　② 사과하기
③ 변명하기　　　　④ 음식 권유하기
⑤ 음식 거절하기

04 다음 대화의 빈칸에 알맞은 것은?

dictionary 사전

> A: She's a walking dictionary.
> B: _____
> A: She knows about everything.

① What's wrong?　　　② What's the matter?
③ What is she doing?　　④ What are you going to say?
⑤ What do you mean by that?

[01~04] 다음 대화를 읽고, 물음에 답하시오.

B: It smells nice. (①) What are you cooking, Uncle Abbas?
M: (②) I'm making kebab.
B: Kebab? What is it?
M: (③) We have small pieces of meat and vegetables on a stick.
B: (④) Oh, it sounds ___ⓐ___.
M: _____ⓑ_____
B: Sure. I'd love some.
M: (⑤) Here you are.
B: It tastes great. You should open your own restaurant!
M: Thanks. I'm glad you like it.

01 위 대화의 ①~⑤ 중 다음 문장이 들어갈 알맞은 곳은?

> It's a traditional Turkish food.

①   ②   ③   ④   ⑤

02 위 대화의 빈칸 ⓐ에 들어갈 말로 알맞은 것은?

① sour
② dull
③ cold
④ terrible
⑤ delicious

03 위 대화의 빈칸 ⓑ에 알맞은 것은?

① Can you help me?
② Can you do me a favor?
③ May I have some kebab?
④ Would you like some?
⑤ Do you like kebab?

04 위 대화의 내용과 일치하지 않는 것은?

① Uncle Abbas is making kebab.
② Kebab is a traditional Turkish food.
③ We need meat and vegetables to make kebab.
④ Uncle Abbas is going to open a new restaurant.
⑤ Uncle Abbas is glad the boy likes kebab.

[05~06] 다음 대화를 읽고, 물음에 답하시오.

G: Hurry up, everyone. ⓐHit the road!
B: I'm sorry, but ⓑwhat do you mean by that?
G: I mean it's time to start moving.
B: Like, "It's time to go"?
G: Yes.

05 위 대화의 밑줄 친 ⓐ의 의미로 알맞은 것은?

① 출발해라.
② 차를 타라.
③ 줄을 서라.
④ 일찍 자라.
⑤ 엎드려라.

06 위 대화의 밑줄 친 ⓑ와 바꿔 쓸 수 있는 것은?

① what are you planning to do?
② what do you think about that?
③ what is the meaning of that?
④ do you know about the idiom?
⑤ have you heard about the idiom?

[07~11] 다음 대화를 읽고, 물음에 답하시오.

G: Hey, Jongha!
B: Hi, Claire. Those cookies look delicious.
G: Would you like some?
B: ___ⓐ___ (①) I'm too nervous.
G: Why are you so nervous?
B: (②) I have my audition for the school radio station ___ⓑ___ half an hour. (③)
G: Oh, really? ⓒBreak a leg!
B: *Break a leg?* (④) What do you mean?
G: I mean "Good luck."
B: (⑤) Thanks! Save some cookies for me, okay?

07 위 대화의 ①~⑤ 중 다음 문장이 들어갈 알맞은 곳은?

That's a funny expression.

①   ②   ③   ④   ⑤

08 위 대화의 빈칸 ⓐ에 들어갈 말로 적절한 것은?

① Yes, please.   ② Sure, thanks.
③ Okay, I'll try it.   ④ No problem.
⑤ No, thanks.

09 위 대화의 빈칸 ⓑ에 들어갈 말로 가장 적절한 것은?

① to   ② in
③ on   ④ off
⑤ about

서답형
10 위 대화의 밑줄 친 ⓒ가 의미하는 것을 우리말로 쓰시오.

➡ _____

서답형
11 위 대화를 읽고, 다음 질문에 대한 답을 완성하시오.

Q: Why is Claire so nervous?
A: Because _____
_____.

[12~14] 다음 대화를 읽고, 물음에 답하시오.

W: What are you going to do today, Kevin?
B: I'm going to look around the city. (①)
W: Do you know ___ⓐ___ to find your way?
B: Sure. I have a map on my phone! (②)
W: Okay. (③)
B: I'm sorry, but what do you ___ⓑ___ by "landmarks"?
W: I ___ⓒ___ important places or special buildings. (④)
B: All right. I will try to remember the places that I see. (⑤)

12 위 대화의 ①~⑤ 중 다음 문장이 들어갈 알맞은 곳은?

Try to remember landmarks, too.

①   ②   ③   ④   ⑤

13 위 대화의 빈칸 ⓐ에 문맥상 알맞은 것은?

① why   ② how   ③ what
④ when   ⑤ where

14 위 대화의 빈칸 ⓑ와 ⓒ에 공통으로 알맞은 것은?

① put   ② mean   ③ learn
④ follow   ⑤ understand

01 다음 대화의 빈칸에 들어갈 문장을 〈보기〉의 단어들을 이용해 완성하시오.

┌─ 보기 ─┐
what   mean

A: She is all ears.
B: _____
A: She is listening very carefully.

02 다음 대화의 밑줄 친 우리말을 괄호 안의 단어를 이용하여 영작하시오. (필요하면 단어의 형태를 바꿀 것.)

(1) A: 너 피자 좀 먹을래? (would, like, some)
   B: Yes, please. I love pizza.
   ➡ _____

(2) A: Do you want some bread?
   B: 아닙니다, 괜찮습니다. (thank)
   ➡ _____

03 다음 대화의 문맥상 알맞은 말을 주어진 철자로 시작하여 쓰시오.

A: I have my audition for the school radio station in half an hour.
B: Oh, really? B_____ a l_____!
A: B_____ a l_____? What do you mean?
B: I mean "Good luck."

04 다음 대화의 순서를 바르게 배열하시오.

(A) Yes, please.
(B) No, thanks. I don't like vegetables.
(C) Then how about pizza?
(D) Would you like some *bibimbap*?

➡ _____

[05~08] 다음 대화를 읽고, 물음에 답하시오.

W: What are you going to do today, Kevin?
B: I'm going to look around the city.
W: Do you know how (A)[finding / to find] your way?
B: Sure. I have a map on my phone!
W: Okay. Try (B)[remembering / to remember] landmarks, too.
B: I'm sorry, but what do you mean by "landmarks"?
W: I mean important places or special buildings.
B: All right. I will try to remember the places (C)[that / what] I see.

05 What is Kevin going to do today? Answer the English.

➡ _____

06 위 대화의 괄호 (A)~(C)에서 어법상 알맞은 것을 골라 쓰시오.

(A) _____ (B) _____ (C) _____

07 What is the meaning of "landmarks"? Answer the Korean.

➡ _____

08 What will Kevin use to find his way?

➡ _____

Grammar

① 목적격 관계대명사

- The woman **whom** I love most is my grandmother. 내가 가장 사랑하는 여인은 나의 할머니이시다.
- The book **which** I read on the bus was a movie magazine.
  내가 버스에서 읽은 책은 영화 잡지였다.
- The snack **that** I ate at night was Hawaiian pizza. 내가 밤에 먹은 간식은 하와이안 피자였다.

■ 관계대명사는 선행사와 뒤에 이어지는 문장을 연결해 주는 역할을 하며, 문장 내에서의 역할에 따라 주격, 목적격, 소유격으로 나뉜다.

	사람	사물/동물	사람/사물/동물
주격	who	which	that
목적격	who(m)	which	that

■ 목적격 관계대명사는 선행사가 뒤에 이어지는 문장(관계대명사절)에서 목적어 역할을 할 때 쓰며, 생략할 수 있다. 선행사가 사람이면 who(m) 또는 that을, 사물이나 동물이면 which 또는 that을 쓴다. 일반적으로 선행사가 사람일 때 whom보다는 who를 더 많이 쓴다.

- Ann was the person. I met her on the way home.

  → Ann was the person **who[whom, that]** I met on the way home.
  Ann은 내가 집에 오늘 길에 만난 사람이었다.

■ 선행사가 최상급이거나 서수, -thing으로 끝나는 경우, 또는 the very, the only가 선행사를 수식하는 경우에는 which 대신 that을 쓸 때가 많다.

- This is the biggest dog **that** I have ever seen. 이것은 지금까지 내가 본 가장 큰 개다.

■ 관계대명사가 전치사의 목적어로 쓰일 때는 who(m)이나 which 대신 that을 전치사와 함께 사용할 수 없다.

- The bed in **which** I slept was comfortable. (○) 내가 잔 침대는 편안했다.

  The bed in that I slept was comfortable. (✕)

핵심 Check

1. 다음 괄호 안에서 알맞은 것을 고르시오.

(1) I know the doctor (which / that) everyone likes.

(2) That is the very problem (that / what) I wanted to solve.

(3) The man to (whom / that) you spoke is my homeroom teacher.

(4) This is the book (who / which) I read yesterday.

(5) Police found the knife with (which / that) the man killed her.

② 의문사+to부정사

> • Please tell me **when to help** you. 너를 언제 돕는게 좋을지 내게 말해라.
>
> • Jake has to decide **where to shop**. Jake는 어디에서 쇼핑을 할 것인지 결정해야 한다.

■ 의문사 바로 뒤에 to부정사를 써서 '~해야 하는지, ~하는 것이 좋을지'라는 의무의 뜻을 나타낼 수 있다. 이때 「의문사+to부정사」는 문장 안에서 보통 동사의 목적어 역할을 한다. 또, 의문사 대신 접속사 whether를 쓸 수도 있다.

   • Will you advise me **whether to help** her **or not**? 그녀를 도와주어야 할지 말아야 할지 충고해 주겠니?

   • Decide **what to do** when you plan a trip. 여행 계획을 할 때 무엇을 해야 할지 결정해라.

■ 의문사와 to부정사 사이에 명사가 오면 의문사와 함께 하나의 의문사구를 형성한다.

   • She decides **what time to wake** up according to a class schedule.
     그녀는 시간표에 따라 몇 시에 일어날지를 정한다.

의문사+to부정사		의문사+명사+to부정사	
what to do where to go when to start which to choose how to swim	무엇을 해야 하는지 어디에 가야 하는지 언제 출발해야 하는지 어느 것을 골라야 할지 어떻게 수영해야 할지	what book to read which way to go what time to get up how many books to read	어떤 책을 읽어야 할지 어느 길로 가야 할지 몇 시에 일어나야 할지 얼마나 많은 책을 읽어야 할지

■ 「의문사+to부정사」는 조동사 should를 써서 「의문사+주어+should+동사원형」 구문으로 바꿔 쓸 수 있다. 이때 의문사절의 주어는 주절의 주어와 일치시킨다.

   • I don't know **what to make** next. 다음에 무엇을 만들어야 할지 모르겠다.
     → I don't know what I should make next.

핵심 Check

2. 다음 괄호 안에서 알맞은 것을 고르시오.

   (1) I want to travel this summer, but I don't know (where / when) to go.

   (2) The doctor told me (what / when) to take medicine.

   (3) Please tell him (why / where) to buy the doll.

   (4) He doesn't know (which / how) to play chess.

   (5) I asked him (which / where) book to buy.

01 다음 괄호 안에서 알맞은 것을 고르시오.

(1) Can you tell me (when / what) to leave?

(2) They showed me (how / who) to bake the cake.

(3) This is the boy (whom / which) I play basketball with every weekend.

(4) I am reading the letter (whom / which) you gave me yesterday.

> bake 굽다

02 다음 우리말과 일치하도록 빈칸에 알맞은 말을 쓰시오.

(1) 그는 김치 만드는 법을 알고 싶어 한다.

➡ He wants to know _____ _____ _____ kimchi.

(2) 우리는 중국 식당에서 무엇을 먹을지 얘기하고 있다.

➡ We're talking about _____ _____ _____ at the Chinese restaurant.

(3) 우체국에 어떻게 가는지 알려 줄래요?

➡ Could you tell me _____ _____ _____ to the post office?

(4) 그들은 휴가를 어디로 가야 하는지에 대해 이야기하고 있다.

➡ They are talking about _____ _____ _____ on a vacation.

> make kimchi 김치를 만들다
> restaurant 식당
> post office 우체국

03 다음 빈칸에 알맞은 말을 〈보기〉에서 골라 쓰시오. (한 단어를 중복해서 쓸 수 없음.)

┌─ 보기 ─────────────────────────────┐
│   that   which   whom   who   │
└─────────────────────────────────────┘

(1) Look at the boy _____ is watering a flower.

(2) You are the only friend with _____ I can talk.

(3) I need a knife with _____ I can cut the rope.

(4) Money is the only thing _____ he wants.

[01~02] 다음 문장의 빈칸에 알맞은 것을 고르시오.

01

The gentleman _____ I met yesterday was a teacher.

① which　　② who
③ at which　④ with who
⑤ with that

02 중요

She wants to learn _____ to play the guitar.

① how　　② what
③ which　④ whom
⑤ who

03 다음 두 문장이 같은 뜻이 되도록 빈칸에 알맞은 것은?

I don't know what to say about it.
= I don't know what I _____ say about it.

① will　　② should
③ would　④ need
⑤ could

서답형

04 다음 문장에서 어법상 어색한 곳을 찾아 바르게 고쳐 쓰시오.

(1) He is an engineer which my father knows very well.

_____ ➡ _____

(2) The village in that I live is very small.

_____ ➡ _____

서답형

05 다음 문장의 빈칸에 공통으로 알맞은 말을 쓰시오.

• I can't decide what _____ do.
• Can you show me how _____ use this washing machine?

[06~07] 다음 중 어법상 어색한 문장을 고르시오.

06 ① This is the pen I lost yesterday.
② I will give you everything that you need.
③ I forgot to bring the homework which I did yesterday.
④ The music which we listened is by Mozart.
⑤ The car which I bought last month already has engine problems.

07 중요

① Can you tell me what to do first?
② She decided what to eat lunch.
③ They showed him how to make it.
④ I didn't know where to find her.
⑤ Jack explains them how to finish it quickly.

서답형

08 다음 문장과 뜻이 같도록 빈칸에 알맞은 말을 쓰시오.

He didn't tell them what to read.
= He didn't tell them what _____ _____ read.

09 다음 두 문장에서 생략된 말이 바르게 짝지어진 것은?

> • He ate the food everyone hated.
> • The tree I cut yesterday was very big.

① who – who   ② who – that
③ that – who   ④ what – which
⑤ that – which

10 다음 문장의 빈칸에 공통으로 알맞은 말을 쓰시오.

> • The building _____ I visited yesterday is a museum.
> • The man _____ everyone knows well built this house for himself.

11 다음 두 문장의 빈칸에 공통으로 알맞은 것은?

> • Can you show me how _____ make *gimbap*?
> • They knew what _____ buy at the mall.

① to   ② on
③ for   ④ must
⑤ should

12 다음 우리말과 일치하도록 주어진 단어를 바르게 배열하시오.

> 그 남자는 자기가 갖고 있는 모든 돈을 내게 주었다.
> (he / gave / had / the / man / me / money / all / that / the)

➡ _____

13 다음 밑줄 친 ①~⑤ 중 어법상 어색한 것은?

> ①Before winter comes, many different ②kinds of birds ③head south. How do they know ④when to migrate? How do they know ⑤where should go?

①   ②   ③   ④   ⑤

14 다음 중 밑줄 친 부분의 쓰임이 옳은 것은?

① The man which I met yesterday will call me this afternoon.
② I can give you the textbook what I bought last week.
③ The rumor who Jeff told me was very interesting.
④ This is the pen with which he wrote the novel.
⑤ Thanks to the textbooks whom you gave me, I could pass the exam.

15 다음 문장의 빈칸에 알맞은 말이 바르게 짝지어진 것은?

> • She didn't decide _____ to wear that morning.
> • Can you tell me _____ to cook it?

① what – why   ② how – who
③ what – how   ④ when – which
⑤ where – what

서답형

16 다음 두 문장이 같은 의미를 지니도록 빈칸에 알맞은 말을 써 넣으시오.

> The teacher told us when to begin the test.
>
> = The teacher told us when we _____ _____ the test.

서답형

17 다음 문장에서 어법상 어색한 부분을 찾아 바르게 고쳐 쓰시오.

(1) The girl which I like will leave this town.

_____ ➡ _____

(2) The knife with which I cut these apples were very sharp.

_____ ➡ _____

중요

18 다음 밑줄 친 부분 중 생략할 수 없는 것은?

① This is the piano <u>which</u> Mozart played.

② The boy <u>who</u> is throwing a ball is my brother.

③ Rome is the place <u>that</u> I really want to visit again.

④ These are the gifts <u>which</u> she gave me on my birthday.

⑤ I'm going to return the book <u>that</u> I borrowed last week.

19 다음 중 어법상 올바른 문장을 모두 고른 것은?

> ⓐ Please show me how to solve this problem.
> ⓑ They decided what to do after school.
> ⓒ We want to know where to go next time.
> ⓓ Do you know who to tell me about it?
> ⓔ Let me tell you when to finish it tomorrow.

① ⓐ   ② ⓐ, ⓑ

③ ⓐ, ⓑ, ⓒ   ④ ⓐ, ⓑ, ⓒ, ⓓ

⑤ ⓐ, ⓑ, ⓒ, ⓔ

중요

20 다음 중 밑줄 친 that의 쓰임이 나머지와 다른 하나는?

① It is true <u>that</u> we were a little late.

② This is the bag <u>that</u> I bought yesterday.

③ This is the hotel <u>that</u> I stayed at last time.

④ Do you know the boy <u>that</u> I met yesterday?

⑤ This is the tree <u>that</u> I planted five years ago.

21 다음 중 밑줄 친 부분의 문장 성분이 다른 하나는?

① He told me <u>where to go</u>.

② The important thing is <u>what to read</u>.

③ I don't know <u>which book to buy</u>.

④ I didn't know <u>whether to take</u> this bus or not.

⑤ I have no idea about <u>how to solve</u> this problem.

01 다음 두 문장을 관계대명사를 써서 한 문장으로 바꿔 쓰시오.

(1) I know the man. You are looking for the man.

➡ _____

(2) This is the bag. I got it from Nancy.

➡ _____

(3) He is the boy. I meet him at the bus stop every morning.

➡ _____

_____

02 다음 빈칸에 알맞은 말을 〈보기〉에서 골라 쓰시오. (한 단어를 중복해서 쓸 수 없음)

┌─── 보기 ───┐
what   where   which   how
└─────────────┘

(1) Jim learned _____ to ride a bike.

(2) I wanted to know _____ time to start.

(3) I asked her _____ book to read.

(4) Can I ask you _____ to write my name?

03 다음 빈칸에 공통으로 알맞은 말을 쓰시오.

• This is the hat _____ Ann bought yesterday.
• I know the girl _____ is playing the drums.

04 다음 문장을 should를 써서 같은 의미의 문장으로 바꿔 쓰시오.

(1) My brother doesn't know where to go.

➡ _____

(2) Alice doesn't know what to cook.

➡ _____

(3) Please tell me when to help you.

➡ _____

05 다음 빈칸에 공통으로 알맞은 말을 쓰시오. (대 · 소문자 무시)

• _____ is your birthday?
• I don't know _____ to meet him.

06 다음 주어진 문장을 어법에 맞게 고쳐 쓰시오.

(1) I bought my sister a blouse who was made in France.

➡ _____

_____

(2) Do you know the boy whom I met him on the street yesterday?

➡ _____

_____

(3) This is the city that are famous for its beautiful buildings.

➡ _____

_____

07 다음 문장에서 어색한 부분을 찾아 바르게 고쳐 쓰시오.

(1) I can't decide what will buy for my mother's birthday.

➡ _____

_____

(2) Bill didn't tell us where to staying.

➡ _____

08 다음 우리말과 일치하도록 빈칸에 알맞은 말을 쓰시오.

(1) 이 아이가 내 남동생이 지난밤에 만난 소년이다.

➡ This is the boy _____ my brother met last night.

(2) 이것이 나의 부모님이 나에게 사 주신 자전거이다.

➡ This is the bike _____ my parents bought for me.

09 다음 주어진 단어를 바르게 배열하여 문장을 완성하시오.

(1) (didn't, leave, I, to, when, know).

➡ _____

(2) (do, how, know, the guitar, play, to, you)?

➡ _____

(3) (to, I, her, where, meet, know, don't).

➡ _____

10 다음 두 문장을 관계대명사를 이용하여 한 문장으로 쓰시오.

(1) I saw a man and his dog. They looked very tired.

➡ _____

(2) John is the best player in this town. I played tennis with him yesterday.

➡ _____

_____

(3) This bike is my treasure. My father bought it for me last year.

➡ _____

_____

(4) My sister ate the ice cream. My mother bought it for me.

➡ _____

_____

(5) The house was in Incheon. We lived in it two years ago.

➡ _____

_____

11 다음 우리말과 의미가 같도록 문장을 완성하시오.

(1) 어디서 노래 연습을 해야 할지 선생님에게 물어보자.

➡ Let's ask our teacher _____ _____ _____ singing songs.

(2) 나는 언제 서울을 방문해야 할지 결정하지 못했다.

➡ I didn't decide _____ _____ _____ Seoul.

(3) 너는 누구와 그곳에 가야 하는지 아니?

➡ Do you know _____ _____ _____ there with?

(4) 나는 무엇을 사야 할지 몰랐다.

➡ I didn't know _____ _____ _____ .

Reading

The Translation App

Jaden's family <u>is</u> in Florence, Italy. They <u>are visiting</u> <u>Ms. Gambini,</u>
있다(완전자동사)   현재진행형

his mother's friend. Today his parents <u>are going</u> to museums, but Jaden
Ms. Gambini와 동격어구   = are going to go to

<u>wants to</u> stay behind. He thinks the translation app <u>on his phone</u> will
want to: ~하기를 원하다   전화기에 있는(형용사구)

<u>help him communicate.</u>
= help him to communicate: 그가 의사소통하도록 돕다

His stomach growls, <u>so</u> he <u>enters</u> the kitchen. When Ms. Gambini
그래서   enter into (x)

sees Jaden, she says "Buon giorno. Vuoi un pezzo di pane e un

bicchiere di latte?" Jaden does not know <u>how to respond.</u> Then the app
= how he should respond

says, "Good morning. <u>Would you like</u> a piece of bread and a glass of
~을 드시겠어요

milk?" Jaden answers, "Yes, please."

<u>There is a knock</u> on the door, and a woman <u>whom</u> Ms. Gambini
노크 소리가 난다   목적격 관계대명사

invited walks in. The two women <u>begin speaking</u> Italian very fast. So
= begin to speak: 말하기 시작하다

the translator does not understand.

Jaden <u>turns off</u> the phone and leaves it on the table. He goes out <u>to</u>
~을 끄다 ↔ turn on(~을 켜다)

<u>enjoy</u> the sunny morning. He follows a thumping sound and finds a girl
목적을 나타내는 부사적 용법

<u>who is kicking</u> a soccer ball against a wall. She <u>turns to</u> him and says,
관계대명사 주격 현재진행형   ~에게로 몸을 돌리다

"Buon giorno."

stay behind 뒤에 남다. 출발하지 않다
translation 번역
communicate 의사소통을 하다
stomach 위, 배
growl 꼬르륵거리다
enter ~에 들어가다
respond 응답하다
translator 번역기
turn off ~을 끄다
thump 쿵쾅거리다
sound 소리
kick 차다
turn to ~으로 몸을 돌리다

 확인문제

● 다음 문장이 본문의 내용과 일치하면 T, 일치하지 <u>않으면</u> F를 쓰시오.

1 Jaden wants to visit museums. ☐

2 Jaden goes into the kitchen as he is hungry. ☐

3 Jaden thinks he can communicate thanks to the translation app. ☐

4 The two women spoke Italian very slowly. ☐

5 Jaden saw a girl kicking a soccer ball against the wall. ☐

His phone is in the kitchen, so Jaden does not know what to say. He
just repeats the words that the girl said, "Buon giorno." The girl kicks
the ball to him. Jaden needs no translator for that. For a while, the
two play with the ball. Finally, the girl points at herself and says, "Mi
chiamo Rosabella." "My name is Jaden," he responds.

Suddenly Rosabella says, "Arrive l'autobus." Jaden understands the
words that sound like *bus* and *arrive*. Sure enough, a bus appears.
Kids in soccer uniforms shout from the windows, "Ciao, Rosabella!"
As Rosabella steps onto the bus, Jaden says, "Good luck." She does
not understand. So Jaden thinks and says, "Buon, buon ...." He points
to the soccer ball that she is holding in her hand.

Rosabella shouts, "Fortuna! Buona fortuna!" Fortuna sounds like
fortune. "Buona fortuna!" he shouts. Rosabella and her friends shout
back, "Molte grazie!" The bus rolls away.

Jaden goes back to the kitchen. He says into the translation app,
"Learning from people is more fun. Can you teach me some Italian,
Ms. Gambini?"

Ms. Gambini says, "Si," and laughs.

respond 응답하다
sure enough 물론, 아니나 다를까
appear 나타나다
onto ~로
fortune 운, 행운
shout 소리치다
roll 구르다
fun 재미있는
laugh 웃다

확인문제

● 다음 문장이 본문의 내용과 일치하면 T, 일치하지 <u>않으면</u> F를 쓰시오.

1 Jaden's phone is in his hand. ☐

2 The girl's name is Rosabella. ☐

3 Jaden sees children in school uniforms. ☐

4 Jaden wants to learn some Italian from Ms. Gambini. ☐

● 우리말을 참고하여 빈칸에 알맞은 말을 쓰시오.

1 Jaden's _____ is _____ Florence, Italy.

2 They are _____ Ms. Gambini, his mother's _____.

3 Today his parents are _____ to museums, but Jaden _____ to stay _____.

4 He _____ the translation app _____ his phone will help him _____.

5 His _____ growls, _____ he enters the kitchen.

6 _____ Ms. Gambini sees Jaden, she _____ "Buon giorno. Vuoi un pezzo di pane e un bicchiere di latte?"

7 Jaden does not _____ how to _____.

8 Then the app says, "Good morning. _____ you like a _____ of bread and a _____ of milk?"

9 Jaden answers, "Yes, _____."

10 There is a _____ on the door, and a woman _____ Ms. Gambini invited _____ in.

11 The two women _____ speaking Italian very _____.

12 So the _____ does not _____.

13 Jaden turns _____ the phone and _____ it on the table.

14 He goes _____ to enjoy the _____ morning.

15 He follows a thumping _____ and finds a girl _____ is kicking a soccer ball _____ a wall.

16 She turns _____ him and _____, "Buon giono."

1 Jaden의 가족은 이탈리아 플로렌스에 있다.

2 그들은 그의 어머니의 친구인 Gambini 씨를 방문하고 있다.

3 오늘 그의 부모님은 박물관에 갈 예정이지만, Jaden은 집에 남고 싶어 한다.

4 그는 자신의 전화기에 있는 번역 앱이 의사소통을 하는 데 도움이 될 것이라고 생각한다.

5 그는 배가 꼬르륵거려서 부엌으로 들어간다.

6 Gambini 씨가 Jaden을 보자, 그녀는 "Buon giorno. Vuoi un pezzo di pane e un bicchiere di latte?"라고 말한다.

7 Jaden은 어떻게 대답해야 할지 모른다.

8 그러자 앱이 "좋은 아침입니다. 빵 한 개와 우유 한 잔 드시겠어요?"라고 말한다.

9 Jaden은 "네, 부탁해요."라고 대답한다.

10 문을 두드리는 소리가 들리고 Gambini 씨가 초대한 한 여자가 안으로 들어온다.

11 두 여자는 아주 빨리 이탈리아어를 말하기 시작한다.

12 그래서 번역 앱은 이해하지 못한다.

13 Jaden은 전화기를 끄고 그것을 탁자 위에 둔다.

14 그는 화창한 아침을 즐기기 위해 밖으로 나간다.

15 그는 쿵쾅거리는 소리를 따라가다 벽에 축구공을 차고 있는 소녀를 발견한다.

16 그녀는 그에게 돌아서서 "Buon giorno."라고 말한다.

17 His phone is in the kitchen, _____ Jaden does not know _____ to say.

18 He just _____ the words _____ the girl said, "Buon giorno."

19 The girl _____ the ball _____ him.

20 Jaden _____ no translator for _____.

21 For a _____, the two play with the _____.

22 _____, the girl points at _____ and says, "Mi chiamo Rosabella."

23 "My name is Jaden," he _____.

24 _____ Rosabella says, "Arrive l'autobus."

25 Jaden _____ the words that _____ like *bus* and *arrive*.

26 Sure _____, a bus _____.

27 Kids _____ soccer uniforms _____ from the windows, "Ciao, Rosabella!"

28 _____ Rosabella steps onto the bus, Jaden says, "Good _____."

29 She does not _____.

30 So Jaden _____ and says, "Buon, buon ...."

31 He points _____ the soccer ball that she is _____ in her hand.

32 Rosabella _____, "Fortuna! Buona fortuna!"

33 Fortuna _____ like *fortune*.

34 "Buona fortuna!" he _____.

35 Rosabella and her friends shout _____, "Molte grazie!"

36 The bus _____ away.

37 Jaden goes _____ to the kitchen.

38 He says _____ the translation app, "_____ from people is more fun. Can you _____ me some Italian, Ms. Gambini?"

39 Ms. Gambini says, "Si," and _____.

17 그의 전화기는 부엌에 있어서 Jaden은 뭐라고 말해야 할지 모른다.

18 그는 단지 소녀가 말한 말들인 "Buon giorno"를 반복한다.

19 소녀는 그에게 공을 찬다.

20 Jaden은 그것 때문에 번역 앱이 필요하지 않다.

21 잠시 동안, 두 사람은 공을 가지고 논다.

22 마침내, 그 소녀는 자신을 가리키며 "Mi chiamo Rosabella." 라고 말한다.

23 "내 이름은 Jaden이야."라고 그가 대답한다.

24 갑자기 Rosabella가 "Arrive l'autobus."라고 말한다.

25 Jaden은 '버스'와 '도착하다'라는 단어와 비슷한 소리가 나는 단어를 알아듣는다.

26 아니나 다를까, 버스 한 대가 나타난다.

27 축구 유니폼을 입은 아이들이 창문에서 "Ciao, Rosabella!"라고 외친다.

28 Rosabella가 버스에 오를 때, Jaden은 "행운을 빌어."라고 말한다.

29 그녀는 이해하지 못한다.

30 그래서 Jaden은 생각하고 "Buon, buon ...."이라고 말한다.

31 그는 그녀가 손에 들고 있는 축구공을 가리킨다.

32 Rosabella가 "Fortuna! Buona fortuna!"라고 소리친다.

33 Fortuna는 '행운'처럼 들린다.

34 "Buona fortuna!"라고 그가 소리친다.

35 Rosabella와 그녀의 친구들은 "Molte grazie!"라고 다시 외친다.

36 버스가 굴러간다.

37 Jaden은 부엌으로 돌아간다.

38 그는 번역 앱에 말한다. "사람들에게서 배우는 것이 더 재미있습니다. 이탈리아어 좀 가르쳐 주실 수 있나요, Gambini 씨?"

39 Gambini 씨는 "Si,"라고 말하고는 웃는다.

● 우리말을 참고하여 본문을 영작하시오.

1 Jaden의 가족은 이탈리아 플로렌스에 있다.

➡ _____

2 그들은 그의 어머니의 친구인 Gambini 씨를 방문하고 있다.

➡ _____

3 오늘 그의 부모님은 박물관에 갈 예정이지만, Jaden은 집에 남고 싶어 한다.

➡ _____

4 그는 자신의 전화기에 있는 번역 앱이 의사소통을 하는 데 도움이 될 것이라고 생각한다.

➡ _____

5 그는 배가 꼬르륵거려서 부엌으로 들어간다.

➡ _____

6 Gambini 씨가 Jaden을 보자, 그녀는 "Buon giorno. Vuoi un pezzo di pane e un bicchiere di latte?"라고 말한다.

➡ _____

_____

7 Jaden은 어떻게 대답해야 할지 모른다.

➡ _____

8 그러자 앱이 "좋은 아침입니다. 빵 한 개와 우유 한 잔 드시겠어요?"라고 말한다.

➡ _____

9 Jaden은 "네, 부탁해요."라고 대답한다.

➡ _____

10 문을 두드리는 소리가 들리고 Gambini 씨가 초대한 한 여자가 안으로 들어온다.

➡ _____

11 두 여자는 아주 빨리 이탈리아어를 말하기 시작한다.

➡ _____

12 그래서 번역 앱은 이해하지 못한다.

➡ _____

13 Jaden은 전화기를 끄고 그것을 탁자 위에 둔다.

➡ _____

14 그는 화창한 아침을 즐기기 위해 밖으로 나간다.

➡ _____

15 그는 쿵쾅거리는 소리를 따라가다 벽에 축구공을 차고 있는 소녀를 발견한다.

➡ _____

16 그녀는 그에게 돌아서서 "Buon giorno."라고 말한다.

➡ _____

17 그의 전화기는 부엌에 있어서 Jaden은 뭐라고 말해야 할지 모른다.
➡ _____

18 그는 단지 소녀가 말한 말들인 "Buon giorno"를 반복한다.
➡ _____

19 소녀는 그에게 공을 찬다.
➡ _____

20 Jaden은 그것 때문에 번역 앱이 필요하지 않다.
➡ _____

21 잠시 동안, 두 사람은 공을 가지고 논다.
➡ _____

22 마침내, 그 소녀는 자신을 가리키며 "Mi chiamo Rosabella."라고 말한다.
➡ _____

23 "내 이름은 Jaden이야."라고 그가 대답한다.
➡ _____

24 갑자기 Rosabella가 "Arrive l'autobus."라고 말한다.
➡ _____

25 Jaden은 '버스'와 '도착하다'라는 단어와 비슷한 소리가 나는 단어를 알아듣는다.
➡ _____

26 아니나 다를까, 버스 한 대가 나타난다.
➡ _____

27 축구 유니폼을 입은 아이들이 창문에서 "Ciao, Rosabella!"라고 외친다.
➡ _____

28 Rosabella가 버스에 오를 때, Jaden은 "행운을 빌어요."라고 말한다.
➡ _____

29 그녀는 이해하지 못한다.
➡ _____

30 그래서 Jaden은 생각하고 "Buon, buon ...."이라고 말한다.
➡ _____

31 그는 그녀가 손에 들고 있는 축구공을 가리킨다.
➡ _____

32 Rosabella가 "Fortuna! Buona fortuna!"라고 소리친다.
➡ _____

33 Fortuna는 '행운'처럼 들린다.
➡ _____

34 "Buona fortuna!"라고 그가 소리친다.
➡ _____

35 Rosabella와 그녀의 친구들은 "Molte grazie!"라고 다시 외친다.
➡ _____

36 버스가 굴러간다
➡ _____

37 Jaden은 부엌으로 돌아간다.
➡ _____

38 그는 번역 앱에 말한다. "사람들에게서 배우는 것이 더 재미있습니다. 이탈리아어 좀 가르쳐 주실 수 있나요, Gambini 씨?"
➡ _____
_____

39 Gambini 씨는 "Si,"라고 말하고는 웃는다.
➡ _____

[01~04] 다음 글을 읽고, 물음에 답하시오.

Jaden's family is in Florence, Italy. They are visiting Ms. Gambini, his mother's friend. Today his parents are going to museums, ___ⓐ___ Jaden wants to stay behind. He thinks the translation app on his phone will help him communicate.

His stomach growls, ___ⓑ___ he enters the kitchen. When Ms. Gambini sees Jaden, she says "Buon giorno. Vuoi un pezzo di pane e un bicchiere di latte?" Jaden does not know ___ⓒ___ to respond. Then the app says, "Good morning. ⓓWill you like a piece of bread and a glass of milk?" Jaden answers, "Yes, please."

01 위 글의 빈칸 ⓐ에 ⓑ에 알맞은 것으로 짝지어진 것은?

① and – so
② but – so
③ but – or
④ and – for
⑤ but – for

02 위 글의 빈칸 ⓒ에 알맞은 것은?

① how
② why
③ what
④ when
⑤ which

서답형
03 위 글의 밑줄 친 ⓓ에서 어법상 어색한 것을 고치시오.

_____ ➡ _____

04 위 글의 내용으로 보아 대답할 수 <u>없는</u> 질문은?

① Where is Jaden's family now?
② Who is Ms. Gambini?
③ Why doesn't Jaden want to go to museums?
④ What does Jaden think will help him communicate?
⑤ Why does Jaden enter the kitchen?

[05~09] 다음 글을 읽고, 물음에 답하시오.

(①) There is a knock on the door, and a woman ___ⓐ___ Ms. Gambini invited walks in. (②) The two women begin speaking Italian very fast. (③) Jaden turns ___ⓑ___ the phone and leaves it on the table. (④) He goes out to enjoy the sunny morning. (⑤) He follows a thumping sound and finds a girl who is kicking a soccer ball ⓒagainst a wall. She turns to him and says, "Buon giorno."

05 위 글의 ①~⑤ 중 다음 주어진 문장이 들어갈 알맞은 곳은?

So the translator does not understand.

①   ②   ③   ④   ⑤

06 위 글의 빈칸 ⓐ에 알맞은 것은? (3개)

① who
② what
③ whom
④ that
⑤ which

07 위 글의 빈칸 ⓑ에 알맞은 것은?

① on   ② off
③ to   ④ for
⑤ from

08 위 글의 밑줄 친 ⓒ와 같은 의미로 쓰인 것은?

① Ted played against the champion.
② We are against the war.
③ She is against seeing him.
④ The rain beat against the windows.
⑤ His red clothes stood out clearly against the snow.

서답형

09 Why does Jaden go out? Answer in English.

➡ _____

[10~14] 다음 글을 읽고, 물음에 답하시오.

ⓐHis phone is in the kitchen, so Jaden does not know what to say. He just repeats the words ____ⓑ____ the girl said, "Buon giorno." The girl kicks the ball to him. Jaden needs no translator for ⓒthat. For a while, the two play with the ball. Finally, the girl points at ⓓher and says, "Mi chiamo Rosabella." "My name is Jaden," he responds.

10 위 글의 밑줄 친 ⓐ와 문형이 같은 것은?

① Mike likes music very much.
② The man is strong.
③ Birds fly in the sky.
④ The news made her glad.
⑤ Jane sent me a birthday card.

11 위 글의 빈칸 ⓑ에 알맞은 것은? (2개)

① who   ② what
③ whom   ④ that
⑤ which

서답형

12 위 글의 밑줄 친 ⓒ가 구체적으로 가리키는 것을 우리말로 쓰시오.

➡ _____

서답형

13 위 글의 밑줄 친 ⓓ를 알맞게 고치시오.

➡ _____

14 위 글의 내용과 일치하지 않는 것은?

① Jaden의 전화기는 부엌에 있다.
② Jaden은 전화기가 없어서 소녀의 말에 대답할 수 없다.
③ 소녀와 Jaden은 잠시 공을 가지고 논다.
④ Jaden은 소녀와 이야기하기 위해 번역 앱이 필요하다.
⑤ Jaden은 소녀의 이름이 Rosabella라는 것을 알았다.

[15~19] 다음 글을 읽고, 물음에 답하시오.

Suddenly Rosabella says, "Arrive l'autobus." Jaden understands the words that sound ⓐ(like, alike) *bus* and *arrive*. Sure enough, a bus ___ⓑ___ .

Kids in soccer uniforms shout from the windows, "Ciao, Rosabella!" ⓒAs Rosabella steps onto the bus, Jaden says, "Good luck." She does not understand. So Jaden thinks and says, "Buon, buon ...." He points ___ⓓ___ the soccer ball that she is holding in her hand.

서답형

15 위 글의 괄호 ⓐ에서 알맞은 것을 고르시오.

➡ _____

중요

16 위 글의 빈칸 ⓑ에 알맞은 것은?

① happens ② starts
③ enters ④ presents
⑤ appears

17 위 글의 밑줄 친 ⓒ와 같은 의미로 쓰인 것은?

① Leave the papers as they are.
② As she grew older, she gained in confidence.
③ She may need some help as she's new here.
④ As you know, Julia is leaving soon.
⑤ Don't read a book as you walk.

18 위 글의 빈칸 ⓓ에 알맞은 것은?

① in ② for
③ to ④ with
⑤ upon

19 위 글의 내용으로 보아 알 수 없는 것은?

① Rosabella는 버스가 온다고 말했다.
② Jaden은 Rosabella가 말한 것을 이해했다.
③ 버스에 탄 아이들은 축구 유니폼을 입고 있다.
④ Rosabella가 버스를 탈 때 Jaden은 행운을 빌어 주었다.
⑤ Rosabella는 축구팀의 주장이다.

[20~23] 다음 글을 읽고, 물음에 답하시오.

Rosabella shouts, "Fortuna! Buona fortuna!" Fortuna sounds ⓐlike *fortune*. "Buona fortuna!" he shouts. Rosabella and her friends shout back, "Molte grazie!" The bus ___ⓑ___ away. Jaden goes back to the kitchen. He says into the translation app, "Learning from people is more fun. ⓒCan you teach me some Italian, Ms. Gambini?" Ms. Gambini says, "Si," and laughs.

중요

20 위 글의 밑줄 친 ⓐ와 쓰임이 같은 것은?

① Do you like their new house?
② This soap smells like a rose.
③ I didn't like to watch TV.
④ At weekends I like to sleep late.
⑤ We'd like you to come and visit us.

서답형

21 위 글의 빈칸 ⓑ에 다음 정의에 해당하는 단어를 쓰시오.

> to move along a surface

➡ _____

서답형

22 위 글의 밑줄 친 ⓒ와 같은 뜻이 되도록 다음 문장의 빈칸에 알맞은 말을 쓰시오.

> Can you teach some Italian _____ me

서답형

23 Jaden이 Gambini 씨에게 이탈리아어를 가르쳐 달라고 말한 이유를 우리말로 간단히 쓰시오.

➡ _____

[24~29] 다음 글을 읽고, 물음에 답하시오.

Gestures can have different meanings in different cultures. ___ⓐ___ example, the "OK sign" means "okay" or "all right" in many countries. (①) ⓑThe gesture means something good. (②) It means "money" in some cultures. (③) ⓒThat is also something good. (④) It means there is nothing, ___ⓓ___ it is not a very happy gesture. (⑤) When we travel, we should use gestures carefully.

중요

24 위 글의 ①~⑤ 중 다음 주어진 문장이 들어갈 알맞은 곳은?

> The same sign, however, means "O" in France.

①   ②   ③   ④   ⑤

25 위 글의 빈칸 ⓐ에 알맞은 것은?

① To   ② For
③ In   ④ From
⑤ With

서답형

26 위 글의 밑줄 친 ⓑ를 우리말로 옮기시오.

➡ _____

서답형

27 위 글의 밑줄 친 ⓒ가 가리키는 것을 영어로 쓰시오.

➡ _____

중요

28 위 글의 빈칸 ⓓ에 알맞은 것은?

① so   ② or
③ but   ④ for
⑤ when

29 위 글의 요지로 가장 알맞은 것은?

① 제스처는 사용되는 문화에 따라 여러 의미가 있다.
② OK 사인은 보통 좋다는 것을 의미한다.
③ OK 사인은 어떤 문화들에서는 돈을 의미한다.
④ OK 사인은 프랑스에서는 제로를 의미한다.
⑤ 우리는 여행할 때 제스처를 주의 깊게 사용해야 한다.

[01~04] 다음 글을 읽고, 물음에 답하시오.

Jaden's family is in Florence, Italy. They are visiting Ms. Gambini, his mother's friend. ⓐ Today his parents are going to museums, but Jaden wants to stay behind. He thinks the translation app on his phone will help him communicate.

His _____ⓑ growls, so he enters the kitchen. When Ms. Gambini sees Jaden, she says "Buon giorno. Vuoi un pezzo di pane e un bicchiere di latte?" ⓒJaden does not know how to respond. Then the app says, "Good morning. Would you like a piece of bread and a glass of milk?" Jaden answers, "Yes, please."

01 위 글의 밑줄 친 ⓐ를 우리말로 옮기시오.

➡ _____

_____

02 위 글의 빈칸 ⓑ에 다음 정의에 해당하는 말을 쓰시오.

> the organ inside your body where food is digested before it moves into the intestines

➡ _____

03 위 글의 밑줄 친 ⓒ와 같은 뜻이 되도록 빈칸에 알맞은 말을 쓰시오.

> Jaden does not know _____ he _____ respond.

04 What does Jaden think will help him communicate? Answer in Korean.

➡ _____

_____

[05~07] 다음 글을 읽고, 물음에 답하시오.

ⓐThere is a knock on the door, and a woman whom Ms. Gambini invited walks in. The two women begin ⓑspeak Italian very fast. So the translator does not understand.

Jaden turns off the phone and leaves it on the table. He goes out to enjoy the sunny morning. He follows a thumping sound and finds a girl ⓒwho is kicking a soccer ball against a wall. She turns to him and says, "Buon giorno."

05 위 글의 밑줄 친 ⓐ와 같은 뜻이 되도록 다음 문장의 빈칸에 알맞은 말을 쓰시오.

> Someone _____ _____ the door

06 위 글의 밑줄 친 ⓑ를 알맞은 형으로 고치시오.

➡ _____

07 위 글의 밑줄 친 ⓒ 대신 쓸 수 있는 말을 쓰시오.

➡ _____

[08~12] 다음 글을 읽고, 물음에 답하시오.

ⓐHis phone is in the kitchen, so Jaden does not know what to say. He just repeats the words ⓑthat the girl said, "Buon giorno." The girl kicks the ball to him. Jaden needs no translator for that. ____ⓒ____ a while, the two play with the ball. Finally, the girl points at herself and says, "Mi chiamo Rosabella." "My name is Jaden," he responds.

Suddenly Rosabella says, "Arrive l'autobus." ⓓJaden은 bus와 arrive처럼 들리는 단어들을 이해한다. Sure enough, a bus appears.

08 위 글의 밑줄 친 ⓐ를 우리말로 옮기시오.

➡ _____

_____

09 위 글의 밑줄 친 ⓑ 대신 쓸 수 있는 말을 쓰시오.

➡ _____

10 위 글의 빈칸 ⓒ에 알맞은 말을 쓰시오.

➡ _____

11 위 글의 밑줄 친 ⓓ를 주어진 단어를 이용해서 영어로 옮기시오.

(words, that, sound)

➡ _____

_____

12 Why doesn't Jaden need a translator?

➡ _____

[13~16] 다음 글을 읽고, 물음에 답하시오.

Kids ____ⓐ____ soccer uniforms shout from the windows, "Ciao, Rosabella!" As Rosabella ____ⓑ____ onto the bus, Jaden says, "Good luck." She does not understand. So Jaden thinks and says, "Buon, buon ...." ⓒ그는 그녀가 손에 들고 있는 축구공을 가리킨다.

Rosabella shouts, "Fortuna! Buona fortuna!" Fortuna sounds ____ⓓ____ fortune. "Buona fortuna!" he shouts. Rosabella and her friends shout back, "Molte grazie!" The bus rolls away.

13 위 글의 빈칸 ⓐ에 알맞은 전치사를 쓰시오.

➡ _____

14 위 글의 빈칸 ⓑ에 다음 정의에 해당하는 말을 쓰시오. (필요하면 어형을 바꿀 것.)

to put your foot on something or move your foot in a particular direction

➡ _____

15 위 글의 밑줄 친 ⓒ를 주어진 단어를 이용해서 영어로 옮기시오.

(point to, that, hold)

➡ _____

_____

16 위 글의 빈칸 ⓓ에 알맞은 말을 쓰시오.

➡ _____

구석구석

My Writing Portfolio - Step 1

Our Travel App

"The name of our app is *Enjoy Paris*. It focuses on what to see in Paris. It
= our app   what to+동사원형: 무엇을 ~할지
gives information on opening hours and admission fees of museums and
정보를 제공하다   개장 시간   입장료
theaters. It also tells you how to get there. Our app will be useful for travelers.
how to+동사원형: ~하는 방법 = to museums and theaters ~에 유용하다

구문해설 • travel: 여행 • app: 앱, 어플리케이션 • focus on: ~에 초점을 맞추다
• museum: 박물관 • theater: 극장 • traveler: 여행객

우리의 여행 앱

　우리 앱의 이름은 "파리를 즐겨라"이다. 그것은 파리에서 무엇을 볼 것인가에 초점을 맞추고 있다. 그것은 박물관과 극장의 개장 시간과 입장료에 대한 정보를 제공한다. 그것은 또한 그곳에 가는 방법을 알려 준다. 우리 앱은 여행객들에게 유용할 것이다.

Wrap Up - Reading

Gestures can have different meanings in different cultures. For example, the
다른 문화에서   예를 들면(= For instance)
"OK sign" means "okay" or "all right" in many countries. The gesture means
괜찮다
something good. It means "money" in some cultures. That is also something
something+형용사   = the OK sign
good. The same sign, however, means "O" in France. It means there is nothing,
그러나
so it is not a very happy gesture. When we travel, we should use gestures
그래서   접 ~할 때   ~해야 한다
carefully.

구문해설 • gesture: 제스처, 몸짓 • different 다른 • meaning: 의미 • mean: 의미하다
• travel: 여행하다 • use: 사용하다 • carefully: 신중하게

　제스처는 다른 문화에서 다른 의미를 가질 수 있다. 예를 들어, 'OK 사인'은 많은 나라에서 '좋다' 또는 '괜찮다'를 의미한다. 그 제스처는 좋은 것을 의미한다. 그것은 어떤 문화에서는 '돈'을 의미한다. 그것 또한 좋은 것이다. 그러나 같은 사인이 프랑스에서는 '제로'를 의미한다. 그것은 아무것도 없다는 것을 의미하기 때문에, 별로 행복한 제스처가 아니다. 우리는 여행할 때, 신중하게 제스처를 사용해야 한다.

Reading for Fun 1

A Different Day   색다른 하루

"Same, same–
SAME," I say.
Today I want a
Different Day!

"같아, 같아–
똑같아" 나는 말한다.
오늘 나는
색다른 하루를 원해!

Walking–NO!
I jump and run.
Bag on my head,
I have some fun.

걸어가는 것.-아니야!
나는 뛰고 달린다.
가방을 머리에 이고,
난 즐겁다.

Notes in blue?
No, no–PINK!
Hello in Spanish,
Is "Hola," I think.

파란색으로 필기?
아니지, 아니야–분홍색
으로!
안녕은 스페인어로
"Hola." 나는 그렇게 생각해.

Different snack,
Old friends and new.
We laugh and ask,
"What shall we do?"

색다른 간식
오랜 친구들과 새로 사귄
친구들
우리는 웃으며 묻는다.
"우리 무얼 할까?"

"Throw a ball?
play a game?"
I'm tired but happy,
It's not the same.

"공을 던질까?
놀이를 할까?"
나는 피곤하지만 행복해,
똑같지가 않아.

"Fun, fun–
FUN," I say.
Today I had an
exciting day!

"재미있어, 재미있어–
진짜 재미있어." 나는 말한다.
오늘 나는
신나는 하루를 보냈어!

영역별 핵심문제

Words & Expressions

01 다음 두 단어의 관계가 같도록 빈칸에 알맞은 말을 쓰시오.

France : French = Turkey : _____

02 다음 중 짝지어진 단어의 관계가 나머지 넷과 <u>다른</u> 것은?

① wrong – right
② delicious – tasty
③ appear – disappear
④ forget – remember
⑤ important – unimportant

03 다음 우리말과 같도록 빈칸에 알맞은 말을 쓰시오.

예를 들면, 나는 사과, 포도 그리고 딸기를 좋아한다.

➡ _____ _____, I like apples, grapes and strawberries.

04 다음 중 영영풀이가 <u>잘못된</u> 것은?

① repeat: to say something again
② mean: to have a particular meaning
③ kick: to hit something with your foot
④ save: to use more of something than is necessary
⑤ enough: as many or as much as someone needs or wants

05 다음 우리말과 같도록 빈칸에 알맞은 말을 쓰시오.

스페인어는 이 나라의 공용어이다.
➡ Spanish is the _____ _____ of the country.

06 다음 빈칸에 공통으로 알맞은 것은?

• The movie will start _____ half an hour.
• As the door was open, Jenny walked _____.

① at
② in
③ on
④ for
⑤ after

07 다음 영영풀이에 해당하는 단어를 주어진 철자로 시작하여 쓰시오.

words that have been changed from one language into a different language

➡ t_____

Conversation

08 다음 대화의 밑줄 친 부분과 바꾸어 쓸 수 있는 것은?

A: Would you like some more cake?
B: Yes, please.

① Can you make the cake?
② Can you put this cake on the plate?
③ Did you eat the cake?
④ How about having some more cake?
⑤ Why don't you make the cake?

09 다음 대화의 빈칸에 알맞은 것은?

> A: She's a busy bee.
> B: What do you mean by that?
> A: _____

① She's very beautiful.
② She's a busy worker.
③ She likes bees very much.
④ She knows about everything.
⑤ She paid too much money for it.

10 다음 대화의 순서를 바르게 배열하시오.

> (A) How do you like it?
> (B) Yes, please.
> (C) Oh, it's delicious.
> (D) Would you like some *bibimbap*?

➡ _____

11 다음 대화의 빈칸에 공통으로 알맞은 것은?

> A: What does it _____ by "A.S.A.P" at the end of the invitation card?
> B: It _____s "as soon as possible."

① put
② follow
③ mean
④ repeat
⑤ understand

12 다음 질문의 응답 중 의도가 나머지와 다른 것은?

> Would you like to have some cake?

① No, thank you.
② I'm not hungry.
③ I've had enough.
④ Thanks, it looks delicious.
⑤ I'd love to, but I'm full.

[13~17] 다음 대화를 읽고, 물음에 답하시오.

> G: Hurry ___ⓐ___ , everyone. Hit the road!
> B: I'm sorry, but _____ⓑ_____ ?
> G: I mean it's time to start moving.
> B: ___ⓒ___ , "ⓓIt's time to go"?
> G: Yes.
> B: Great! ⓔLet's hit the road.

13 위 대화의 빈칸 ⓐ에 알맞은 단어를 쓰시오.

➡ _____

14 위 대화의 빈칸 ⓑ에 알맞은 것은?

① you know what
② do you understand
③ what does it like
④ can you guess what it is
⑤ what do you mean by that

15 위 대화의 빈칸 ⓒ에 알맞은 것은?

① By　　　　　② With
③ From　　　　④ Like
⑤ Through

16 위 대화의 밑줄 친 ⓓ와 쓰임이 다른 것은?

① It is dark outside.
② It rains a lot in summer.
③ It is two o'clock now.
④ How far is it from here to the subway station?
⑤ I cleaned the room, but it is a mess again.

17 위 대화의 밑줄 친 ⓔ를 우리말로 쓰시오.

➡ _____

Grammar

[18~19] 다음 문장의 빈칸에 알맞은 것을 고르시오.

18

> This is the ring _____ my best friend Yujin gave me.

① who

② how

③ what

④ which

⑤ where

19

> You'll never forget how _____ a bicycle once you have learned.

① ride

② to ride

③ riding

④ to riding

⑤ about riding

20 다음 두 문장을 한 문장으로 만들 때 빈칸에 알맞은 말을 쓰시오.

> You are the only friend. I can tell you a secret.
>
> ➡ You are the only friend to _____ I can tell a secret.

[21~22] 다음 중 어법상 어색한 문장을 고르시오.

21 ① Can you tell me when to get up?

② They told me where to go.

③ Jack decided what to eat in the morning.

④ Will you tell me who to invite Jack?

⑤ I learned how to make lemonade.

22 ① The woman with whom I went there is my aunt.

② The man with whom she is talking is Mr. Allen.

③ I have no friends with whom I can talk about it.

④ The people whom I work are all very kind.

⑤ Those whom he lived with respected him.

23 다음 두 문장의 뜻이 같도록 빈칸에 알맞은 말을 쓰시오.

> We could not agree as to where we should go.
> = We could not agree as to _____ _____ _____.

24 다음 〈보기〉의 밑줄 친 부분과 쓰임이 <u>다른</u> 하나는?

> ┤ 보기 ├
> Do you know the boy <u>that</u> you saw at the library?

① Meryl Streep is a famous actress <u>that</u> I like a lot.

② He is the smartest boy <u>that</u> I've ever met.

③ The tomato pasta <u>that</u> we ate for lunch was a little spicy.

④ I thought <u>that</u> I had to finish my homework.

⑤ The pants <u>that</u> I'm wearing are very comfortable.

25 다음 우리말을 영어로 옮길 때 빈칸에 알맞은 말을 쓰시오.

> 내 여동생은 자신의 머리를 갈색으로 염색할 것인지 말 것인지를 결정하는 데 어려움을 겪고 있다.
> ➡ My sister is having trouble deciding _____ _____ dye her hair brown or not.

26 다음 중 밑줄 친 부분의 쓰임이 바르지 <u>않은</u> 것은?

① I know the girl <u>whom</u> you met at the store.
② The woman <u>whom</u> we saw on the street is a famous singer.
③ This is the house in <u>that</u> she was born.
④ Do you know the doctor <u>who</u> I visited last night?
⑤ I cannot find the watch <u>which</u> I bought last week.

27 다음 중 빈칸에 들어갈 말이 나머지 넷과 <u>다른</u> 것은?

① What _____ learn in youth is very important.
② I want you to decide where _____ go first.
③ We discussed who _____ take the resposibility.
④ She completely forgot how _____ make a paper crane.
⑤ I will tell you what _____ see in London.

[28~31] 다음 글을 읽고, 물음에 답하시오.

> Today Jaden's parents are going to museums, but Jaden wants ⓐ<u>to stay</u> behind. He thinks the translation app on his phone will help him _____ ⓑ . ⓒ<u>His stomach growls, so he enters into the kitchen.</u> When Ms. Gambini sees Jaden, she says "Buon giorno. Vuoi un pezzo di pane e un bicchiere di latte?" ⓓ<u>Jaden does not know how to respond.</u>

28 위 글의 밑줄 친 ⓐ와 같은 용법으로 쓰인 것은? (2개)

① We wished to reach the North Pole.
② He made a promise to come again.
③ Kate was excited to see the scenery.
④ The boy grew up to be a poet.
⑤ We decided to go shopping at the mart.

29 위 글의 빈칸 ⓑ에 알맞은 것은? (2개)

① communicate   ② communicates
③ communicating   ④ to communicate
⑤ to communicating

30 위 글의 밑줄 친 ⓒ에서 어법상 어색한 것을 고쳐 다시 쓰시오.

➡ _____

31 위 글의 밑줄 친 ⓓ와 같은 뜻이 되도록 다음 문장의 빈칸에 알맞은 말을 쓰시오.

> Jaden does not know _____ _____ _____ respond.

[32~34] 다음 글을 읽고, 물음에 답하시오.

> **April 10**
> Today I had an ___ⓐ___ for the school radio station. Claire offered me some cookies, ___ⓑ___ I couldn't eat. She said, "ⓒBreak a leg!" and it worked! I passed!

32 위 글의 빈칸 ⓐ에 다음 정의에 해당하는 단어를 쓰시오.

> a short performance given by an actor, dancer, or musician so that a director or conductor can decide if they are good enough to be in a play, film, or orchestra

➡ _____

33 위 글의 빈칸 ⓑ에 알맞은 것은?

① so   ② but
③ for   ④ and
⑤ that

34 위 글의 밑줄 친 ⓒ가 의도하는 것은?

① 칭찬하기   ② 변명하기
③ 비난하기   ④ 기원하기
⑤ 축하하기

[35~39] 다음 글을 읽고, 물음에 답하시오.

> **Our Travel App**
> The name of our app is *Enjoy Paris.* ⓐIt focuses on ___ⓑ___ to see in Paris. It gives information on opening hours and ___ⓒ___ fees of museums and theaters. It also tells you how to get there. Our app will be ⓓuse for travelers.

35 위 글의 밑줄 친 ⓐ가 가리키는 것을 영어로 쓰시오.

➡ _____

36 위 글의 빈칸 ⓑ에 알맞은 것은?

① how   ② who
③ what   ④ where
⑤ which

37 위 글의 빈칸 ⓒ에 다음 정의에 해당하는 단어를 쓰시오.

> the act of entering a place

➡ _____

38 위 글의 밑줄 친 ⓓ를 알맞은 형으로 옮기시오.

➡ _____

39 위 글의 내용과 일치하지 <u>않는</u> 것은?

① 우리 앱의 이름은 '파리를 즐겨라'이다.
② 우리의 앱은 파리의 볼 장소들에 대한 정보를 알려준다.
③ 우리의 앱을 이용하면 파리의 박물관들과 극장의 개관 시간을 일 수 있다.
④ 우리의 앱은 파리의 박물관들과 극장에 가는 방법을 알려준다.
⑤ 우리의 앱은 주로 파리 시민들이 많이 이용한다.

01 출제율 95%

다음 중 단어의 성격이 나머지와 <u>다른</u> 것은?

① Thai　　　　② Russian
③ Spanish　　　④ Germany
⑤ Portuguese

02 출제율 85%

다음 우리말과 같도록 할 때 빈칸에 알맞은 것은?

> 그들은 기차에 올라타고 있다.
> ➡ They are stepping _____ the train.

① in　　　　② to
③ up　　　　④ at
⑤ onto

03 출제율 90%

다음 영영풀이에 해당하는 단어로 알맞은 것은?

> to have the intended effect or result

① need　　　② work
③ hold　　　④ change
⑤ match

04 출제율 100%

다음 빈칸에 공통으로 알맞은 단어를 쓰시오. (대·소문자 무시)

> • I need to relax _____ a while.
> • _____ example, people like to talk about the leisure time.

➡ _____

05 출제율 95%

다음 빈칸에 들어갈 말로 적절하지 <u>않은</u> 것은?

> • Let's _____ the road.
> • I know how to _____ there.
> • What do you _____ by that?
> • The boy is kicking a ball _____ a wall.

① get　　　　② hit
③ mean　　　④ against
⑤ understand

06 출제율 90%

다음 대화의 밑줄 친 말의 문맥상 의미로 알맞은 것은?

> A: I will buy this cell phone. <u>It's a steal.</u>
> B: What do you mean by that?
> A: It's very cheap.

① 그것은 훔친 거야.
② 그것은 불량품이야.
③ 그것은 너무 비싸.
④ 그것은 최신형이야.
⑤ 그것은 공짜나 다름없어.

07 출제율 85%

다음 대화의 빈칸에 들어갈 말로 알맞지 <u>않은</u> 것은?

> A: Would you like some *bibimbap*?
> B: _____

① No, thanks. I'm full.
② No, thanks. I'll try some *bibimbap*.
③ No, thank you. I had enough.
④ Yes, please. It smells nice.
⑤ Yes, please. It looks wonderful.

[08~12] 다음 대화를 읽고, 물음에 답하시오.

> B: It smells nice. What are you cooking, Uncle Abbas?
> M: I'm making kebab.
> B: Kebab? What is it?
> M: It's a traditional Turkish food. We have small pieces of meat and vegetables on a stick.
> B: Oh, it sounds delicious.
> M: ⓐWould you like some?
> B: Sure. _____ⓑ_____
> M: ⓒ여기 있어.
> B: It tastes great. You should open your own restaurant!
> M: Thanks. I'm glad you like it.

출제율 95%

08 위 대화의 밑줄 친 ⓐ를 다음과 같이 바꿔 쓸 때 빈칸에 알맞은 말을 쓰시오.

_____ _____ you have some?

출제율 85%

09 위 대화의 빈칸 ⓑ에 알맞은 것은?

① I'm full.　　　② I had enough.
③ I'm not hungry　④ I don't like kebab.
⑤ I'd love some.

출제율 100%

10 위 대화의 밑줄 친 ⓒ의 우리말을 세 단어로 쓰시오.

➡ _____

출제율 85%

11 위 대화에서 다음 영영풀이에 해당하는 단어를 찾아 쓰시오

> being part of the beliefs, customs, or way of life of a particular group of people, that have not changed for a long time

➡ _____

출제율 85%

12 위 대화를 통해 알 수 있는 것은?

① Uncle Abbas lives in Turkey.
② The boy likes Turkish food a lot.
③ The boy has never eaten kebab before.
④ The boy loves Turkey.
⑤ Uncle Abbas hopes to run a restaurant.

출제율 95%

13 다음 빈칸에 공통으로 알맞은 말은?

> • I like the doll _____ my mom made.
> • Do you know the man _____ Jane wants to meet?

① how　　　　② who
③ whom　　　④ which
⑤ that

출제율 90%

14 다음 문장에서 어법상 어색한 것을 고치시오.

> When you read, you will often find words you don't know them.

_____ ➡ _____

출제율 95%

15 다음 중 어법상 어색한 문장은?

① Does she know when to start?
② I don't know how use this camera.
③ We don't know which bus to get on.
④ They had no idea where to go.
⑤ I'm wondering what to buy for my mother's birthday.

16 다음 중 밑줄 친 관계대명사가 <u>잘못</u> 쓰인 것은?

① Jack needs a car <u>which</u> he can drive.

② I need a man <u>that</u> can speak English.

③ I know the girl <u>which</u> you are looking for.

④ This is the book <u>which</u> I bought two days ago.

⑤ They saw the old man and his dog <u>that</u> were running in the park.

17 다음 우리말을 영어로 바르게 옮긴 것은?

> 나는 내 남동생에게 중국어 읽는 법을 가르쳤다.

① I taught my brother how to read Chinese.

② I taught my brother where to read Chinese.

③ I taught my brother why to read Chinese.

④ I taught my brother what to read Chinese.

⑤ I taught my brother how he can read Chinese.

18 다음 문장의 밑줄 친 부분 중 생략할 수 <u>없는</u> 것은?

① This is the story <u>that</u> Kevin wrote.

② The dress <u>which</u> she is wearing is pink.

③ This is the table <u>which</u> his father made.

④ The man <u>whom</u> I saw yesterday was Mr. Brown.

⑤ The man <u>who</u> lives in Seoul will come tomorrow.

[19~23] 다음 글을 읽고, 물음에 답하시오.

Jaden does not know how to respond. Then the app says, "Good morning. Would you like a ⓐ of bread and a ⓑ of milk?" Jaden answers, "Yes, please."

ⓒ<u>누군가 문을 노크한다</u>, and a woman ⓓ Ms. Gambini invited walks in. The two women begin ⓔ<u>speak</u> Italian very fast. So the translator does not understand.

19 위 글의 빈칸 ⓐ와 ⓑ에 알맞은 말이 바르게 짝지어진 것은? (2개)

① piece – glass   ② piece – cups

③ pair – cup   ④ pair – glasses

⑤ slice – glass

20 위 글의 밑줄 친 ⓒ를 주어진 말을 이용해 영어로 옮기시오.

> (there, knock, on)

➡ _____

21 위 글의 빈칸 ⓓ에 알맞지 <u>않은</u> 것은? (2개)

① who   ② what

③ that   ④ which

⑤ whom

22 위 글의 밑줄 친 ⓔ를 알맞은 형으로 고치시오.

➡ _____

23 위 글의 내용으로 보아 대답할 수 <u>없는</u> 질문은?

① Why doesn't Jaden know how to respond?
② What helps Jaden respond?
③ Who knocks on the door?
④ Who is the woman Ms. Gambini invited?
⑤ Why doesn't the translator understand?

26 위 글의 밑줄 친 ⓑ 대신 쓸 수 있는 것을 쓰시오.

➡ _____

27 위 글의 밑줄 친 ⓒ와 같은 뜻이 되도록 바꿔 쓸 때 빈칸에 알맞은 것으로 짝지어진 것은?

> Jaden does not know what he _____ say _____ his phone is in the kitchen.

① would – for
② would – as
③ might – because
④ should – though
⑤ should – because

[24~29] 다음 글을 읽고, 물음에 답하시오.

Jaden turns _____ⓐ the phone and leaves it on the table. He goes out to enjoy the sunny morning. He follows a thumping sound and finds a girl ⓑ<u>who</u> is kicking a soccer ball against a wall. She turns to him and says, "Buon giorno."

(①) ⓒ<u>His phone is in the kitchen, so Jaden does not know what to say.</u> (②) He just repeats the words that the girl said, "Buon giorno." (③) Jaden needs no translator for that. (④) For a while, the two play with the ball. (⑤) ⓓ<u>Finally, the girl points at her and says,</u> "Mi chiamo Rosabella." "My name is Jaden," he responds.

24 위 글의 ①~⑤ 중 다음 주어진 문장이 들어갈 알맞은 곳은?

> The girl kicks the ball to him.

① ② ③ ④ ⑤

28 위 글의 밑줄 친 ⓓ에서 어법상 어색한 것을 고치시오.

_____ ➡ _____

25 위 글의 빈칸 ⓐ에 알맞은 말을 쓰시오.

➡ _____

29 위 글의 내용과 일치하지 <u>않는</u> 것은?

① Jaden은 전화기를 테이블에 놓는다.
② Jaden은 화창한 아침을 즐기기를 원한다.
③ Jaden은 벽에 축구공을 차고 있는 소녀를 발견한다.
④ Jaden은 소녀와 대화하기 위해 번역 앱이 필요하다.
⑤ 소녀와 Jaden은 서로의 이름을 말한다.

01 다음 주어진 단어를 바르게 배열하시오.

> A: Bonjour.
> B: (that / does / what / mean / ?)
> A: It's means "Hello," in French.

➡ _____

02 다음 밑줄 친 부분과 바꿔 쓸 수 있는 표현을 두 가지 이상 쓰시오.

> A: <u>Do you want some juice?</u>
> B: No, thanks. I'm full.

➡ _____

_____

03 다음 대화의 빈칸에 알맞은 말을 넣어 대화를 완성하시오.

> A: Hurry up, everyone. Hit the road!
> B: _____
> A: It means it's time to start moving.

➡ _____

_____

04 다음 대화의 밑줄 친 우리말을 영어로 옮길 때 빈칸에 알맞은 말을 쓰시오.

> A: What is "Hello," in Spanish?
> B: It is "Hola." <u>독일어로 "고맙습니다,"를 어떻게 말하니?</u>
> A: "Danke."

_____ _____ _____ _____

"Thank you," in German?

05 다음 괄호 안에 주어진 단어를 배열하여 문장을 완성하시오.

(1) Mr. Brown is a teacher (everyone, class, my, whom, in) respects.

➡ Mr. Brown is a teacher _____

_____ respects.

(2) The movie (I, to, watch, want, which) is *Shrek*.

➡ The movie _____ is

Shrek.

06 다음 〈조건〉에 맞게 괄호 안의 단어를 이용하여 우리말을 영어로 옮기시오.

> ┤ 조건 ├
> 1. 주어진 단어를 모두 이용할 것.
> 2. 필요시 어형을 바꾸거나 단어를 추가할 것.
> 3. '의문사+to부정사'를 이용할 것.
> 4. 대·소문자 및 구두점에 유의할 것.

(1) 나는 어느 것을 골라야 할지 결정할 수 없었다. (make / which / mind / choose / can / my / up)

➡ _____

(2) 그는 언제 공부하고 언제 놀아야 할지 알지 못한다. (when / play / and / he / know / does / study)

➡ _____

_____

07 다음 문장에서 어법상 어색한 부분을 찾아 바르게 고쳐 쓰시오.

> I have a pen what my father gave me.

_____ ➡ _____

08 다음 〈보기〉에서 알맞은 것을 골라 문장을 완성하시오.

┌─── 보기 ├─────────────────┐
│   when   what   where   │
└───────────────────────────┘

(1) Birds know _____ to fly without a compass.

(2) I don't know _____ to go. Should I go now, or in two hours?

(3) The problem is _____ to do first.

[09~13] 다음 글을 읽고, 물음에 답하시오.

ⓐSudden Rosabella says, "Arrive l'autobus." Jaden understands the words ___ⓑ___ sound like *bus* and *arrive*. Sure enough, a bus appears. Kids ___ⓒ___ soccer uniforms shout from the windows, "Ciao, Rosabella!" As Rosabella steps onto the bus, Jaden says, "Good luck." She does not ___ⓓ___. So Jaden thinks and says, "Buon, buon ...." He points to the soccer ball that she is holding in her hand.

09 위 글의 밑줄 친 ⓐ를 알맞은 형으로 고치시오.

➡ _____

★ 중요

10 위 글의 빈칸 ⓑ에 알맞은 말을 쓰시오.

➡ _____

11 위 글의 빈칸 ⓒ에 알맞은 전치사를 쓰시오.

➡ _____

12 위 글의 빈칸 ⓓ에 다음 정의에 해당하는 말을 쓰시오.

┌───────────────────────────┐
│   to know what someone means   │
└───────────────────────────┘

➡ _____

13 What is Rosabella holding in her hand? Answer in English.

➡ _____

[14~16] 다음 글을 읽고, 물음에 답하시오.

Rosabella shouts, "Fortuna! Buona fortuna!" Fortuna sounds ___ⓐ___ *fortune*. "Buona fortuna!" he shouts. Rosabella and her friends shout back, "Molte grazie!" The bus rolls away.

Jaden goes back ___ⓑ___ the kitchen. He says into the translation app, "Learning from people is more fun. Can you teach me some Italian, Ms. Gambini?"

Ms. Gambini says, "Si," and laughs.

★ 중요

14 위 글의 빈칸 ⓐ에 알맞은 말을 쓰시오.

➡ _____

15 위 글의 빈칸 ⓑ에 알맞은 말을 쓰시오.

➡ _____

16 What can Ms. Gambini teach to Jaden? Answer in English.

➡ _____

➡ _____

01 다음 대화문을 읽고, 여행 앱을 소개하는 글을 완성하시오.

> G: Look. The name of our app is *Enjoy Paris*!
>
> B: Enjoy Paris? Sounds interesting!
>
> G: This app focuses on what to see in Paris.
>
> B: Does it give information on famous museums and theaters?
>
> G: Yes. You can find out about opening hours and admission fees.
>
> B: Fantastic.
>
> G: It also tells you how to get there.
>
> B: Oh, I'll download it right now!
>
> G: I'm sure you'll like it.

> The name of our app is _____. It focuses on _____ in Paris. It gives information on _____ and _____ of museums and theaters. It also tells you _____ there. Our app will be useful for travelers.

02 「의문사+to부정사」 구문을 이용하여 〈보기〉와 같이 자신의 입장에서 문장을 만드시오.

> ┌─ 보기 ─
> I know how to swim.

(1) _____

(2) _____

(3) _____

(4) _____

03 다음 빈칸에 자신이 원하는 것을 써 넣은 후, 문장을 완성하시오.

> • 사고 싶은 것: _____   • 보고 싶은 영화: _____
> • 먹고 싶은 음식: _____   • 만나고 싶은 사람: _____

(1) The thing that I want to buy is _____.

(2) The movie that I _____.

(3) The food _____.

(4) The person who(m) _____.

단원별 모의고사

01 다음 짝지어진 단어의 관계가 같도록 빈칸에 알맞은 단어를 쓰시오.

> important : unimportant
>
> = appear : _____

02 다음 영영풀이에 해당하는 단어로 알맞은 것은?

> an object or structure on land that is easy to see and recognize

① admission
② building
③ department
④ landmark
⑤ information

03 다음 빈칸에 공통으로 알맞은 것은?

> • The computer still doesn't _____.
> • She said, "Good luck!" and it _____ed.

① need
② turn
③ pass
④ work
⑤ follow

04 다음 영영풀이에 해당하는 단어를 주어진 철자로 시작하여 쓰시오.

> to make your ideas, feelings, thoughts, etc. known to other people so that they understand them

➡ c_____

05 다음 중 밑줄 친 부분의 뜻풀이가 잘못된 것은?

① He is going to step onto a bus.
　　　　　　　　　～쪽으로 걸어가다
② The concert starts in half an hour.
　　　　　　　　　　　30분 후에
③ You'd better hurry up and decide.
　　　　　　　　　서두르다
④ The woman is pointing to the man.
　　　　　　　　　～을 가리키다
⑤ Go outside and look around the city.
　　　　　　　　　～을 둘러보다

06 다음 짝지어진 대화 중 어색한 것은?

① A: Do you want some hamburgers?
　　B: Yes, please. I love them.
② A: What is "Hello," in Spanish?
　　B: It is "Hola."
③ A: Would you like some cheese?
　　B: No, I'm on a diet.
④ A: What's "끝" in English, Minsu?
　　B: It means no more; it's the end.
⑤ A: What would you like to eat?
　　B: I ate some pizza.

07 다음 대화의 순서를 바르게 배열한 것은?

> (A) Hey, Kate, would you like to have some rice cake?
> (B) Yes, thank you.
> (C) Yes, please. Oh! It's delicious.
> (D) Would you like some more?

① (A) – (C) – (D) – (B)
② (A) – (D) – (B) – (C)
③ (C) – (D) – (A) – (B)
④ (D) – (C) – (A) – (B)
⑤ (D) – (B) – (A) – (C)

[08~11] 다음 대화를 읽고, 물음에 답하시오.

> W: What are you going to do today, Kevin?
> B: I'm going to look ___ⓐ___ the city.
> W: Do you know ___ⓑ___ to find your way?
> B: Sure. I have a map on my phone!
> W: Okay. Try to remember landmarks, (A)[too / either].
> B: I'm sorry, but ___ⓒ___ do you mean by "landmarks"?
> W: I mean ___ⓓ___ .
> B: All right. I will try to remember the places (B)[what / that] I see.

08 위 대화의 빈칸 ⓐ에 '~을 둘러보다'라는 의미가 되도록 빈칸에 알맞은 말을 쓰시오.

➡ _____

09 위 대화의 빈칸 ⓑ와 ⓒ에 알맞은 말이 바르게 짝지어진 것은?

① when – how
② how – why
③ where – what
④ what – why
⑤ how – what

10 위 대화의 빈칸 ⓓ에 들어갈 말로 가장 적절한 것은?

① pictures or charts
② houses in the country
③ interesting and valuable things
④ an opinion or way of thinking
⑤ important places or special buildings

11 위 대화의 괄호 (A)와 (B)에서 알맞은 것을 골라 쓰시오

(A) _____ (B) _____

12 다음 빈칸에 공통으로 알맞은 것은?

> • My dad bought me a bag _____ was black.
> • I know the man _____ you are looking for.

① how
② who
③ that
④ whom
⑤ which

13 다음 중 밑줄 친 부분이 어색한 것은?

① Can you show me how to cook it?
② I didn't know what to wear.
③ They decided where to go first.
④ Jack explained them how to make next.
⑤ She told me when to start the work.

14 다음 중 밑줄 친 that의 쓰임이 나머지와 다른 하나는?

① He is the man that I can trust.
② That is the dog that I really love.
③ I know the man that is singing a song.
④ I like the car that you bought yesterday.
⑤ She is wearing a sweater that she bought yesterday.

15 다음 두 문장의 뜻이 같도록 빈칸에 알맞은 말을 쓰시오.

> I want to learn cooking.
> = I want to learn _____ _____ _____ .

16 다음 문장의 빈칸에 알맞은 것은? (2개)

> Javalon's father got a new job in Korea, so his family moved to Seoul three months ago. Let's look at the writings _____ Javalon posted on his blog.

① who ② whom
③ what ④ that
⑤ which

17 다음 중 빈칸에 들어갈 말이 나머지와 다른 하나는?

① Can you tell me what _____ buy at the mall?
② They didn't know where _____ go.
③ Let me know how _____ cook *bulgogi*.
④ He is _____ short to touch the ceiling.
⑤ I can't decide what _____ wear today.

18 다음 중 어법상 알맞지 않은 문장은?

① It is the same shirt that Tom has.
② I know a girl whom name is Nancy.
③ This is the bicycle that I lost yesterday.
④ She bought a bag that I really wanted to have.
⑤ He is the man who likes playing baseball.

19 다음 밑줄 친 부분 중 생략할 수 있는 것은?

① I know a boy whose name is Mark.
② He bought me a bag which was red.
③ I don't like the boy who makes a noise.
④ The cake that he baked was very nice.
⑤ Do you know the man who is playing with a ball?

20 다음 문장에서 어색한 곳을 찾아 바르게 고쳐 쓰시오.

> That is the most interesting movie which I have ever seen.

_____ ➡ _____

[21~25] 다음 글을 읽고, 물음에 답하시오.

> (①) There is a knock on the door, and a woman ⓐwhom Ms. Gambini invited walks in. (②) The two women begin speaking Italian very fast. (③)
> Jaden turns off the phone and leaves it on the table. (④) He goes out to enjoy the ⓑsun morning. (⑤) He follows a thumping sound and finds a girl ___ⓒ___ is kicking a soccer ball against a wall. She turns to him and says, "Buon giorno."

21 위 글의 ①~⑤ 중 다음 주어진 문장이 들어갈 알맞은 곳은?

> So the translator does not understand.

① ② ③ ④ ⑤

22 위 글의 밑줄 친 ⓐ 대신 쓸 수 있는 것은? (2개)

① who ② what
③ which ④ that
⑤ whose

23 위 글의 밑줄 친 ⓑ를 알맞은 형으로 고치시오.

➡ _____

24 위 글의 빈칸 ⓒ에 알맞은 것은? (2개)

① who　　　　② what
③ which　　　④ that
⑤ whose

25 위 글의 내용으로 보아 대답할 수 없는 질문은?

① Who is knocking on the door?
② Whom did Ms. Gambini invite?
③ What language does the two women begin speaking?
④ Why does Jaden go out?
⑤ Who is the girl kicking a soccer ball against a wall?

[26~30] 다음 글을 읽고, 물음에 답하시오.

Gestures can have different meanings in different cultures. ⓐ example, ①the "OK sign" means "okay" or "all right" in many countries. ②The gesture means something good. ③It means "money" in some cultures. ④That is also something good. ⑤The same sign, however, means "O" in France. It means there is nothing, ⓑ it is not a very happy gesture. ⓒ we travel, we should use gestures ⓓcare.

26 위 글의 밑줄 친 ①~⑤ 중 가리키는 대상이 다른 것은?

①　　②　　③　　④　　⑤

27 위 글의 빈칸 ⓐ에 알맞은 것은?

① At　　　　② On
③ To　　　　④ For
⑤ With

28 위 글의 빈칸 ⓑ와 ⓒ에 알맞은 것으로 짝지어진 것은?

① for – If　　　② or – If
③ so – When　　④ so – Though
⑤ for – When

29 위 글의 밑줄 친 ⓓ를 알맞은 형으로 고치시오.

➡ _____

30 위 글의 내용과 일치하지 않는 것은?

① 제스처는 문화에 따라 다르다.
② OK 사인은 많은 나라에서 okay를 의미한다.
③ OK 사인은 몇몇 나라에서는 돈을 의미한다.
④ OK 사인은 프랑스에서는 좋은 의미로 쓰인다.
⑤ 외국에 여행할 때는 제스처의 사용에 신중해야 한다.

Lesson 3

Healthy Life, Happy Life

의사소통 기능

- 증상 묻고 답하기
  A: What's wrong with you?
  B: I have a toothache.

- 약속 정하기
  A: Can you make it at three?
  B: That's fine with me.

언어 형식

- 가주어 it
  It is good **to exercise** regularly.

- to부정사의 형용사적 용법
  I need something **to eat** for lunch.

Words & Expressions

Key Words

- **actually**[ǽktʃuəli] 부 실제로, 정말로
- **against**[əgénst] 전 ~에 붙여[맞아], ~에 반대하여
- **antibody**[ǽntibadi] 명 항체
- **appointment**[əpɔ́intmənt] 명 약속
- **attack**[ətǽk] 동 공격하다 명 공격
- **bacteria**[bæktíəriə] 명 박테리아, 세균
- **bad breath** 입 냄새
- **balanced**[bǽlənst] 형 균형 잡힌, 안정된
- **break**[breik] 동 부러지다
- **cell**[sel] 명 세포
- **copy**[kápi] 동 복제하다, 복사하다
- **creature**[krí:tʃər] 명 생물
- **dangerous**[déindʒərəs] 형 위험한 (↔ safe)
- **defend**[difénd] 동 방어하다 (↔ attack)
- **defense**[diféns] 명 방어
- **different**[dífərənt] 형 다른 (↔ same)
- **digest**[didʒést] 동 소화하다, 소화시키다
- **everywhere**[evriwer] 부 모든 곳, 어디나
- **exercise**[éksərsàiz] 동 운동하다
- **fever**[fí:vər] 명 열
- **finally**[fáinəli] 부 마지막으로, 마침내 (= at last)
- **flu**[flu:] 명 독감
- **form**[fɔ:rm] 명 형태
- **germ**[dʒəːrm] 명 세균, 미생물
- **happen**[hǽpən] 동 발생하다, 일어나다
- **hard**[ha:rd] 형 어려운 (↔easy)
- **healthy**[hélθi] 형 건강한
- **hiccup**[híkʌp] 명 딸꾹질
- **hurt**[həːrt] 동 다치게 하다, 아프다
- **impossible**[impásəbl] 형 불가능한 (↔ possible)
- **invade**[invéid] 동 침입하다
- **luckily**[lʌkili] 부 다행히도
- **macrophage**[mǽkrəfèidʒ] 명 대식 세포
- **major**[méidʒər] 형 주요한, 중대한
- **medicine**[medsn] 명 약
- **multiply**[mʌltəplài] 동 증식[번식]하다
- **necessary**[nésəsèri] 형 필요한
- **regularly**[régjulərli] 부 규칙적으로
- **remember**[rimémbər] 동 기억하다 (↔ forget)
- **scratch**[skrætʃ] 동 긁다, 할퀴다
- **several**[sévərəl] 형 몇의
- **shot**[ʃot] 명 주사
- **skin**[skin] 명 피부
- **sore throat** 인후염
- **spot**[spat] 명 (특정한) 곳[장소/자리]
- **step**[step] 명 단계
- **stomachache** 명 위통, 복통
- **success**[səksés] 명 성공
- **terrible**[térəbl] 형 끔찍한, 소름끼치는
- **through**[θru:] 전 ~을 통하여
- **trick**[trik] 동 속이다
- **victim**[víktim] 명 피해자, 희생자
- **virus**[váiərəs] 명 바이러스
- **white blood cell** 백혈구
- **zone**[zoun] 명 지역

Key Expressions

- **at last** 마침내, 드디어
- **be famous for** ~으로 유명하다
- **be good for** ~에 좋다
- **be ready to** ~할 준비가 되어 있다
- **be thinking of** ~을 생각하고 있다
- **by the way** 그런데
- **catch a cold** 감기에 걸리다
- **give up** 포기하다
- **go well** 잘되어 가다
- **in a few days** 며칠 후에
- **make it** (모임 등에) 가다[참석하다]
- **plenty of** 많은
- **protect A from B** A를 B로부터 보호하다
- **show up** 나타나다
- **such as** ~와 같은
- **watch out** 조심하다

Word Power

※ 동사에 -er, -or을, 명사에 -ist를 붙여서 행위자를 나타내는 단어

☐ act (연기하다) → actor (배우)

☐ paint (그리다) → painter (화가)

☐ invent (발명하다) → inventor (발명가)

☐ write (쓰다) → writer (작가)

☐ science (과학) → scientist (과학자)

☐ visit (방문하다) → visitor (방문객)

☐ translate (번역[통역]하다) → translator (번역가, 통역사)

☐ direct (감독하다) → director (감독)

☐ art (미술, 예술) → artist (미술가, 예술가)

☐ cartoon (만화) → cartoonist (만화가)

English Dictionary

☐ **appointment** 약속
→ an agreement to meet with someone at a particular time 특정한 때에 어떤 사람을 만나기로 하는 약속

☐ **bacteria** 박테리아, 세균
→ any one of a group of very small living things that often cause disease
흔히 질병을 일으키는 아주 작은 생물 무리의 하나

☐ **balanced** 균형 잡힌
→ having good or equal amounts of all the necessary parts of something
필요한 요소를 빠짐없이 잘 또는 고르게 갖춘

☐ **cell** 세포
→ any one of the very small parts that together form all living things
모든 생물을 구성하는 아주 작은 부분들의 어느 하나

☐ **defend** 방어하다
→ to fight in order to keep someone or something safe
누군가 또는 어떤 것을 안전하게 지키기 위해 싸우다

☐ **digest** 소화하다, 소화시키다
→ to change food that you have eaten by a biological process into simpler forms that can be used by the body
섭취한 음식물을 신체가 사용할 수 있도록 생리 과정을 거쳐 더 단순한 형태로 변화시키다

☐ **flu** 독감
→ an infectious disease like a very bad cold, which causes fever, pains, and weakness
고열, 통증, 약화를 일으키는 매우 심한 감기 같은 전염병

☐ **germ** 세균, 미생물
→ a very small living thing that causes disease
병을 일으키는 아주 작은 생물

☐ **invade** 침입하다
→ to enter or be in a place where you are not wanted
남이 원하지 않는 곳에 들어가거나 있다

☐ **luckily** 다행히도
→ used to say that something good or lucky has happened
좋은 일이나 다행스러운 일이 일어났다고 말할 때 사용되는

☐ **major** 주요한, 중대한
→ very important
매우 중요한

☐ **multiply** 증식[번식]하다
→ to increase in number by reproducing
번식해서 수가 증가하다

☐ **scratch** 긁다
→ to rub your skin with your fingernails because it feels uncomfortable
불편해서 손톱 같은 날카로운 것으로 피부를 긁다

☐ **shot** 주사
→ an act of putting something such as medicine or vaccine into the body with a needle
약이나 백신 같은 어떤 것을 바늘로 몸 안에 주입하는 일

☐ **success** 성공
→ the fact of getting or achieving wealth, respect, or fame
부, 존경 또는 명성을 얻거나 달성함

☐ **victim** 피해자, 희생자
→ a person who has been attacked, injured, robbed, or killed by someone else
다른 누군가에게 공격받거나 다치거나 강탈당하거나 죽임을 당한 사람

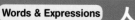
01 다음 중 단어의 성격이 <u>다른</u> 하나는?

① writer ② danger
③ traveler ④ director
⑤ invader

중요
02 다음 빈칸에 알맞은 말이 바르게 짝지어진 것은?

• Mary didn't show _____ for the meeting yesterday.
• Eating too many snacks is not good _____ your health.

① into – at ② up – for
③ on – in ④ out – with
⑤ off – over

중요
03 다음 영영풀이에 해당하는 단어로 알맞은 것은?

to increase in number by reproducing

① defend ② scratch
③ invade ④ multiply
⑤ protect

서답형
04 다음 짝지어진 단어의 관계가 같도록 빈칸에 알맞은 말을 쓰시오.

hard : easy = defend : _____

05 다음 우리말에 맞게 빈칸에 알맞은 것은?

너는 다음 월요일에 참석할 수 있니?
➡ Can you _____ it next Monday?

① do ② take
③ get ④ have
⑤ make

서답형
06 다음 영영풀이에 해당하는 단어를 쓰시오.

any one of the very small parts that together form all living things

➡ _____

서답형
07 다음 우리말에 맞게 빈칸에 알맞은 말을 쓰시오.

그런데, 너는 누구와 함께 갔니?
➡ _____ _____ _____, who did you go with?

08 다음 빈칸에 공통으로 알맞은 것은?

• I like films with plenty _____ action.
• I can't think _____ her name at the moment.

① in ② of
③ up ④ about
⑤ at

01 다음 짝지어진 두 단어의 관계가 같도록 빈칸에 알맞은 말을 쓰시오.

(1) paint : painter = act : _____

(2) art : artist = cartoon : _____

(3) invent : _____ = write : writer

02 다음 우리말에 맞게 빈칸에 알맞은 말을 쓰시오.

(1) 바이러스는 독감과 같은 질병을 일으킨다.

➡ Viruses cause diseases _____ _____ the flu.

(2) 그녀는 그녀의 독특한 그림으로 유명하다.

➡ She _____ _____ _____ her unique paintings.

(3) 며칠 후에, 너는 기분이 좋아지기 시작한다.

➡ In a _____ _____, you start to feel better.

03 다음 빈칸에 들어갈 알맞은 말을 〈보기〉에서 골라 쓰시오.

┤ 보기 ├
digest balanced germs multiply

(1) When _____ enter your body, they can make you sick.

(2) When we eat, our bodies _____ food.

(3) Bacteria _____ quickly in warm food.

(4) A _____ diet will keep your body strong and healthy.

04 다음 괄호 안의 말을 문맥에 맞게 고쳐 쓰시오.

(1) I hope you are always _____ and happy. (health)

(2) _____, we arrived there on time. (luck)

(3) Some robots do _____ jobs for humans. (danger)

05 다음 빈칸에 알맞은 말을 〈보기〉에서 골라 쓰시오.

┤ 보기 ├
plenty of   good for
show up   catch a cold

(1) Still, Jane does not _____.

(2) Fruits are _____ your health.

(3) That store has _____ customers.

(4) If you _____, you will cough a lot.

06 다음 영영풀이에 해당하는 단어를 주어진 철자로 시작하여 쓰시오.

(1) s_____ : to rub your skin with your fingernails because it feels uncomfortable

(2) v_____ : a person who has been attacked, injured, robbed, or killed by someone else

(3) b_____ : any one of a group of very small living things that often cause disease

Conversation

교과서

1 증상 묻고 답하기

A What's wrong with you? 무슨 일이니?
B I have a toothache. 이가 아파.

■ What's wrong with you?는 '무슨 일이니?'의 뜻으로 상대방이 몸이 아파 보이거나 우울해 보일 때 사용하는 표현이다.
  • A: What's wrong with you, Jake? 너 왜 그래, Jake?
    B: I have a terrible headache. 머리가 몹시 아파.

증상을 묻는 표현

  • What's wrong (with you)?
  • What's the matter (with you)?
  • What happened (to you)?
  • What's the problem (with you)?
  • What seems to be the problem?

증상 묻기에 답하기

  • I have a cold. 감기에 걸렸어.
  • I have a stomachache. 배가 아파.
  • I have a sore throat. 목이 아파.
  • I cut my finger. 손가락을 베었어.
  • I broke my leg. 다리가 부러졌어.

  • I have a toothache. 이가 아파.
  • I have a runny nose. 콧물이 나와.
  • I have a headache. 머리가 아파.
  • I have a fever. 열이 나.

핵심 Check

1. 다음 우리말과 일치하도록 빈칸에 알맞은 말을 쓰시오.

(1) **A:** What's _____? (무슨 일이야?)
    B: I have a _____. (배가 아파.)

(2) **A:** What's the _____? You look worried. (무슨 일이야? 걱정돼 보인다.)
    B: I have a _____ _____. (콧물이 나와.)

(3) **A:** _____ seems to be the _____? (무슨 문제가 있니?)
    B: I _____ _____ _____. (이가 아파.)

② 약속 정하기

A Can you make it at three? 3시에 올 수 있니?

B That's fine with me. 난 괜찮아.

■ Can you make it at three?는 '3시에 올 수 있니?'라는 뜻으로 약속을 정할 때 쓰는 표현이다. make it 은 '해내다, 성공하다'라는 의미를 갖고 있지만, 시간이나 장소의 표현과 함께 쓰여 '시간에 맞춰 가다' 또는 '도착하다'라는 의미를 갖는다.

약속 정하기 표현

- Can we meet at six? 6시에 만날까?
- Why don't we meet at six?
- How[What] about meeting at six?
- Shall we meet at six?
- Let's meet at six.

약속 정하기에 답하는 표현

승낙하기 • That's fine with me. / No problem. / Why not? / Sure, I'd love to. / That's a good idea. / (That) Sounds great.

거절하기 • I'm sorry, I can't. / I'm afraid not. / I'd love to, but I can't. / Not this time, thanks. / Maybe next time.

핵심 Check

2. 다음 우리말과 일치하도록 빈칸에 알맞은 말을 쓰시오.

(1) **A:** Can you _____ _____ at five at the bus stop? (너는 5시에 버스 정류장에 올 수 있니?)

　　B: _____. See you _____. (물론이지. 그때 보자.)

(2) **A:** _____ _____ _____ to the movie theater tomorrow?

　　(우리 내일 영화관에 가는 게 어때?)

　　B: No _____. (문제없어.)

(3) **A:** _____ _____ basketball this Saturday. (이번 토요일에 농구하자.)

　　B: _____, _____ _____. (미안하지만, 못하겠어.)

Communicate: Listen - Listen and Answer Dialog 1

B: ❶Can I go home early, Ms. Song? I don't feel so good.

W: ❷What seems to be the problem?

B: ❸I have a terrible stomachache. ❹It really hurts.

W: ❺Why don't you get some medicine at the nurse's office?

B: I already did. But it didn't help.

W: Okay. ❻You can go. ❼Go see a doctor, okay?

B: ❽Sure. Thanks.

B: 송 선생님, 집에 일찍 가도 될까요? 몸이 너무 안 좋아요.

W: 무슨 문제가 있니?

B: 배가 너무 아파요. 정말 아파요.

W: 양호실에서 약을 좀 먹는 게 어떠니?

B: 벌써 먹었어요. 하지만 도움이 되지 않았어요.

W: 알겠다. 가도 돼. 병원에 가봐, 알았지?

B: 물론이죠. 고맙습니다.

❶ Can{May] I + 동사원형 ~?: 내가 ~해도 될까?(상대방에게 허락을 구할 때 쓰는 표현) ❷ What seems to be the problem?: 어디가 안 좋으니? (증상을 물을 때 쓰는 표현) ❸ have a terrible stomachache: 배가 너무 아프다 ❹ hurt: 아프다 ❺ Why don't you + 동사원형 ~?: ~하는 게 어때? / get some medicine: 약을 좀 먹다 / nurse's office: 양호실 ❻ can: ~해도 좋다, ~해도 된다(허락의 의미를 나타냄) ❼ go see a doctor = go and see a doctor = go to see a doctor / 명령어, okay?: ~해라, 알았지? (제안, 권유하는 표현) ❽ 제안이나 권유에 승낙하는 표현이다.

Check(√) True or False

(1) The boy has a terrible stomachache. T ☐ F ☐

(2) The boy got some medicine at the hospital. T ☐ F ☐

Communicate: Listen - Listen and Answer Dialog 2

(*The phone rings.*)

B: Hello, Sora.

G: Hi, Jongha. ❶I heard you were sick. ❷Are you okay now?

B: Yes, ❸I went to the doctor, and I feel better now.

G: Good to hear that. ❹By the way, I called you to talk about our science project.

B: Yeah, we should meet. ❺Can you make it tomorrow?

G: Okay. ❻Let's meet at Simpson's Donuts at nine.

B: At nine? That's too early. I sleep late on the weekend.

G: ❼How about 10 then?

B: ❽That sounds fine.

(전화벨이 울린다.)

B: 여보세요, 소라야.

G: 안녕, 종하야. 아프다고 들었어. 이제 좀 괜찮니?

B: 응. 병원에 갔었는데, 이제 좀 나아졌어.

G: 다행이구나. 그런데, 우리 과학 프로젝트에 대해 얘기하려고 전화했어.

B: 그래. 우리 만나야겠다. 내일 만날 수 있니?

G: 좋아. 9시에 Simpson's Donuts에서 만나자.

B: 9시? 너무 일러. 난 주말에 늦잠을 자.

G: 그럼 10시는 어때?

B: 괜찮아.

❶ I heard (that) + 주어 + 동사 ~: 나는 ~라고 들었어.(들은 사실을 말할 때 쓰는 표현) ❷ 상대방이 안 좋아 보일 때 사용하는 표현이다. ❸ go to the doctor: 의사의 진찰을 받다, 병원에 가다 / feel better: 몸이 나아지다 ❹ by the way: 그런데, 그건 그렇고(화제를 바꿀 때 사용하는 표현) / to talk: to부정사의 부사적 용법(목적) ❺ Can you make it ~?: ~에 만날 수 있니? (약속 시간을 제안하는 표현) ❻ Let's meet + 동사원형 ~: ~에서 만나자 ❼ How about ~?: ~은 어때? ❽ 약속 제안에 승낙하는 표현이다.

Check(√) True or False

(3) Sora called Jongha to talk about their science project. T ☐ F ☐

(4) Sora and Jongha will meet at nine. T ☐ F ☐

Communicate: Listen - Listen More

M: Hi, Minsol. ❶What's wrong with your dog?

G: ❷She keeps scratching herself. ❸Actually, she lost some hair.

M: When did she first have the problem?

G: ❹About three days ago.

M: ❺Let me see. (*pause*) She has a virus on her skin. ❻I'll give you some medicine.

G: Thank you.

M: I need to check your dog again. Can you make it next Monday?

G: ❽That's fine with me.

M: Okay. See you.

❶ What's wrong with ~?: ~에게 무슨 문제가 있니?

❷ keep -ing: 계속해서 ~하다

❸ actually: 사실 / lose some hair: 털이 좀 빠지다

❹ about three days ago: 약 3일 전에

❺ Let me see.: 어디 보자

❻ give + 간접목적어 + 직접목적어 = give + 직접목적어 + to + 간접목적어: ~에게 ...을 주다

❼ Can you make it ~?: ~에 올 수 있니?

❽ That's fine with me.: 전 괜찮아요.

 Communicate: Listen - All Ears

W: 1. ❶Can you make it next Friday?
　　2. ❷What's wrong with your cat?

❶ Can you make it ~?: ~에 만날까?

❷ What's wrong with ~?: ~에게 무슨 문제가 있니?

 Communicate: Speak 2 - Talk in pairs

A: ❶What's wrong with you?

B: ❷I have a sore throat.

A: ❸That's too bad. ❹You should drink some water.

B: ❺Okay, I will.

❶ What's wrong with you?: 무슨 일 있니? = What's the matter? = Is something wrong? = What's the problem? = What happened (to you)?

❷ have a sore throat: 목이 아프다

❸ That's too bad.: 안됐구나. (동정하는 표현)

❹ You should + 동사원형 ~.: 너는 ~해야 해. (충고하는 표현)

❺ 충고에 수락하는 표현이다.

 Communicate: Speak 2 - Talk in groups

A: ❶Let's play basketball this Saturday.

B: ❷Sure, why not?

A: ❸Can you make it at ten?

B: That's fine with me. ❹Where should we meet?

A: ❺Let's meet at the school gym.

B: ❻Okay. See you there.

❶ Let's ~: ~하자

❷ 제안에 수락하는 표현이다. / Why not?: 좋고말고.

❸ Can you make it at ~?: ~에 만날 수 있니?

❹ 약속 장소를 정할 때 사용하는 표현이다.

❺ Let's meet at ~: ~에서 만나자.(약속 장소를 정할 때 쓰는 표현) / school gym: 학교 체육관

❻ Okay.: 좋아. (제안을 수락하는 표현) = Sure. = Of course. = No problem. = Why not? 등

 Wrap Up - Listening ❺

B: Mom, ❶I don't feel well.

W: ❷What seems to be the problem?

B: ❸I think I have a fever.

W: Really? Let me see. Umm, ❹you do have a fever. ❺I'll get you some medicine.

B: Thank you, Mom.

❶ I don't feel well: 몸이 좋지 않아.

❷ What seems to be the problem?: 어디가 안 좋으니?

❸ have a fever: 열이 나다

❹ do: 동사를 강조하는 do

❺ get + 간접목적어 + 직접목적어 = get + 직접목적어 + for + 간접목적어: ~에게 ...을 갖다 주다

Wrap Up - Listening ❻

G: ❶I'm thinking of going to the Comics Museum tomorrow. ❷Will you come with me?

B: I really want to go.

G: ❸Can you make it at 11?

B: ❹That's fine with me.

G: Okay. ❺Let's meet at the subway station.

❶ I'm thinking of -ing ~: 나는 ~할 생각이다

❷ Will you + 동사원형 ~?: ~할 거니?

❸ Can you make it at ~?: ~에 만날 수 있니?

❹ That's fine with me. 난 괜찮아. (제안에 수락하는 표현) = Sure. = Of course. = No problem. = Why not? 등

❺ Let' meet at + 장소: ~에서 만나자. / subway station: 지하철역

● 다음 우리말과 일치하도록 빈칸에 알맞은 말을 쓰시오.

 해석

Communicate: Listen - Listen and Answer Dialog 1

B: _____ I go home _____, Ms. Song? I _____ _____ so good.

W: What _____ _____ be the problem?

B: I _____ a terrible _____. It really _____.

W: _____ _____ you get some _____ at the nurse's office?

B: I _____ did. But it _____ _____.

W: Okay. You _____ go. _____ _____ a doctor, okay?

B: _____. Thanks.

B: 송 선생님, 집에 일찍 가도 될까요? 몸이 너무 안 좋아요.
W: 무슨 문제가 있니?
B: 배가 너무 아파요. 정말 아파요.
W: 양호실에서 약을 좀 먹는 게 어떠니?
B: 벌써 먹었어요. 하지만 도움이 되지 않았어요.
W: 알겠다. 가도 돼. 병원에 가봐, 알았지?
B: 물론이죠. 고맙습니다.

Communicate: Listen - Listen and Answer Dialog 2

(The phone rings.)

B: Hello, Sora.

G: Hi, Jongha. I _____ you were sick. Are you _____ now?

B: Yes, I went to _____ _____, and I _____ _____ now.

G: Good _____ _____ that. _____ _____ _____, I called you _____ _____ about our science project.

B: Yeah, we _____ _____. Can you _____ _____ tomorrow?

G: Okay. _____ _____ at Simpson's Donuts _____ nine.

B: At nine? That's too _____. I sleep _____ on the weekend.

G: _____ _____ 10 then?

B: That _____ fine.

(전화벨이 울린다.)
B: 여보세요, 소라야.
G: 안녕, 종하야. 아프다고 들었어. 이제 좀 괜찮니?
B: 응, 병원에 갔었는데, 이제 좀 나아졌어.
G: 다행이구나. 그런데, 우리 과학 프로젝트에 대해 얘기하려고 전화했어.
B: 그래, 우리 만나야겠다. 내일 만날 수 있니?
G: 좋아. 9시에 Simpson's Donuts에서 만나자.
B: 9시? 너무 일러. 난 주말에 늦잠을 자.
G: 그럼 10시는 어때?
B: 괜찮아.

Communicate: Listen - Listen More

M: Hi, Minsol. What's _____ _____ your dog?

G: She keeps _____ herself. Actually, she _____ some _____.

M: When did she first _____ _____ _____?

G: _____ three days _____.

M: _____ me _____. *(pause)* She _____ _____ _____ on her skin. I'll give you some medicine.

G: Thank you.

M: I _____ _____ _____ your dog again. _____ you _____ it next Monday?

G: That's _____ _____ me.

M: Okay. _____ you.

M: 안녕, 민솔. 너의 개에게 무슨 문제가 있니?
G: 계속 자기 몸을 긁어요. 사실, 털이 좀 빠졌어요.
M: 너의 개는 언제 처음으로 문제가 생겼니?
G: 약 3일 전에요.
M: 어디 보자. (잠시 멈춘다) 피부에 바이러스가 있어. 약을 좀 줄게.
G: 감사합니다.
M: 네 개를 다시 확인할 필요가 있어. 다음 주 월요일에 올 수 있니?
G: 좋아요.
M: 알겠다. 나중에 보자.

해석

Communicate: Listen - All Ears

M: 1. Can you _____ it next Friday?

2. What's _____ with your cat?

W 1. 다음 주 금요일에 만날까?
2. 너의 고양이에게 무슨 문제가 있니?

Communicate: Speak 2 - Talk in pairs

A: _____ _____ with you?

B: I _____ a _____ _____.

A: That's too _____. You _____ _____ some water.

B: Okay, I _____.

A: 무슨 일 있니?
B: 목이 아파.
A: 그것 참 안됐구나. 너는 물을 좀 마셔야 해.
B: 알았어, 그럴게.

Communicate: Speak 2 - Talk in groups

A: _____ play basketball this Saturday.

B: Sure, _____ _____?

A: _____ _____ _____ it at ten?

B: That's fine _____ me. Where _____ we _____?

A: _____ meet _____ the school gym.

B: Okay. _____ _____ there.

A: 이번 토요일에 농구하자.
B: 물론, 좋고말고.
A: 10시에 만날 수 있니?
B: 난 괜찮아. 우리 어디서 만날까?
A: 학교 체육관에서 만나자.
B: 알았어, 거기서 보자.

Wrap Up - Listening ❺

B: Mom, I _____ _____ well.

W: _____ seems to be the _____?

B: I think I _____ _____ _____.

W: Really? _____ _____ _____. Umm, you _____ have a fever. I'll _____ _____ _____ _____.

B: _____ you, Mom.

B: 엄마, 몸이 안 좋아요.
W: 뭐가 문제인 것 같니?
B: 열이 있는 것 같아요.
W: 정말? 어디 보자. 음, 정말 열이 있네. 약을 좀 갖다 줄게.
B: 고마워요, 엄마.

Wrap Up - Listening ❻

G: I'm _____ _____ going to the Comics Museum tomorrow. Will you _____ _____ me?

B: I really want _____ _____.

G: Can you _____ _____ _____ 11?

B: That's _____ _____ me.

G: Okay. _____ meet _____ the subway station.

G: 내일 만화 박물관에 갈 생각이야. 나하고 같이 갈래?
B: 정말 가고 싶어.
G: 11시에 만날 수 있니?
B: 난 괜찮아.
G: 좋아, 지하철역에서 만나자.

[01~02] 다음 밑줄 친 말과 바꾸어 쓸 수 있는 것을 고르시오.

01

A: What time should we meet tomorrow?
B: <u>Can you make it at five?</u>

① Let's go there.
② Let's meet tomorrow.
③ Let's meet at five.
④ How about meeting together?
⑤ I can't make it at five.

02

A: <u>What's wrong?</u>
B: I have a terrible headache.

① Why not?
② What's that?
③ How are you?
④ What's the problem?
⑤ What are you doing?

[03~04] 다음 대화의 빈칸에 알맞은 것을 고르시오.

03

A: Let's go see a movie tomorrow.
B: Good idea!
A: _____
B: Okay. Let's meet at 5 o'clock.

① Where can we meet?
② When can you come?
③ How would you like it?
④ Can you make it at 5?
⑤ What time shall we meet?

04

A: _____
B: Well, I have a sore throat.

① How come?
② What's wrong?
③ How are you?
④ How do you do?
⑤ What are you doing?

[01~05] 다음 대화를 읽고, 물음에 답하시오.

B: Can I go home early, Ms. Song? I don't feel so good.
W: ⓐWhat seems to be the problem?
B: I have a terrible stomachache. It really hurts.
W: ⓑWhy don't you get some medicine at the nurse's office?
B: I already did. But it didn't help.
W: Okay. You ⓒcan go. Go see a doctor, okay?
B: Sure. Thanks.

01 위 대화의 밑줄 친 ⓐ와 바꿔 쓸 수 있는 것은?

① What's your opinion?
② How's it going?
③ How did it happen?
④ Why is it a problem?
⑤ What's the matter with you?

서답형
02 위 대화의 밑줄 친 ⓑ를 다음과 같이 바꿔 쓸 때 빈칸에 알맞은 말을 쓰시오.

_____ _____ _____ some medicine at the nurse's office?

03 위 대화의 밑줄 친 ⓒ와 쓰임이 같은 것은?

① The child can't walk yet.
② He can speak German very well.
③ Can the rumor be true?
④ You can go out and play outdoors.
⑤ Can you speak any foreign languages?

서답형
04 위 대화에서 다음 영영풀이에 해당하는 단어를 찾아 쓰시오.

pain in or near your stomach

➡ _____

05 위 대화의 내용과 일치하지 않는 것은?

① 소년은 몸이 좋지 않다.
② 소년은 배가 약간 아프다.
③ 소년은 약을 먹었지만 소용이 없었다.
④ 송 선생님은 소년이 집에 가는 것을 허락해 주었다.
⑤ 소년은 병원에 갈 것이다.

[06~09] 다음 대화를 읽고, 물음에 답하시오.

A: Let's play basketball this Saturday.
B: _____ ⓐ _____
A: ⓑCan you make it at ten?
B: That's fine with me. _____ ⓒ _____
A: Let's meet at the school gym.
B: Okay. See you there.

06 위 대화의 빈칸 ⓐ에 알맞지 않은 것은?

① Of course.
② No problem.
③ That's a good idea.
④ I'm afraid I can't.
⑤ Sure, why not?

서답형
07 위 대화의 밑줄 친 ⓑ를 다음과 같이 바꿔 쓸 때 빈칸에 알맞은 말을 쓰시오.

Can we _____ at ten?

08 위 대화의 빈칸 ⓒ에 알맞은 것은?

① When can you come?
② Where should we meet?
③ How would you like it?
④ Who can play with us?
⑤ What time shall we meet?

09 위 대화를 읽고, 다음 질문에 완전한 문장으로 답하시오.

Q: What time and where will "A" and "B" meet?
A: ______________________

[10~15] 다음 대화를 읽고, 물음에 답하시오.

(*The phone rings.*)
B: Hello, Sora.
G: Hi, Jongha. I heard you were sick. _______ⓐ_______
B: Yes, I went to the doctor, and I feel better now.
G: Good to hear that. ⓑ그런데, I called you to talk about our science project.
B: Yeah, we should meet. ⓒCan you make it tomorrow?
G: Okay. _______ⓓ_______ meet at Simpson's Donuts at nine.
B: At nine? That's too early. I sleep ___ⓔ___ on the weekend.
G: How about 10 then?
B: That sounds fine.

10 위 대화의 빈칸 ⓐ에 알맞은 것은?

① Are you busy now?
② Do you feel sad?
③ Are you okay now?
④ What are you doing?
⑤ Did you take your medicine?

서답형

11 위 대화의 밑줄 친 ⓑ의 우리말을 세 단어로 쓰시오.

➡ ______________________

중요

12 위 대화의 밑줄 친 ⓒ와 바꿔 쓸 수 없는 것은?

① Let's meet tomorrow.
② Shall we meet tomorrow?
③ How about meeting tomorrow?
④ Will you meet tomorrow?
⑤ Why don't we meet tomorrow?

13 위 대화의 빈칸 ⓓ에 알맞은 것은?

① You can
② Let's
③ I'd like to
④ We will
⑤ You have to

서답형

14 위 대화의 빈칸 ⓔ에 다음 영영풀이에 해당하는 단어를 쓰시오.

after the usual or expected time

➡ ______________________

중요

15 위 대화를 읽고, 답할 수 없는 질문은?

① Why did Jongha go to the doctor?
② Why did Sora call Jongha?
③ Where will Sora and Jongha meet?
④ What time will they meet?
⑤ Until when should they finish their science project?

[01~02] 다음 대화를 읽고, 물음에 답하시오.

A: _____ ⓐ _____
B: Well, I have a headache.
A: That's too bad. ⓑ좀 쉬는 게 어때?
B: OK, I will.

01 위 대화의 빈칸 ⓐ에 들어갈 말을 2가지 이상 쓰시오.

➡ _____

_____

02 위 대화의 밑줄 친 ⓑ의 우리말을 괄호 안의 단어를 이용하여 영어로 쓰시오.

(why, get, rest)

➡ _____

[03~05] 다음 대화를 읽고, 물음에 답하시오.

A: Let's play basketball this Saturday.
B: Sure, why not?
A: ⓐCan you make it at ten?
B: That's fine with me. ⓑ우리 어디서 만날까?
A: Let's meet at the school gym.
B: Okay. See you ⓒthere.

03 위 대화의 밑줄 친 ⓐ를 다음과 같이 바꿔 쓸 때 빈칸에 알 맞은 말을 쓰시오.

How about _____ at ten?

04 위 대화의 밑줄 친 ⓑ의 우리말을 주어진 단어를 이용하여 영작하시오. (4 words)

(should)

➡ _____

05 위 대화의 밑줄 친 ⓒ가 가리키는 말을 영어로 쓰시오.

➡ _____

[06~09] 다음 대화를 읽고, 물음에 답하시오.

M: Hi, Minsol. ⓐWhat's wrong with your dog?
G: She keeps (A)[scratching / to scratch] herself. Actually, she lost some hair.
M: When did she first have the problem?
G: About three days (B)[before / ago].
M: Let me see. (*pause*) She has a virus on her skin. I'll give you some medicine.
G: Thank you.
M: I need to check your dog again. ⓑ다음 월요일에 올 수 있니?
G: That's fine with me.
M: Okay. See you.

06 위 대화의 밑줄 친 ⓐ를 다음과 같이 바꿔 쓸 때 빈칸에 알 맞은 말을 쓰시오.

What's the _____ with your dog?

07 위 대화의 밑줄 친 ⓑ의 우리말을 주어진 단어를 이용하여 영작하시오.

(make)

➡ _____

08 위 대화의 (A)~(B)에서 어법상 알맞은 것을 골라 쓰시오.

(A) _____ (B) _____

09 위 대화를 읽고, 민솔이네 개의 증상을 우리말로 모두 쓰시오.

➡ _____

Grammar

교과서

① 가주어 it

> • **It** is not easy **to take** good care of a pet. 애완동물을 잘 돌보는 것은 쉽지 않다.
> • **It** is fun **to learn** to swim. 수영을 배우는 것은 재미있다.
> • **It** will be nice **to become** a musician. 음악가가 되는 것은 멋질 거야.

■ **가주어 it**

to부정사구가 문장 안에서 주어로 쓰일 경우, to부정사구를 문장의 뒤로 보내고 그 자리에 it을 쓴다. 이때의 it은 아무런 의미가 없는 주어로 '가주어'라고 하고, to부정사구를 '진주어'라고 한다.

• To master English in a month is impossible. 영어를 한 달 동안에 습득하는 것은 불가능하다.

→ **It** is impossible **to master** English in a month.
　　가주어　　　　　　　　진주어

cf. to부정사 이외에도 진주어로 명사절이 쓰일 때가 있다. 이때 명사절을 이끄는 접속사는 보통 that이 쓰인다.

• **It** is a bad habit **that** people read in bed. 침대에서 독서하는 것은 나쁜 버릇이다.

■ **to부정사의 의미상의 주어**

to부정사의 의미상 주어가 문장의 주어와 일치하지 않는 경우, 일반적으로 「for+목적격」의 형태로 진주어 앞에 쓴다. kind, foolish, wise, honest, polite 등과 같이 사람의 성격을 나타내는 형용사가 보어로 쓰이면 의미상의 주어로 「of+목적격」의 형태를 쓴다.

• **It** is natural **for** your parents **to get** angry. 너의 부모님이 화를 내시는 것은 당연하다.

• **It** is very kind **of** you **to help** me. 나를 도와주다니 넌 참 친절하다.

핵심 Check

1. 다음 괄호 안에서 알맞은 것을 고르시오.

(1) It is hard (understanding / to understand) his words.

(2) (It / That) is interesting to watch basketball.

(3) It is good for your health (to exercise / exercise) every day.

(4) It is honest (for / of) you to say so.

(5) It is not easy (for / of) us to learn foreign languages.

2 to부정사의 형용사적 용법

- Jay has the ability **to make** people happy. Jay는 사람들을 행복하게 만드는 능력이 있다.
- They need something **to drink**. 그들은 마실 것이 필요하다.
- I have a lot of homework **to do** tonight. 나는 오늘밤 해야 할 숙제가 많다.

■ to부정사의 형용사적 용법은 명사나 대명사 뒤에서 '~하는, ~할'의 뜻으로 쓰인다. 이 때 앞의 명사는 to부정사의 주어 또는 목적어 역할을 한다.

- I have no money **to give** you. (목적어) 나는 너에게 줄 돈이 없다.
  = I have no money that I can give you.
- He had no friends **to help** him. (주어) 그는 자기를 도와줄 친구가 하나도 없었다.
  = He had no friends who would help him.

■ to부정사의 수식을 받는 명사가 전치사의 목적어일 경우, to부정사 뒤에 전치사가 온다.

- Ann has elderly parents **to look** after. Ann은 돌보아야 할 나이 드신 부모가 있다.
- I want a small room **to live** in by myself. 나는 혼자 살 작은 방을 원한다.

■ -thing으로 끝나는 부정대명사는 「-thing+(형용사+)to부정사」의 어순을 따른다.

- I want something cold **to drink**. 나는 차가운 마실 것을 원한다.
- You think that you have nothing **to wear**. 너는 입을 것이 아무것도 없다고 생각한다.

핵심 Check

2. 다음 괄호 안에서 알맞은 것을 고르시오.
   (1) It's time (going / to go) to school.
   (2) Jack has a lot of friends (helping / to help).
   (3) Give me a pen (to write / to write with).
   (4) Would you like something (to cold drink / cold to drink)?

01 다음 괄호 안에서 알맞은 것을 고르시오.

(1) (It / That) is fun to travel to some countries in Asia.

(2) Do you have anything (to do / doing) this evening?

(3) There are many places (visit / to visit) in Jeju.

(4) It is hard (of / for) me to solve this problem.

(5) It is very kind (of / for) you to help me.

travel 여행하다
solve 풀다

02 다음 우리말과 일치하도록 빈칸에 알맞은 말을 쓰시오.

(1) 우리는 일정을 바꿀 시간이 없다.

➡ We have no time _____ _____ the schedule.

(2) 그는 우리나라를 방문한 최초의 미국인이었다.

➡ He was the first American _____ _____ our country.

(3) 우리에게 그늘을 드리워줄 나무가 전혀 없었다.

➡ There were no trees _____ _____ us shade.

schedule 일정
offer 제공하다
shade 그늘

03 다음 문장에서 어법상 틀린 것을 찾아 바르게 고쳐 쓰시오.

(1) It's difficult exercise every day.

_____ ➡ _____

(2) It is impossible finish this work in an hour.

_____ ➡ _____

(3) That is very important to learn a foreign language.

_____ ➡ _____

(4) It was brave for him to save the child.

_____ ➡ _____

(5) It was easy of me to answer all the questions.

_____ ➡ _____

exercise 운동하다
impossible 불가능한
save 구하다

01 다음 중 밑줄 친 부분의 쓰임이 나머지 넷과 다른 것은?

① He is always the first to come.
② He has nothing to write with.
③ He went to England to study English.
④ There are a lot of things for him to do.
⑤ He was looking for an apartment to live in.

[02~03] 다음 문장의 빈칸에 알맞은 것을 고르시오.

02
It is good for the health _____ early.

① get up
② got up
③ to get up
④ to getting up
⑤ to be getting up

03
Do you have anything _____ ?

① read
② reads
③ reading
④ to read
⑤ to be reading

서답형
04 다음 두 문장의 뜻이 같도록 빈칸에 알맞은 말을 쓰시오.

I have a lot of letters _____ _____.
= I have a lot of letters that I should write.

서답형
05 다음 두 문장의 뜻이 같도록 빈칸에 알맞은 말을 쓰시오.

To change the schedule is very difficult.
= _____ is very difficult _____ the schedule.

06 다음 중 밑줄 친 부분의 쓰임이 〈보기〉와 같은 것은?

보기
I have lots of books to read by next month.

① Jina has no chair to sit on.
② My hobby is to listen to music.
③ She is glad to get a letter from Ted.
④ He wants to play baseball after school.
⑤ I went to the market to buy some eggs.

07 다음 우리말과 같도록 할 때, 빈칸에 알맞은 말이 바르게 짝 지어진 것은?

자전거를 탈 때는 헬멧을 쓰는 것이 안전하다.
= _____ is safe _____ a helmet when you ride a bike.

① It − to wear
② This − wear
③ It − wears
④ It − wear
⑤ That − to wear

서답형

08 다음 우리말과 일치하도록 주어진 단어를 바르게 배열하여 문장을 완성하시오.

> 너 뭐 좀 먹을래?
> (anything, you, want, do, eat, to)

➡ _____

_____

09 다음 밑줄 친 it의 쓰임이 나머지 넷과 <u>다른</u> 하나는?

① <u>It</u>'s important to be kind to others.
② Is <u>it</u> fun to play computer games?
③ <u>It</u> is not surprising for him to say so.
④ It's hard to believe, but <u>it</u>'s a flower.
⑤ <u>It</u>'s not easy to understand other cultures.

중요

10 다음 중 어법상 <u>어색한</u> 문장은?

① It's almost time to go to bed.
② It's time to get aboard a plane.
③ It is time to eat dinner.
④ It's time for the children to going to bed.
⑤ It's time for my dad to buy a new car.

서답형

11 다음 괄호 안에 주어진 말을 사용하여 우리말을 영작하시오.

> 그 기계를 고치는 것은 어렵다.
> (it, difficult, fix, machine)

➡ _____

12 다음 빈칸에 알맞은 말이 바르게 짝지어진 것은?

> • It is very kind _____ you to say so.
> • It is natural _____ a baby to cry.

① of – of
② of – for
③ for – for
④ for – of
⑤ for – with

중요

13 다음 빈칸에 공통으로 알맞은 것은?

> • It was honest _____ you to tell the truth.
> • It is wise _____ her to make such a decision.

① of
② for
③ with
④ at
⑤ upon

14 다음 빈칸에 들어갈 동사의 형태로 적절한 것은?

> It's necessary _____ on time.

① to be
② is
③ be
④ are
⑤ will be

서답형

15 다음 빈칸에 공통으로 알맞은 말을 쓰시오.

> • You don't have _____ worry about it.
> • I have no reason _____ be angry at you.

16 다음 문장의 빈칸에 to를 쓸 수 <u>없는</u> 것은?

① It is natural for your mom _____ get angry.
② She hopes _____ visit her uncle.
③ He is kind enough _____ help us.
④ It is easy _____ speak English.
⑤ She made me _____ wash the dishes.

서답형

17 다음 문장에서 어법상 <u>어색한</u> 부분을 찾아 바르게 고쳐 쓰시오.

I need a chair to sit.

_____ ➡ _____

18 다음 중 밑줄 친 부분의 쓰임이 나머지 넷과 <u>다른</u> 것은?

① <u>It</u> will soon be a new year.
② Is <u>it</u> easy to use this camera?
③ <u>It</u> is a lot of fun to ski in winter.
④ <u>It</u> isn't difficult to use the computer.
⑤ <u>It</u> is interesting to read English books.

19 다음 밑줄 친 부분의 쓰임이 바르지 <u>않은</u> 것은?

① There is no chair <u>to sit on</u>.
② I have no money <u>to give</u> you.
③ Judy has a lot of friends <u>to talk</u>.
④ She doesn't have a house <u>to live in</u>.
⑤ Do you have a pen <u>to write with</u>?

20 다음 중 밑줄 친 to부정사의 쓰임이 나머지와 <u>다른</u> 하나는?

① It is important <u>to try</u> your best.
② My dream is <u>to be</u> a singer.
③ I want a house <u>to live</u> in.
④ I decided <u>to study</u> Spanish.
⑤ It is very kind of you <u>to help</u> me.

서답형

21 다음 주어진 어구를 이용하여 〈보기〉와 같이 문장을 쓰시오.

┌─ 보기 ─┐

boring, watch news on TV
→ It is boring to watch news on TV.

pleasant, listen to music

➡ _____

22 다음 빈칸에 들어갈 말이 바르게 짝지어진 것은?

• It's time for our children _____ to bed.
• You don't have _____ an umbrella with you.

① go – take
② to go – taken
③ going – taking
④ going – to take
⑤ to go – to take

서답형

23 다음 문장에서 어법상 <u>어색한</u> 부분을 찾아 바르게 고쳐 쓰시오.

It is necessary for you going there as soon as possible.

_____ ➡ _____

01 다음 빈칸에 공통으로 알맞은 말을 쓰시오.

- Mike had no time _____ do his homework.
- We are going to buy some paper _____ write on.

02 다음 두 문장의 뜻이 같도록 빈칸에 알맞은 말을 쓰시오.

To cook French food is difficult.
= _____ is difficult _____ cook French food.

03 다음 주어진 단어를 바르게 배열하여 문장을 완성하시오.

(1) (difficult / it / learn / is / to / English)
➡ _____

(2) (a magazine / on / he / read / the train / bought / to)
➡ _____

04 다음 밑줄 친 단어를 알맞은 형태로 고쳐 쓰시오.

It is strange for her <u>receive</u> fan letters.

➡ _____

05 다음 괄호 안에 주어진 말을 사용하여 우리말을 영작하시오. (가주어 – 진주어 구문을 사용할 것.)

(1) 주말마다 그를 방문하는 것은 쉽지 않았다.
(visit, easy, every)
➡ _____

(2) 다른 나라에서 사는 것은 재미있는 경험이다.
(it, exciting, live, another)
➡ _____
_____

06 다음 괄호 안에 주어진 단어를 이용하여 우리말을 영어로 옮기시오.

(1) 그녀는 가수가 되려는 강한 욕망을 갖고 있다.
(strong desire, be, singer)
➡ _____

(2) 우리는 이야기할 것이 있었다.
(something, talk about)
➡ _____

(3) 나는 쓸 종이를 한 장 원한다.
(want, write)
➡ _____

(4) 제게 뜨거운 마실 것을 좀 주십시오.
(please, something, drink)
➡ _____

07 다음 문장에서 어법상 어색한 곳을 찾아 바르게 고쳐 쓰시오.

(1) He doesn't have time play with his friends.

_____ ➡ _____

(2) It is important of you to study hard.

_____ ➡ _____

08 다음 빈칸에 알맞은 말을 〈보기〉에서 골라 쓰시오. (중복해서 사용할 수 없음)

┌─ 보기 ─┐
to   on   with   it

(1) _____ is hard to follow good advice.
(2) Do you have anything to write _____?
(3) I need a knife to cut the rope _____.
(4) I have a lot of things _____ do today.

09 다음 두 문장의 뜻이 같도록 빈칸에 알맞은 말을 쓰시오

나는 같이 놀 친한 친구가 필요하다.
= I need my best friend _____
_____ _____.

10 다음 빈칸에 공통으로 들어갈 알맞은 말을 쓰시오.

• It's time for my father _____ come home.
• You don't have _____ water the flowers.

11 다음 두 문장이 같은 뜻이 되도록 빈칸에 알맞은 말을 쓰시오.

To learn to ride a bike was not difficult.
= _____ was not difficult _____ _____ to ride a bike.

12 다음 문장에서 어법상 어색한 곳을 찾아 바르게 고쳐 쓰시오.

(1) It was stupid for you to believe the rumor.

_____ ➡ _____

(2) It isn't necessary of you to come here today.

_____ ➡ _____

13 다음 주어진 단어를 이용하여 우리말을 영어로 옮기시오.

그곳은 24시간 동안 많은 물건들을 파는 장소이다.
(it's, a place, to sell, things)

➡ _____

Reading

Germs: The War Inside

Germs are everywhere, but it is impossible to see them with your
eyes.

There are two major kinds of germs: bacteria and viruses. Bacteria
are very small creatures. Some are good. They can help you digest the
food that you eat. Others are bad and can make you sick. Viruses are
germs that can only live inside the cells of other living bodies. They
cause diseases such as the flu.

"Bad" germs can enter your body through your skin, mouth, nose,
and eyes. What happens when they invade?

The germs multiply in the body. Your body becomes a war zone. You
start to feel tired and weak.

Luckily, your body has an army of defense. The T cells sound the
alarm! The B cells arrive to fight the germs with antibodies. The
macrophage cells show up and eat the germs. Together, this army is
called the white blood cells. If all goes well, they win the fight. In a
few days, you start to feel better.

germ 세균
everywhere 도처에
impossible 불가능한
major 주요한
bacteria 박테리아
virus 바이러스
creature 생물
digest 소화하다
inside ~ 안에서
cell 세포
body 신체, 몸
cause 일으키다, 야기하다
disease 병
such as ~와 같은
flu 독감
skin 피부
happen 일어나다
invade 침략하다
multiply 증식하다
zone 지역
army 부대, 군대
defense 방어
antibody 항체

확인문제

● 다음 문장이 본문의 내용과 일치하면 T, 일치하지 않으면 F를 쓰시오.

1 We can see germs with our eyes. ☐

2 Bacteria and viruses are two major germs. ☐

3 Most bacteria are bad. ☐

4 Viruses cause diseases like the flu. ☐

5 Our body has an army of defense. ☐

The body remembers the invader, so it cannot make copies of itself
그래서   자기 자신을 복제하다

again. But the germs are smart, too. They can change form and trick
모양을 바꾸다

the body. There are several ways to protect yourself from germs. First,
형용사적 용법의 to부정사   재귀 용법의 재귀대명사

wash your hands with soap and warm water. A balanced diet will keep
동사원형으로 시작하는 명령문   ~으로(도구)   불완전 타동사

your body strong and healthy. It is also important to exercise regularly
목적어   목적보어   가주어   to부정사(진주어)

and get plenty of sleep. Finally, get the necessary shots. They are the
exercise와 함께 to에 연결   필요한 주사를 맞다   = The necessary shots

best defense against germs. If you follow these steps, you will not be a
~에 대항하여   이러한 조치들을 따르다

victim of "bad" germs.

Watch out! This is my spot! Hands off! Time to attack! Make more
watch out: 조심하다   손 치워!   형용사적 용법의 to부정사   many의 비교급

copies of me. It's my job to defend the body. That was a nice meal! Are
가주어   진주어가 되는 to부정사   멋진 식사

there any more germs to eat? Next year, I'll send in my cousin. He'll
형용사적 용법의 to부정사   send in: ~을 파견하다

see you then for another fight! I'm ready to fight any germs. We give
another+단수 명사   be ready to: ~할 준비가 되다   give up: 포기하다

up. We can't make you sick.
불완전 타동사+목적어+목적보어

invader 침입자
copy 복사, 복제
smart 영리한
form 형태
trick 속이다
several 몇 개의
protect 보호하다
soap 비누
balanced 균형 잡힌
diet 다이어트, 식단
heathy 건강한
important 중요한
regularly 규칙적으로
plenty of 충분한
finally 마지막으로
necessary 필요한
shot 주사
step 단계, 조치
victim 희생자

확인문제

● 다음 문장이 본문의 내용과 일치하면 T, 일치하지 않으면 F를 쓰시오.

1 The invader can make copies of itself again though the body remembers it. ☐

2 The germs are smart enough to trick the body. ☐

3 You should wash your hands with soap and warm water to protect yourself from germs. ☐

4 The shots are not the best defense against the germs ☐

● 우리말을 참고하여 빈칸에 알맞은 말을 쓰시오.

1 Germs are _____, but it is impossible to _____ them with your eyes.

2 There are two major _____ of germs: _____ and viruses.

3 Bacteria are very small _____.

4 _____ are good.

5 They can help you _____ the food _____ you eat.

6 _____ are bad and can _____ you sick.

7 Viruses are germs _____ can only live _____ the cells of other _____ bodies.

8 They _____ diseases _____ as the flu.

9 "Bad" germs can _____ your body _____ your skin, mouth, nose, and eyes.

10 What _____ when they invade?

11 The germs _____ in the body.

12 Your _____ _____ a war _____.

13 You _____ to feel tired and _____.

14 Luckily, your _____ has an army of _____.

15 The T cells _____ the alarm!

16 The B cells _____ to fight the _____ with antibodies.

17 The macrophage cells _____ up and _____ the germs.

18 Together, this army is _____ the white blood _____.

19 If all _____ well, they win the _____.

20 In a _____ days, you start to _____ better.

---

1 세균은 어디에나 있지만 눈으로 세균을 보는 것은 불가능하다.

2 세균에는 두 가지 주요한 종류가 있다: 박테리아와 바이러스이다.

3 박테리아는 매우 작은 생물이다.

4 어떤 것들은 좋다.

5 그것들은 당신이 먹는 음식을 소화하는 데 도움을 줄 수 있다.

6 다른 것들은 나쁘고 당신을 아프게 할 수 있다.

7 바이러스는 다른 살아 있는 몸의 세포 안에서만 살 수 있는 세균이다.

8 그들은 독감과 같은 질병을 일으킨다.

9 '나쁜' 세균은 피부, 입, 코, 눈을 통해 몸에 들어갈 수 있다.

10 그들이 침입하면 어떻게 되는가?

11 세균은 몸속에서 증식한다.

12 당신의 몸은 전쟁 지역이 된다.

13 당신은 피곤하고 약해지는 것을 느끼기 시작한다.

14 다행히도, 당신의 몸은 방어 부대를 가지고 있다.

15 T세포가 경보를 발한다!

16 B세포는 항체로 세균과 싸우기 위해 도착한다.

17 대식 세포가 나타나서 세균을 먹는다.

18 이 군대는 함께 백혈구라고 부른다.

19 모든 것이 잘되면 싸움에서 이긴다.

20 며칠 후면 당신은 회복되기 시작한다.

21 The body remembers the _____, so it cannot make _____ of _____ again.

22 But the germs are _____, too.

23 They can _____ form and _____ the body.

24 There are _____ ways to _____ yourself from germs.

25 First, _____ your hands with soap and _____ water.

26 A balanced _____ will keep your body strong and _____.

27 It is also important to _____ regularly and get _____ of sleep.

28 _____, get the necessary _____.

29 They are the best _____ against _____.

30 If you follow these _____, you will not be a _____ of "bad" germs.

31 Make more _____ of me.

32 It's my job to _____ the body.

33 That was a nice _____!

34 Are _____ any more germs to _____?

35 _____ year, I'll _____ in my cousin.

36 He'll _____ you then for _____ fight!

37 What _____ I do now?

38 I'm _____ to fight _____ germs.

39 We give _____.

40 We can't _____ you sick.

21 몸은 침입자를 기억하므로 침입자는 다시 복제할 수 없다.

22 하지만 세균들도 영리하다.

23 그들은 형태를 바꿀 수 있고 몸을 속일 수 있다.

24 세균으로부터 당신 자신을 보호하는 몇 가지 방법이 있다.

25 먼저 비누와 따뜻한 물로 손을 씻어라.

26 균형 잡힌 식단은 당신의 몸을 튼튼하고 건강하게 해줄 것이다.

27 규칙적으로 운동하고 충분한 잠을 자는 것도 중요하다.

28 마지막으로 필요한 주사를 맞아라.

29 그것들은 세균을 막는 최고의 방어이다.

30 만약 당신이 이 단계를 따른다면, 당신은 "나쁜" 세균의 희생자가 되지 않을 것이다.

31 나를 더 복제해 줘.

32 몸을 지키는 게 내 일이야.

33 정말 맛있는 식사였어!

34 먹을 세균이 더 있니?

35 내년에는 내 사촌을 보낼게.

36 그때 그가 또 싸우려고 널 보게 될 거야!

37 지금 내가 무엇을 할 수 있을까?

38 나는 어떤 세균과도 싸울 준비가 되어 있어.

39 우리는 포기한다.

40 우리는 널 아프게 할 수 없어.

● 우리말을 참고하여 본문을 영작하시오.

1 세균은 어디에나 있지만 눈으로 세균을 보는 것은 불가능하다.
➡ _____

2 세균에는 두 가지 주요한 종류가 있다: 박테리아와 바이러스이다.
➡ _____

3 박테리아는 매우 작은 생물이다.
➡ _____

4 어떤 것들은 좋다.
➡ _____

5 그것들은 당신이 먹는 음식을 소화하는 데 도움을 줄 수 있다.
➡ _____

6 다른 것들은 나쁘고 당신을 아프게 할 수 있다.
➡ _____

7 바이러스는 다른 살아 있는 몸의 세포 안에서만 살 수 있는 세균이다.
➡ _____

8 그들은 독감과 같은 질병을 일으킨다.
➡ _____

9 '나쁜' 세균은 피부, 입, 코, 눈을 통해 몸에 들어갈 수 있다.
➡ _____

10 그들이 침입하면 어떻게 되는가?
➡ _____

11 세균은 몸속에서 증식한다.
➡ _____

12 당신의 몸은 전쟁 지역이 된다.
➡ _____

13 당신은 피곤하고 약해지는 것을 느끼기 시작한다.
➡ _____

14 다행히도, 당신의 몸은 방어 군대를 가지고 있다.
➡ _____

15 T세포가 경보를 발한다!
➡ _____

16 B세포는 항체로 세균과 싸우기 위해 도착한다.
➡ _____

17 대식 세포가 나타나서 세균을 먹는다.
➡ _____

18 이 군대는 함께 백혈구라고 부른다.
➡ _____

19 모든 것이 잘되면 싸움에서 이긴다.
➡ _____

20 며칠 후면 당신은 회복되기 시작한다.
➡ _____

21 몸은 침입자를 기억하므로 다시 복제할 수 없다.
➡ _____

22 하지만 세균들도 영리하다.
➡ _____

23 그들은 형태를 바꿀 수 있고 몸을 속일 수 있다.
➡ _____

24 세균으로부터 여러분 자신을 보호하는 몇 가지 방법이 있다.
➡ _____

25 먼저 비누와 따뜻한 물로 손을 씻어라.
➡ _____

26 균형 잡힌 식단은 당신의 몸을 튼튼하고 건강하게 해줄 것이다.
➡ _____

27 규칙적으로 운동하고 충분한 잠을 자는 것도 중요하다.
➡ _____

28 마지막으로 필요한 주사를 맞아라.
➡ _____

29 그것들은 세균을 막는 최고의 방어이다.
➡ _____

30 만약 당신이 이 단계를 따른다면, 당신은 "나쁜" 세균의 희생자가 되지 않을 것이다.
➡ _____

31 나를 더 복제해 주세요.
➡ _____

32 몸을 지키는 게 내 일이야.
➡ _____

33 정말 맛있는 식사였어!
➡ _____

34 먹을 세균이 더 있니?
➡ _____

35 내년에는 내 사촌을 보낼게.
➡ _____

36 그때 그가 또 싸우려고 널 보게 될 거야!
➡ _____

37 지금 내가 무엇을 할 수 있을까?
➡ _____

38 나는 어떤 세균과도 싸울 준비가 되어 있어.
➡ _____

39 우리는 포기한다.
➡ _____

40 우리는 널 아프게 할 수 없어.
➡ _____

[01~06] 다음 글을 읽고, 물음에 답하시오.

> Germ 1: Watch ___ⓐ___ !
>
> Germ 2: This is my spot!
>
> Germ 3: ⓑHands off!
>
> Germ 4: Hey!
>
> (①) Germs are everywhere, ___ⓒ___ it is impossible to see them with your eyes. (②)
>
> There are two major kinds of germs: bacteria and viruses. (③) Bacteria are very small creatures. (④) They can help you digest the food ⓓthat you eat. (⑤) Others are bad and can make you sick.

01 위 글의 ①~⑤ 중 다음 주어진 문장이 들어갈 알맞은 곳은?

> Some are good.

①   ②   ③   ④   ⑤

02 위 글의 빈칸 ⓐ에 알맞은 것은?

① on   ② out
③ at   ④ for
⑤ with

서답형

03 위 글의 밑줄 친 ⓑ를 우리말로 옮기시오.

➡ _____

중요

04 위 글의 빈칸 ⓒ에 알맞은 것은?

① read   ② or
③ but   ④ for
⑤ because

중요

05 위 글의 밑줄 친 ⓓ와 바꿔 쓸 수 있는 것은?

① who   ② whom
③ what   ④ where
⑤ which

06 위 글의 내용과 일치하지 않는 것은?

① 균은 어디에나 있다.
② 균을 눈으로 볼 수 없다.
③ 박테리아와 바이러스는 균이다.
④ 박테리아는 아주 작은 생명체다.
⑤ 박테리아는 대부분 몸에 해롭다.

[07~10] 다음 글을 읽고, 물음에 답하시오.

> Germ 1: I'm in! Time to ___ⓐ___ !
>
> Germ 2: Yay! Success!
>
> Germ 3: Make more copies of me. Now!
>
> Viruses are germs ___ⓑ___ can only live inside the cells of other living bodies. They cause diseases ⓒsuch as the flu.
>
> "Bad" germs can enter your body through your skin, mouth, nose, and eyes. What happens when they invade? The germs ___ⓓ___ in the body. Your body becomes a war zone. You start to feel tired and weak.

07 위 글의 빈칸 ⓐ에 알맞은 것은?

① attack   ② eat
③ die   ④ escape
⑤ repair

08 위 글의 빈칸 ⓑ에 알맞은 것은? (2개)

① who   ② that

③ what   ④ why

⑤ which

서답형

09 위 글의 밑줄 친 ⓒ를 한 단어로 바꿔 쓰시오.

➡ _____

서답형

10 위 글의 빈칸 ⓓ에 다음 정의에 해당하는 단어를 쓰시오.

> to increase greatly in number or amount

➡ _____

[11~15] 다음 글을 읽고, 물음에 답하시오.

A: We have an ⓐinvade! Come quickly.
B: It's my job to ___ⓑ___ the body.
C: That was a nice meal! Are there any more germs to eat?

Luckily, your body has an army of defense. The T cells sound the alarm! The B cells arrive ⓒto fight the germs with antibodies. The macrophage cells show ___ⓓ___ and eat the germs.

Together, this army is called the white blood cells. If all goes well, they win the fight. In a few days, you start to feel better.

서답형

11 위 글의 밑줄 친 ⓐ를 알맞은 형으로 바꿔 쓰시오.

➡ _____

12 위 글의 빈칸 ⓑ에 알맞은 것은?

① defend   ② attack

③ live   ④ fix

⑤ fight

중요

13 위 글의 밑줄 친 ⓒ와 같은 용법으로 쓰인 것은?

① My hope is to become a doctor.
② It's time to go to bed now.
③ My job is to report the news.
④ He tried to find the lost key.
⑤ Kathy came to Korea to be a K pop singer.

14 위 글의 빈칸 ⓓ에 알맞은 것은?

① on   ② up

③ off   ④ with

⑤ from

15 위 글의 내용으로 보아 대답할 수 없는 질문은?

① What did 'C' eat?
② What does our body have?
③ Why does B cells arrive?
④ How does the T cells sound the alarm?
⑤ What is the army called?

[16~21] 다음 글을 읽고, 물음에 답하시오.

The army of defense: Game ___ⓐ___.

Germ: Fine. Next year, I'll send ___ⓑ___ my cousin. He'll see you then for ©(other, another) fight!

ⓓThe body remembers the invader, so it cannot make copies of it again. But the germs are smart, too. ⓔThey can change form and trick the body.

16 위 글의 빈칸 ⓐ에 알맞은 것은?

① Up   ② On
③ Over   ④ Off
⑤ From

중요

17 위 글의 빈칸 ⓑ에 알맞은 것은?

① on   ② to
③ off   ④ in
⑤ for

서답형

18 위 글의 괄호 ©에서 알맞은 것을 고르시오.

➡ _____

서답형

19 위 글의 밑줄 친 ⓓ에서 어법상 어색한 것을 고치시오.

_____ ➡ _____

서답형

20 위 글의 밑줄 친 ⓔ를 우리말로 옮기시오.

➡ _____

21 위 글의 내용에서 언급되지 않은 것은?

① 방어 군대가 전쟁에서 승리했다.
② 균들은 내년에 다시 올 것이다.
③ 균들은 자신들이 침입한 몸을 기억하고 있다.
④ 한 번 침입한 균들은 자신을 복제할 수 없다.
⑤ 균들은 형태를 바꿀 수 있다.

[22~24] 다음 글을 읽고, 물음에 답하시오.

Germ: Oh, no! I can't hold on.
What can I do now?
There are several ways ⓐprotect yourself ___ⓑ___ germs. First, wash your hands ©with soap and warm water.

서답형

22 위 글의 밑줄 친 ⓐ를 알맞은 형태로 고쳐 쓰시오.

➡ _____

23 위 글의 빈칸 ⓑ에 알맞은 것은?

① of   ② from
③ in   ④ off
⑤ with

중요

24 위 글의 밑줄 친 ©와 같은 의미로 쓰인 것은?

① That's all right with me.
② What's the matter with you?
③ Cut the bread with this knife.
④ Do you agree with him?
⑤ Ann was in bed with the flu.

[25~28] 다음 글을 읽고, 물음에 답하시오.

A: I'm ready to ___ⓐ___ any germs.
B: Me, too. ⓑBring it on.
ⓒA balanced diet will keep your body strong and healthy. ⓓIt is also important to exercise regularly and get plenty of sleep.

25 위 글의 빈칸 ⓐ에 알맞은 것은?

① lose   ② win
③ fight   ④ hit
⑤ follow

서답형
26 위 글의 밑줄 친 ⓑ를 우리말로 옮기시오.

➡ _____

중요
27 위 글의 밑줄 친 ⓒ와 문형이 같은 것은?

① These shirts are very small.
② The song made me sad.
③ There are some apples in the basket.
④ She made us some cookies.
⑤ My grandfather planted some trees.

서답형
28 위 글의 밑줄 친 ⓓ가 가리키는 것을 우리말로 쓰시오.

➡ _____

[29~33] 다음 글을 읽고, 물음에 답하시오.

Germ 1: What? ⓐIt's "Game Over" for my cousins, too?
Germ 2: We give ___ⓑ___.
Germ 3: We can't make you sick.
ⓒFinal, get the necessary shots. They are the best defense ___ⓓ___ germs. ___ⓔ___ you follow these steps, you will not be a victim of "bad" germs.

서답형
29 위 글의 밑줄 친 ⓐ를 우리말로 옮기시오.

➡ _____

30 위 글의 빈칸 ⓑ에 알맞은 것은?

① on   ② in
③ for   ④ up
⑤ over

서답형
31 위 글의 밑줄 친 ⓒ를 알맞은 형으로 고치시오.

➡ _____

32 위 글의 빈칸 ⓓ에 알맞은 것은?

① to   ② with
③ over   ④ across
⑤ against

중요
33 위 글의 빈칸 ⓔ에 알맞은 것은?

① If   ② As
③ While   ④ Since
⑤ Though

[01~04] 다음 글을 읽고, 물음에 답하시오.

Germ 1: ⓐ조심해!
Germ 2: This is my spot!
Germ 3: Hands off!
Germ 4: Hey!

  Germs are everywhere, ⓑbut it is impossible to see them with your eyes.

  There are two major kinds of germs: bacteria and viruses. Bacteria are very small creatures. Some are good. They can help you digest the food that you eat. ___ⓒ___ are bad and can make you sick.

01 위 글의 밑줄 친 ⓐ와 같은 뜻이 되도록 빈칸에 알맞은 말을 쓰시오.

_____ out!

02 위 글의 밑줄 친 ⓑ와 같은 뜻이 되도록 빈칸에 알맞은 말을 쓰시오.

but you _____ see them with your eyes.

03 위 글의 빈칸 ⓒ에 알맞은 말을 쓰시오.

➡ _____

04 How do good bacteria help you? Answer in Korean.

➡ _____

[05~08] 다음 글을 읽고, 물음에 답하시오.

Germ 1: I'm in! Time to attack!
Germ 2: Yay! Success!
Germ 3: Make more copies ___ⓐ___ me. Now!

  Viruses are germs that can only live inside the cells of other living bodies. They cause diseases such as the flu. ⓑ"Bad" germs can enter into your body through your skin, mouth, nose, and eyes. What happens when ⓒthey invade? The germs multiply in the body. Your body becomes a war zone. You start to feel tired and weak.

05 위 글의 빈칸 ⓐ에 알맞은 말을 쓰시오.

➡ _____

06 위 글의 밑줄 친 ⓑ에서 어법상 어색한 것을 고치시오.

_____ ➡ _____

07 위 글의 밑줄 친 ⓒ가 가리키는 것을 우리말로 쓰시오.

➡ _____

08 Why does your body become a war zone? Answer in English.

➡ _____

[09~13] 다음 글을 읽고, 물음에 답하시오.

A: We have an invader! Come quickly.

B: It's my job to defend the body.

C: That was a nice meal! ⓐ먹을 균들이 좀 더 있냐?

Luckily, your body has an army of ⓑdefend. The T cells sound the alarm! The B cells arrive to fight the germs with antibodies. The macrophage cells show up and eat the germs.

ⓒTogether, this army is calling the white blood cells. If all goes well, they win the fight. ⓓIn a few days, you start to feel better.

09 위 글의 밑줄 친 ⓐ와 같은 뜻이 되도록 주어진 단어를 써서 영어로 옮기시오.

> (there, any, germs, eat)

➡ _____

10 위 글의 밑줄 친 ⓑ를 알맞은 형으로 고치시오.

➡ _____

11 위 글의 밑줄 친 ⓒ에서 어법상 어색한 것을 고치시오.

_____ ➡ _____

12 위 글의 밑줄 친 ⓓ를 우리말로 옮기시오.

➡ _____

13 What do the T cells do for the body?

➡ _____

[14~18] 다음 글을 읽고, 물음에 답하시오.

Every day you use your hands to touch ⓐdiffer things. You touch your phone and computer. You open and close doors with your hands, too. There are germs on everything ___ⓑ___ you touch. If you eat ___ⓒ___ with your hands, the germs on your hands can get into your body. Then what should you do? Wash your hands ___ⓓ___ soap!

14 위 글의 밑줄 친 ⓐ를 알맞은 형으로 고치시오.

➡ _____

15 위 글의 빈칸 ⓑ에 알맞은 관계대명사를 쓰시오.

➡ _____

16 위 글의 빈칸 ⓒ에 다음 정의에 해당하는 단어를 쓰시오. (필요하면 어형 변화를 할 것.)

> a simple meal that is quick to cook and to eat

➡ _____

17 위 글의 빈칸 ⓓ에 알맞은 말을 쓰시오.

➡ _____

18 위 글의 내용으로 보아 손으로 음식을 먹으면 안 되는 이유를 우리말로 간단히 쓰시오.

➡ _____

My Writing Portfolio - Step 1

Sit Less, Move More

- It is dangerous to play online games too much.
  「가주어 It, 진주어 to부정사」 구문
- It is time to go out and exercise.
  밖에 나가다

Stay Healthy

- Eating too many snacks is not good for your health.
  동명사 주어(동사는 단수 취급)
- It is important to eat enough fruit and vegetables.

구문해설 • less: 더 적게, 덜하게 • dangerous: 위험한 • exercise: 운동하다 • healthy: 건강한
• be not good for: ~에 좋지 않다 • important: 중요한 • enough: 충분한
• vegetables: 채소

Words in Action - B

1. Frida Kahlo was a Mexican painter[artist]. She is famous for her unique
paintings.   ~으로 유명하다

2. Charles Schulz was a cartoonist who created the famous character Charlie
Brown.   주격 관계대명사(선행사: a cartoonist)

3. Park Gyeongri was a great Korean writer. She spent 25 years writing *Toji*.
                                             spend time -ing: ~하면서 시간을 보내다
4. James Cameron is the director of the movie, *Avatar*.
                              the movie와 Avatar는 동격 관계
5. Jang Yeongsil was a(n) inventor[scientist] who created water clocks.
                                        주격 관계대명사

구문해설 • painter: 화가 • unique: 독특한 • painting: 그림 • cartoonist: 만화가
• create: 창조하다 • director: 감독 • inventor: 발명가 • water clock: 물시계

Wrap Up - Reading

Every day you use your hands to touch different things. You touch your phone
매일   to부정사의 부사적 용법(목적)
and computer. You open and close doors with your hands, too. There are
                                   ~으로   There are + 복수명사 ~: ~이 있다
germs on everything that you touch. If you eat snacks with your hands, the
         목적격 관계대명사   조건을 나타내는 접속사 if: (만약) ~이면
germs on your hands can get into your body. Then what should you do? Wash
                        ~에 들어가다   명령문: 동사원형 ~: ~해라
your hands with soap!

구문해설 • use: 사용하다 • touch: 만지다 • different: 다른 • close: (문을) 닫다
• too: ~도 (또한) • everything: 모든 것 • germ: 세균 • wash: 씻다 • soap: 비누

해석

덜 앉고, 더 움직여라
• 온라인 게임을 너무 많이
  하는 것은 위험하다.
• 이제 외출해서 운동할 시간
  이다.
건강을 유지해라
• 과자를 너무 많이 먹는 것
  은 건강에 좋지 않다.
• 과일과 채소를 충분히 먹는
  것이 중요하다.

1. Frida Kahlo는 멕시코 화
   가[예술가]였다. 그녀는 독특
   한 그림으로 유명하다.

2. Charles Schulz는 유명한
   캐릭터인 Charlie Brown
   을 만든 만화가였다.

3. 박경리는 위대한 한국 작가
   였다. 그녀는 토지를 쓰는
   데 25년이 걸렸다.

4. James Cameron은 영화
   '아바타'의 감독이다.

5. 장영실은 물시계를 만든 발
   명가[과학자]였다.

여러분은 매일 다른 것들을 만
지기 위해 손을 사용한다. 여러
분은 여러분의 전화기와 컴퓨
터를 만진다. 여러분은 또한 손
으로 문을 열고 닫는다. 여러분
이 만지는 모든 것에는 세균이
있다. 만약 여러분이 손으로 과
자를 먹는다면, 손에 있는 세균
은 여러분의 몸으로 들어갈 수
있다. 그럼 어떻게 해야 할까?
비누로 손을 씻어라!

01 다음 중 짝지어진 단어의 관계가 나머지 넷과 다른 것은?

① write – writer
② paint – painter
③ act – actor
④ science – scientist
⑤ direct – director

02 다음 빈칸에 들어갈 말로 적절하지 않은 것은?

- This is a very _____ problem.
- The key to _____ is hard work.
- The old bill is too easy to _____.
- She has a virus on her _____.

① skin
② hard
③ germ
④ copy
⑤ success

03 다음 두 단어의 관계가 같도록 빈칸에 알맞은 말을 쓰시오.

easy : difficult = safe : _____

04 다음 빈칸에 들어갈 말이 바르게 짝지어진 것은? (대 · 소문자 무시)

- _____ the way, what should we eat?
- Watch _____! There's a car coming!

① in – on
② on – off
③ by – out
④ for – after
⑤ from – for

05 다음 영영풀이에 해당하는 단어는?

any one of the very small parts that together form all living things

① shot
② cell
③ germ
④ virus
⑤ spot

06 다음 문장의 밑줄 친 부분과 바꿔 쓸 수 있는 것은?

At last, the guests began to arrive.

① Usually
② Finally
③ Actually
④ Extremely
⑤ Especially

07 다음 우리말에 맞게 빈칸에 알맞은 말을 쓰시오.

왜 너는 기타 치는 걸 포기했니?
➡ Why did you _____ _____ playing the guitar?

08 다음 대화의 빈칸에 알맞지 않은 것은?

A: _____
B: Well, I have a stomachache.

① What's wrong?
② Is something wrong?
③ What's the problem?
④ What did you eat for lunch?
⑤ What seems to be the problem?

09 다음 대화의 빈칸에 알맞은 말을 쓰시오.

> A: Can you make it at two?
> B: No _____. Let's meet at the park.

➡ _____

10 다음 대화의 빈칸에 알맞은 것은?

> A: Let's go to the history museum. How about 12 o'clock?
> B: _____ Why don't we meet at 2 o'clock?
> A: Sure, no problem.

① Of course.
② That's a good idea.
③ What time will they meet?
④ Good, I am so excited.
⑤ I'm sorry. I will meet my friend at that time.

11 다음 대화의 순서를 바르게 배열하시오.

> (A) I have a sore throat.
> (B) Okay, I will.
> (C) What's wrong with you?
> (D) That's too bad. You should drink some water.

➡ _____

12 다음 대화의 빈칸에 알맞은 말은?

> A: Let's go to the movies this afternoon.
> _____
> B: I'm sorry, I can't.

① Can you make it at 5?
② Are you interested in films?
③ Do you go to the movies often?
④ Would you like to see the movie?
⑤ What kind of movies do you like?

[13~16] 다음 대화를 읽고, 물음에 답하시오.

> B: Can I go home early, Ms. Song? I don't feel so good.
> W: ⓐWhat seems to be the problem?
> B: I have a terrible stomachache. It really hurts.
> W: Why don't you get some medicine at the nurse's office?
> B: I already did. But ⓑit didn't help.
> W: Okay. You can go. _____ ⓒ _____
> B: Sure. Thanks.

13 위 대화의 밑줄 친 ⓐ와 바꿔 쓸 수 없는 것은?

① What's wrong?
② What's the problem?
③ Is something wrong?
④ Why are you so upset?
⑤ What's the matter?

14 위 대화의 밑줄 친 ⓑ가 의미하는 것을 우리말로 구체적으로 쓰시오.

➡ _____

15 위 대화의 빈칸 ⓒ에 알맞은 것은?

① Do exercise, okay?
② Ride a bike, okay?
③ Go see a doctor, okay?
④ Play basketball, okay?
⑤ Have some pizza, okay?

16 위 대화를 읽고, 다음 질문에 완전한 문장으로 답하시오.

> Q: What's the problem with the boy?
> A: _____

[17~18] 다음 문장의 빈칸에 알맞은 것을 고르시오.

17

Do you have anything _____ this evening?

① do   ② did
③ doing   ④ to do
⑤ to doing

18

It is dangerous _____ swim in this river.

① to   ② in
③ of   ④ for
⑤ with

19 다음 빈칸에 공통으로 알맞은 것은?

- It was stupid _____ you to believe him.
- It is clever _____ him to solve the problem.

① at   ② of
③ for   ④ from
⑤ with

20 다음 대화의 빈칸에 알맞은 말을 쓰시오.

A: I think _____ _____ difficult to find the things I want to buy.
B: You know, they have the information desk.

21 다음 중 어법상 어색한 것은?

① She doesn't have a pen to write with.
② She wants someone to travel with.
③ She wants interesting something to read.
④ She kept her promise to enter a university.
⑤ She was the first woman to land on the moon.

22 다음 밑줄 친 부분의 쓰임이 나머지 넷과 다른 것은?

① It is necessary for you to study hard.
② It is too cold to go swimming in the lake.
③ It's good to try to solve the problem.
④ It is difficult for us to achieve the goal.
⑤ It is dangerous to walk alone at midnight.

23 다음 중 밑줄 친 부분의 쓰임이 〈보기〉와 다른 것은?

| 보기 |

I have a lot of work to do today.

① I need somebody to talk to.
② He must be crazy to quit his job.
③ I don't have time to chat with you.
④ She couldn't find any chairs to sit on.
⑤ Do you know the way to get to City Hall?

24 다음 문장에서 어법상 <u>어색한</u> 부분을 찾아 바르게 고쳐 쓰시오.

> I need a ball point to write.

_____ ➡ _____

25 다음 우리말을 영어로 바르게 옮긴 것은?

> 냉장고에는 먹을 음식이 많이 있다.

① There are a lot of food to eat in the refrigerator.
② There are a lot of food eating in the refrigerator.
③ There is a lot of food eating in the refrigerator.
④ There is a lot of foods to eat in the refrigerator.
⑤ There is a lot of food to eat in the refrigerator.

26 다음 두 문장이 같은 뜻이 되도록 빈칸에 알맞은 말을 쓰시오.

> To read this book is important.
> = _____ is important _____ read this book.

27 다음 단어를 바르게 배열하여 알맞은 문장을 만드시오.

> to / anything / myself / I / do / make / slimmer / look / will

➡ _____

[28~32] 다음 글을 읽고, 물음에 답하시오.

> Germ 1: I'm in! Time to ___ⓐ___ !
> Germ 2: Yay! Success!
> Germ 3: Make more copies of me. Now!
> Viruses are germs that can only live inside the cells of other ⓑlive bodies. (①) They cause diseases such as the flu. (②) "Bad" germs can enter your body through your skin, mouth, nose, and eyes. (③) What happens ___ⓒ___ they invade? (④) The germs multiply in the body. (⑤) You start to feel tired and weak.

28 위 글의 ①~⑤ 중 다음 주어진 문장이 들어갈 알맞은 곳은?

> Your body becomes a war zone.

①   ②   ③   ④   ⑤

29 위 글의 빈칸 ⓐ에 알맞은 것은?

① play   ② attack
③ rest   ④ defend
⑤ advise

30 위 글의 밑줄 친 ⓑ를 알맞은 형으로 고치시오.

➡ _____

31 위 글의 빈칸 ⓒ에 알맞은 것은?

① that   ② till
③ when   ④ since
⑤ which

32 위 글의 내용과 일치하지 <u>않는</u> 것은?

① 균은 자신을 복제할 수 없다.
② 바이러스는 다른 살아 있는 몸의 세포 안에서만 살 수 있다.
③ 바이러스는 병을 유발한다.
④ 나쁜 균은 피부, 입, 코, 눈을 통해 신체로 들어온다.
⑤ 균은 몸 안에서 번식한다.

[33~35] 다음 글을 읽고, 물음에 답하시오.

The army of defense: Game Over
Germ: Fine. Next year, I'll send in my cousin. ⓐHe'll see you then for another fight!
The body remembers the invader, _____ⓑ_____ it cannot make copies of itself again. But the germs are smart, too. They can change form and _____ⓒ_____ the body.

33 위 글의 밑줄 친 ⓐ를 우리말로 옮기시오.

➡ _____

34 위 글의 빈칸 ⓑ에 알맞은 것은?

① or   ② so
③ but   ④ for
⑤ though

35 위 글의 빈칸 ⓒ에 알맞은 것은?

① save   ② live
③ trick   ④ fix
⑤ protect

[36~39] 다음 글을 읽고, 물음에 답하시오.

  Every day you use your hands to touch different things. (①) You touch your phone and computer. (②) There are germs on everything that you touch. (③) If you eat snacks with your hands, the germs ____ⓐ____ your hands can get into your body. (④) Then what should you do? (⑤) Wash your hands with ____ⓑ____ !

36 위 글의 ①~⑤ 중 다음 주어진 문장이 들어갈 알맞은 곳은?

You open and close doors with your hands, too.

①   ②   ③   ④   ⑤

37 위 글의 빈칸 ⓐ에 알맞은 것은?

① on   ② to
③ at   ④ in
⑤ over

38 위 글의 빈칸 ⓑ에 다음 정의에 해당하는 단어를 쓰시오.

a substance that you use with water for washing yourself or sometimes for washing clothes

➡ _____

39 Where are germs? Answer in English.

➡ _____

출제율 90%

01 다음 중 짝지어진 단어의 관계가 나머지 넷과 <u>다른</u> 것은?

① defend : attack
② remember : forget
③ different : same
④ hard : difficult
⑤ dangerous : safe

출제율 95%

02 다음 빈칸에 공통으로 알맞은 것은?

> • I won't give _____ easily.
> • He didn't show _____ for the appointment.

① in
② up
③ out
④ off
⑤ onto

출제율 90%

03 다음 짝지어진 두 단어의 관계가 같도록 빈칸에 알맞은 말을 쓰시오.

> paint : painter = invent : _____

출제율 85%

04 다음 중 영영풀이가 <u>잘못된</u> 것은?

① easy: not hard to do
② major: very important
③ fever: a body temperature that is higher than normal
④ germ: a very small living thing that causes disease
⑤ safe: involving possible injury, harm, or death

출제율 90%

05 다음 우리말에 맞게 빈칸에 알맞은 말을 쓰시오.

(1) 우리는 하루 이틀 뒤에 떠날 준비를 하고 있어야 해.
➡ We should _____ _____ _____ leave in a day or two.

(2) 콧물이 나고 목도 아프고 기침도 납니다.
➡ I have a _____ _____, _____ _____ and a cough.

출제율 90%

06 다음 대화의 빈칸에 알맞은 말이 바르게 짝지어진 것은?

> A: What's wrong?
> B: I have _____.
> A: That's too bad. Why don't you _____?
> B: OK. I will.

① a bad cold — see a doctor
② a pet — get some fresh air
③ a lot of homework — go to sleep
④ some stress — go to see a dentist
⑤ long hair — take some medicine

출제율 85%

07 다음 대화의 빈칸에 알맞은 것은?

> A: Let's go to the concert this Saturday.
> B: Sounds good. _____
> A: Fine with me.

① Can I join you?
② May I go to the concert?
③ How about going to the concert?
④ Do you like the concert?
⑤ Can you make it at 3?

[08~10] 다음 대화를 읽고, 물음에 답하시오.

B: Hello, Sora.
G: Hi, Jongha. I heard you were sick. Are you okay now?
B: (①) Yes, I went to the doctor, and I feel better now.
G: (②) By the way, I called you to talk about our science project.
B: (③) Yeah, we should meet. _____ ⓐ _____
G: Okay. ⓑLet's meet at Simpson's Donuts at nine.
B: At nine? That's too early. I sleep late on the weekend.
G: (④) How about 10 then?
B: (⑤) That sounds fine.

출제율 90%

08 위 대화의 ①~⑤ 중 다음 주어진 문장이 들어갈 알맞은 곳은?

> Good to hear that.

① ② ③ ④ ⑤

출제율 100%

09 위 대화의 빈칸 ⓐ에 들어갈 말을 주어진 단어를 바르게 배열하여 완성하시오.

> (it / you / tomorrow / can / make)

➡ _____

출제율 95%

10 위 대화의 밑줄 친 ⓑ를 다음과 같이 바꿔 쓸 때 빈칸에 알맞은 말을 쓰시오.

> _____ _____ _____ meet at Simpson's Donuts at nine?

출제율 85%

11 다음 빈칸에 들어갈 동사의 형태로 적절한 것은?

> It's necessary for you _____ the piano every day.

① practice
② practiced
③ practicing
④ to practice
⑤ to practicing

출제율 95%

12 다음 빈칸에 알맞은 말이 바르게 짝지어진 것은?

> • It was wise _____ you to agree to the proposal.
> • It is impossible _____ us to win the game.

① of – of
② of – for
③ for – for
④ for – of
⑤ for – with

출제율 90%

13 다음 문장에서 어법상 어색한 부분을 찾아 바르게 고쳐 쓰시오.

> I need some paper to write.

_____ ➡ _____

출제율 100%

14 다음 두 문장의 뜻이 같도록 빈칸에 알맞은 말을 쓰시오.

> To finish this homework is hard.
> = _____ is hard _____ finish this homework.

출제율 85%

15 다음 중 어법상 어색한 문장은?

① I need a chair to sit.
② Columbus was the first man to discover the American continent.
③ We have no house to live in.
④ He has a wish to become a pilot.
⑤ She forgot to bring something to write with.

출제율 90%

16 다음 중 〈보기〉의 밑줄 친 it과 쓰임이 같은 것은?

> ── 보기 ──
> It is bad to use cell phones in class.

① It is very hot in this room.
② It is not my lost puppy.
③ It is fun to play soccer with my friends.
④ It rained a lot yesterday morning.
⑤ It was built by Koreans.

출제율 85%

17 다음 우리말을 영어로 바르게 옮긴 것은?

> 한국에는 방문할 장소가 많이 있다.

① There is many places visit in Korea.
② There are visiting many places in Korea.
③ There are many places visiting in Korea.
④ There are to visit many places in Korea.
⑤ There are many places to visit in Korea.

출제율 100%

18 다음 밑줄 친 부분의 쓰임이 다른 하나는?

① There's nothing to be afraid of any more.
② Ann is coming to Seoul to visit us.
③ I'm going to the park to walk my dogs.
④ Paul drove very quickly to get there on time.
⑤ I went to the post office to send the parcel.

[19~21] 다음 글을 읽고, 물음에 답하시오.

> A: ⓐI'm ready to fight any germs.
> B: Me, too. Bring it ___ⓑ___.
> A balanced diet will keep your body strong and healthy. It is also important to exercise ⓒregular and get plenty of sleep.

출제율 90%

19 위 글의 밑줄 친 ⓐ를 우리말로 옮기시오.

➡ _____

출제율 85%

20 위 글의 빈칸 ⓑ에 알맞은 것은?

① in   ② on
③ to   ④ for
⑤ from

출제율 90%

21 위 글의 밑줄 친 ⓒ를 알맞은 어형으로 고치시오.

➡ _____

[22~26] 다음 글을 읽고, 물음에 답하시오.

Every day you use your hands ⓐto touch different things. You touch your phone and computer. You ___ⓑ___ and close doors with your hands, too. ⓒ여러분이 손대는 모든 것에 균들이 있다. ___ⓓ___ you eat snacks with your hands, the germs on your hands can get ___ⓔ___ your body. Then what should you do? Wash your hands with soap!

✏️ 출제율 90%

22 위 글의 밑줄 친 ⓐ와 같은 용법으로 쓰인 것은?

① My hope is to work as a doctor in Africa.
② It's time to go to bed now.
③ My job is to report the news.
④ The boys hoped to find the hidden treasure.
⑤ Kevin came to Korea to be a K pop singer.

✏️ 출제율 100%

23 위 글의 빈칸 ⓑ에 알맞은 단어를 쓰시오.

➡ _____

✏️ 출제율 90%

24 위 글의 밑줄 친 ⓒ를 주어진 단어를 써서 영어로 옮기시오.

there, germs, on, touch

➡ _____

✏️ 출제율 85%

25 위 글의 빈칸 ⓓ에 알맞은 것은?

① But   ② If
③ Since   ④ Though
⑤ Because

✏️ 출제율 90%

26 위 글의 빈칸 ⓔ에 알맞은 것은?

① at   ② to
③ into   ④ from
⑤ out of

[27~30] 다음 글을 읽고, 물음에 답하시오.

Germ 1: ⓐWhat? It's "Game Over" for my cousins, too?
Germ 2: We give up.
Germ 3: We can't ___ⓑ___ you sick.
  Finally, get the necessary shots. ⓒThey are the best defense against germs. If you follow these steps, you will not be a ___ⓓ___ of "bad" germs.

✏️ 출제율 90%

27 위 글의 Germ 1이 밑줄 친 ⓐ를 말한 이유를 우리말로 간단히 쓰시오.

➡ _____

✏️ 출제율 100%

28 위 글의 빈칸 ⓑ에 알맞은 것은?

① make   ② get
③ do   ④ let
⑤ become

✏️ 출제율 90%

29 위 글의 밑줄 친 ⓒ를 우리말로 옮기시오.

➡ _____

✏️ 출제율 85%

30 위 글의 빈칸 ⓓ에 다음 정의에 해당하는 단어를 쓰시오.

someone who has been hurt or killed

➡ _____

[01~02] 다음 대화를 읽고, 물음에 답하시오.

A: ⓐWhat's wrong with you?
B: ⓑ나는 목이 아파.
A: That's too bad. You should drink some water.
B: Okay, I will.

01 위 대화의 밑줄 친 부분과 바꿔 쓸 수 있는 표현을 두 가지 쓰시오.

➡ _____

_____

_____

02 위 대화의 밑줄 친 우리말을 영어로 쓰시오. (5 words)

➡ _____

03 다음 우리말과 같도록 빈칸에 알맞은 말을 넣어 대화를 완성하시오.

A: _____ go to the library this Saturday.
(우리 이번 토요일에 도서관에 가자.)
B: Sounds good. Can you _____ _____ at 9? (좋아. 너는 9시에 시간 되니?)
A: I'm _____ I can't. _____ about 10? (난 안 될 것 같아. 10시는 어떠니?)
B: Okay. _____ you then. (좋아. 그때 보자.)

04 다음 대화의 순서를 바르게 배열하시오.

(A) OK, I will.
(B) What's wrong?
(C) Well, I have a toothache.
(D) That's too bad. Why don't you go see a dentist?

➡ _____

05 다음 우리말 의미에 맞도록 주어진 표현을 이용하여 영작하시오.

(1) 언덕을 내려가는 것은 쉽지 않다.
(it, easy, go down)

➡ _____

(2) 나는 내 남동생이 찍는 사진들을 좋아한다.
(photographs, which, takes)

➡ _____

_____

06 다음 〈조건〉에 맞게 괄호 안의 단어를 이용하여 우리말을 영어로 옮기시오.

┌─ 조건 ─┐
1. 주어진 단어를 모두 이용할 것.
2. 필요시 관사를 붙이거나 단어를 추가할 것.
3. It으로 시작할 것.
4. 대·소문자 및 구두점에 유의할 것.

(1) 내가 자동차를 주차하기는 어렵다.
(difficult, me, park, car)

➡ _____

(2) 헬멧을 쓰고 자전거를 타는 것이 안전하다.
(safe, ride, bike, with, helmet)

➡ _____

(3) 다른 나라에서 사는 것은 흥미진진한 경험이다.
(exciting, experience, live, another, country)

➡ _____

07 다음 하루 일과표를 보고 빈칸에 알맞은 내용을 쓰시오.

8:00 a.m.	school
12:10 p.m.	lunch
5:00 p.m.	playground
6:30 p.m.	homework

(1) It's 8 a.m. It's time _____.
(2) It's 12:10 p.m. It's time _____.
(3) It's 5 p.m. It's time _____.
(4) It's 6:30 p.m. It's time _____.

[08~11] 다음 글을 읽고, 물음에 답하시오.

Germ: Oh, no! I can't hold on.
___ⓐ___ can I do now?
There are several ways to protect ⓑyou from germs. First, wash your hands ___ⓒ___ soap and warm water.

08 위 글의 빈칸 ⓐ에 알맞은 말을 쓰시오.

➡ _____

09 위 글의 밑줄 친 ⓑ를 알맞은 형으로 고치시오.

➡ _____

10 위 글의 빈칸 ⓒ에 알맞은 말을 쓰시오.

➡ _____

11 위 글의 Germ이 밑줄 친 부분과 같이 말한 이유를 본문에서 유추하여 답하시오.

➡ _____

[12~15] 다음 글을 읽고, 물음에 답하시오.

Germ 1: What? It's "Game Over" for my cousins, too?
Germ 2: ⓐ우리는 포기한다.
Germ 3: We can't make you sick.
　Finally, get the necessary shots. ⓑThey are the best ⓒdefend against germs. ⓓIf you follow these steps, you will not be a victim of "bad" germs.

12 위 글의 밑줄 친 ⓐ와 같은 뜻이 되도록 빈칸에 알맞은 말을 쓰시오.

We give _____.

13 위 글의 밑줄 친 ⓑ가 가리키는 것을 영어로 쓰시오.

➡ _____

14 위 글의 밑줄 친 ⓒ를 알맞은 형으로 고치시오.

➡ _____

15 위 글의 밑줄 친 ⓓ를 우리말로 옮기시오.

➡ _____
_____

01 다음 주어진 상황에 맞게 to부정사와 괄호 안의 단어를 이용하여 〈보기〉처럼 문장을 완성하시오.

┌─ 보기 ─────────────────────────────────┐
I'm hungry. I need some food to eat.(eat)
└───┘

(1) I'm very thirsty. _____ (drink)

(2) There's no chair here. _____ (sit)

(3) Tony feels lonely. _____ (talk)

02 다음 어구들을 연결하여 〈보기〉와 같이 한 문장으로 쓰시오.

• happy	• him	• to visit	• his hometown
• kind	• foreigners	• to watch	• Korean
• exciting	• us	• to play	• the work on time
• boring	• her	• to finish	• the poor
• possible	• you	• to help	• basketball games
• difficult	• me	• to learn	• the game

┌─ 보기 ─────────────────────────────────┐
It is happy for him to visit his hometown.
└───┘

(1) _____

(2) _____

(3) _____

(4) _____

(5) _____

03 Jessica의 이번 주 일정표를 보고, 내용에 맞도록 문장을 완성하시오.

Mon.	Tue.	Wed.	Thu.	Fri.
a movie / watch	a piano lesson / take	a baseball game / watch	a piano lesson / take	four comic books / read

(1) Jessica has _____ this Monday.

(2) Jessica has _____ on TV this Wednesday.

(3) Jessica has _____ on Tuesday and Thursday.

(4) Jessica has _____ on Friday.

단원별 모의고사

01 다음 영영풀이에 해당하는 단어로 알맞은 것은?

> to change food that you have eaten by a biological process into simpler forms that can be used by the body

① multiply ② scratch
③ invade   ④ digest
⑤ exercise

02 다음 중 우리말 뜻이 <u>잘못된</u> 것은?

① at last: 마침내
② feel better: 몸이 좋아지다
③ go well: 잘되어 가다
④ watch out for: ~을 구경하다
⑤ can't hold on: 견뎌낼 수 없다

03 다음 빈칸에 공통으로 알맞은 것은?

> • The nurse gave him a flu _____ .
> • Taylor scored with a low _____ into the corner of the net.

① mask   ② zone
③ way   ④ shot
⑤ spot

04 다음 짝지어진 두 단어의 관계가 같도록 빈칸에 알맞은 말을 쓰시오.

> art : artist = cartoon : _____

05 다음 빈칸에 공통으로 들어갈 말을 쓰시오.

> • It is important to get plenty _____ sleep.
> • I'm thinking _____ going to Greece this summer.

➡ _____

[06~08] 다음 대화를 읽고, 물음에 답하시오.

> A: Let's play basketball this Saturday.
> B: _____ⓐ_____
> A: ⓑCan you make it at ten?
> B: That's fine with me. Where should we meet?
> A: Let's meet at the school gym.
> B: Okay. See you there.

06 위 대화의 빈칸 ⓐ에 알맞은 것은?

① No, thanks.   ② I'm afraid not.
③ It doesn't matter. ④ Sure, why not?
⑤ Sorry, but I can't.

07 위 대화의 밑줄 친 ⓑ와 바꿔 쓸 수 <u>없는</u> 것은?

① Let's meet at ten.
② Do you meet at ten?
③ Shall we meet at ten?
④ What about meeting at ten?
⑤ Why don't we meet at ten?

08 위 대화의 내용과 일치하도록 빈칸에 알맞은 말을 쓰시오.

> "A" and "B" will meet at _____
> _____ _____ at _____ o'clock
> this Saturday to _____ _____ .

[09~11] 다음 대화를 읽고, 물음에 답하시오.

> G: I'm thinking ___ⓐ___ going to the Comics Museum tomorrow. Will you come with me?
> B: I really want to go.
> G: Can you ___ⓑ___ it at 11?
> B: That's fine ___ⓒ___ me.
> G: Okay. ⓓLet's meet at the subway station.

09 위 대화의 빈칸 ⓐ와 ⓒ에 알맞은 말이 바르게 짝지어진 것은?

① at – by
② about – to
③ of – with
④ in – on
⑤ on – to

10 위 대화의 빈칸 ⓑ에 알맞은 단어를 쓰시오.

➡ _____

11 위 대화의 밑줄 친 ⓓ를 다음과 같이 바꿔 쓸 때 빈칸에 알맞은 말을 쓰시오.

> _____ _____ meeting at the subway station?

[12~14] 다음 문장의 빈칸에 알맞은 것을 고르시오.

12 He has many things _____ tonight.

① do
② does
③ doing
④ to do
⑤ to be doing

13 I'm looking for a friend to travel _____.

① at
② in
③ with
④ on
⑤ for

14 Alice and Ken are going to enter Berkeley. They need a dormitory _____.

① live
② to live
③ to live in
④ to live with
⑤ to living

15 다음 밑줄 친 부분의 쓰임이 〈보기〉와 같은 것은?

> ┌── 보기 ──┐
> I have nothing special to eat in my bag.

① She packed her bag to go home.
② I was happy to find my cell phone.
③ He needs someone to look after his cat.
④ To eat breakfast is good for your brain.
⑤ We went to the store to buy some snacks.

16 다음 괄호 안에 주어진 단어의 알맞은 형태를 쓰시오.

> Is it possible _____ the project by tomorrow? (finish)

[17~18] 다음 중 어법상 알맞지 <u>않은</u> 문장을 고르시오.

17 ① It's hard to climb the tree.
② It's great fun skate on ice.
③ It's exciting to watch a baseball game.
④ It's important for us to study English.
⑤ It's interesting to take a trip to strange lands.

18 ① Let me get you a chair to sit on.
② She has no house to live in.
③ There's nothing to worry about.
④ Give me a pen to write with.
⑤ You seem to have important something to tell me.

19 다음 밑줄 친 ⓐ, ⓑ를 어법상 올바른 형태로 쓰시오.

I think shopping on the Internet is good. It's easy ⓐfind the things I want to buy. It's also easy ⓑfind good prices.

ⓐ _____ ⓑ _____

20 다음 괄호 안의 단어 형태가 바르게 짝지어진 것은?

• I have something (tell) you.
• Do you have anything (read)?

① tell – read
② tell – to read
③ to tell – read
④ telling – read
⑤ to tell – to read

[21~24] 다음 글을 읽고, 물음에 답하시오.

Germ 1: Watch out!
Germ 2: This is my spot!
Germ 3: Hands off!
Germ 4: Hey!
   Germs are everywhere, but it is ⓐpossible to see them with your eyes.
   There are two major kinds of germs: bacteria and viruses. Bacteria are very small creatures. _____ⓑ_____ are good. They can help you _____ⓒ_____ the food that you eat. _____ⓓ_____ are bad and can make you sick.

21 위 글의 밑줄 친 ⓐ를 알맞은 어형으로 고치시오.

➡ _____

22 위 글의 빈칸 ⓑ와 ⓓ에 알맞은 것으로 짝지어진 것은?

① Any – Other
② Any – Others
③ Some – Others
④ Some – Other
⑤ Some – The others

23 위 글의 빈칸 ⓒ에 알맞은 것은? (2개)

① digest   ② digestion
③ digesting   ④ to digest
⑤ to digesting

24 위 글의 내용으로 보아 알 수 <u>없는</u> 것은?

① 균들은 도처에 있다.
② 박테리아와 바이러스는 균이다.
③ 박테리아는 아주 작은 생물체이다.
④ 박테리아 중에는 이로운 것들이 있다.
⑤ 바이러스는 박테리아보다 더 해롭다.

[25~28] 다음 글을 읽고, 물음에 답하시오.

A: We have an invader! Come quickly.
B: It's my job to defend the body.
C: That was a nice meal! Are there any more germs ⓐ ?
   Luckily, your body has an army of defense. The T cells sound the alarm! (①) The B cells arrive to fight the germs with antibodies. (②) The macrophage cells ⓑshow up and eat the germs. (③)
   Together, this army is ⓒcall the white blood cells. (④) In a few days, you start to feel better. (⑤)

25 위 글의 ①~⑤ 중 다음 주어진 문장이 들어갈 알맞은 곳은?

| If all goes well, they win the fight. |

①   ②   ③   ④   ⑤

26 위 글의 빈칸 ⓐ에 알맞은 것은?

① eat   ② eating
③ to eat   ④ for eat
⑤ to eating

27 위 글의 밑줄 친 ⓑ와 뜻이 같은 것은?

① seem   ② turn
③ get   ④ become
⑤ appear

28 위 글의 밑줄 친 ⓒ를 알맞은 형으로 고치시오.

➡ _____

[29~31] 다음 글을 읽고, 물음에 답하시오.

The army of defense: Game Over.
Germ: Fine. Next year, I'll send in my cousin. He'll see you then for ⓐ fight!
   The body remembers the invader, so it cannot make copies of itself again. But the germs are smart, too. They can change form and trick the body.

29 위 글의 빈칸 ⓐ에 알맞은 것은?

① other   ② another
③ others   ④ the other
⑤ the others

30 위 글의 내용과 일치하지 <u>않는</u> 것은?

① The army of defense won the fight.
② The germ's cousin will come next year.
③ The invader can't make copies of itself again.
④ The body will remember the germ's cousin.
⑤ The germs can change form.

31 Why can't the invader make copies of itself again? Answer in English.

➡ _____

INSIGHT
on the textbook
교과서 파헤치기

※ 다음 영어를 우리말로 쓰시오.

01 grade

02 hundred

03 add

04 downtime

05 another

06 relax

07 weekly

08 beginning

09 behave

10 waste

11 birth

12 achieve

13 bored

14 however

15 control

16 strange

17 download

18 eco-friendly

19 exercise

20 between

21 manage

22 full

23 goal

24 habit

25 stressful

26 popular

27 heavy

28 death

29 historical

30 text

31 hard

32 magazine

33 useful

34 messy

35 free

36 perfect

37 skill

38 once in a while

39 stand in line

40 look down

41 focus on

42 from now on

43 for a minute

44 drive ~ crazy

45 get some rest

46 get off to a start

※ 다음 우리말을 영어로 쓰시오.

01	무거운	
02	역사적인	
03	예의 바르게 행동하다	
04	휴식을 취하다	
05	문자 메시지를 보내다	
06	지저분한	
07	잡지	
08	유용한	
09	완벽한, 완전한	
10	기술	
11	인기 있는	
12	죽음, 사망	
13	어려운; 열심히	
14	팬티	
15	다른, 또 다른	
16	매주의, 주간의	
17	앱, 어플리케이션	
18	초(반), 시작	
19	백, 100	
20	탄생, 출생	
21	한가한[휴식] 시간	
22	달성하다, 성취하다	
23	지루한	

24	그러나	
25	통제, 규제	
26	이상한	
27	다운로드하다	
28	친환경적인	
29	운동하다	
30	~ 사이에, ~ 중간에	
31	관리하다	
32	배부른	
33	성적	
34	목표	
35	습관	
36	스트레스가 많은	
37	낭비; 낭비하다	
38	약간의 휴식을 취하다	
39	~를 돌보다	
40	한 시간 동안	
41	줄넘기하다	
42	~ 때문에	
43	서로	
44	이제부터	
45	~의 앞쪽에[앞에]	
46	~를 치우다[청소하다]	

※ 다음 영영풀이에 알맞은 단어를 <보기>에서 골라 쓴 후, 우리말 뜻을 쓰시오.

1 _____ : to get or reach something by working hard: _____

2 _____ : helping to do or achieve something: _____

3 _____ : not harmful to the environment: _____

4 _____ : to spend time resting or doing something enjoyable especially after work: _____

5 _____ : the time when something starts; the first part of an event, a story, etc. _____

6 _____ : dirty and not neat: _____

7 _____ : the end of the life of a person or animal: _____

8 _____ : different from what is usual, normal, or expected: _____

9 _____ : the time when someone stops working and is able to relax: _____

10 _____ : to use more of something than is necessary or useful: _____

11 _____ : liked or enjoyed by many people: _____

12 _____ : something that you are trying to do or achieve: _____

13 _____ : to send someone a text message: _____

14 _____ : to act in the way that people think is correct and proper: _____

15 _____ : something that a person does often in a regular and repeated way: _____

16 _____ : full of or causing stress: _____

보기			
stressful	relax	achieve	behave
text	goal	death	popular
habit	beginning	waste	eco-friendly
useful	downtime	messy	strange

※ 다음 우리말과 일치하도록 빈칸에 알맞은 말을 쓰시오.

Communicate: Listen - Listen and Answer Dialog 1

G: Kevin, do you have a _____ _____ _____ the year?

B: Yeah, I want to _____ a gold medal in the _____ swimming contest.

G: Cool!

B: _____ _____ you, Minsol?

G: I'd _____ _____ _____ my time better.

B: How would you _____ _____ _____?

G: I'm _____ to make a _____ and _____ schedule.

B: _____ good.

Communicate: Listen - Listen and Answer Dialog 2

G: Can I talk with you _____ _____ _____ , Minsu?

B: _____ . What is it?

G: I'm _____ _____ my _____ schedule.

B: Really? _____ _____ you, _____ sister.

G: Here. _____ _____ _____ and give me some _____ .

B: Hmm, you have _____ _____ _____ study time.

G: Yeah, I'm _____ _____ study hard.

B: _____ _____ you add some _____ ?

G: Downtime?

B: Yeah, I mean you need to _____ once in a _____ .

Communicate: Listen - Listen More

(The phone rings.)

W: Hi, Jongha.

B: Hello, Grandma. I'd _____ _____ _____ you this Saturday.

W: That'll be great. We can _____ some vegetables _____ .

B: Really? _____ _____ of vegetables?

W: This time, _____ _____ _____ plant some tomatoes and peppers.

B: Wow! That'll _____ _____ .

W: I _____ it's _____ to be sunny this Saturday. You _____ _____ your cap.

B: Okay, I _____ .

W: Why don't you _____ _____ sunscreen _____ you leave?

B: No _____ . I'll see you _____ Saturday.

W: Okay. Bye.

G: Kevin, 올해의 특별한 목표가 있니?

B: 응, 전국 수영 대회에서 금메달을 따고 싶어.

G: 멋지네!

B: 민솔아, 너는?

G: 난 내 시간을 더 잘 관리하고 싶어.

B: 어떻게 네 목표를 달성할 거니?

G: 나는 일일 계획표와 주간 계획표를 만들 계획이야.

B: 좋은 생각이야.

G: 민수 오빠, 잠깐 얘기 좀 할 수 있을까?

B: 물론. 뭔데?

G: 나는 주간 계획표를 작성하고 있어.

B: 정말? 잘했다, 동생아.

G: 여기 있어. 한번 보고 조언 좀 해 줘.

B: 음, 공부 시간이 많구나.

G: 응, 나는 열심히 공부할 계획이야.

B: '다운타임'을 조금 더 추가하는 게 어때?

G: '다운타임'?

B: 응, 내 말은 넌 가끔 쉬어야 한다는 거야.

(전화기가 울린다.)

W: 안녕, 종하구나.

B: 안녕하세요, 할머니. 이번 주 토요일에 할머니를 방문하고 싶어요.

W: 그거 좋겠다. 우리는 함께 채소를 심을 수 있어.

B: 정말요? 어떤 종류의 채소죠?

W: 이번에는 토마토와 고추를 심을 계획이야.

B: 와! 재미있겠는데요.

W: 이번 토요일에 날씨가 맑을 거라고 들었어. 모자를 가져와야 해.

B: 알았어요, 그럴게요.

W: 떠나기 전에 자외선 차단제를 바르는 게 어때?

B: 그럼요. 토요일에 뵙겠습니다.

W: 알았어. 안녕.

Communicate: Listen - Listen and Complete

M: 1. _____ would you _____ your goal?

   2. I'd _____ _____ _____ you this Saturday.

My Speaking Portfolio

1. G: Hello, I'm Nayeon. I'd like to _____ _____ _____ person. I'm planning to _____ _____ _____ every day.

2. B1: Hi, I'm Junho. My goal for the year is _____ _____ the Korean History Test. I'm planning to _____ _____ _____. I'm also _____ to watch _____ _____ _____ historical dramas on TV.

3. B2: Hi, I'm Hojin. I _____ _____ _____ for the year. I want to get good _____ in math. I'm _____ _____ review math lessons _____. I'm also going to _____ 20 math problems every day.

Wrap Up - Listening ❸

B: What _____ you _____ _____ do this weekend, Mina?

G: I'm _____ _____ visit Yeosu _____ my aunt.

B: That _____ great. Do you have _____ _____ in Yeosu?

G: Well, we'll _____ Yeosu Expo Park and eat some _____.

B: That'll _____ _____. _____ your weekend.

Wrap Up - Listening ❹

G: You _____ _____, Yunsu. What's the _____?

B: I have a _____ project, and I _____ _____ any ideas.

G: _____ _____ _____ _____ science magazines in the library?

B: Science _____?

G: Sure. You _____ _____ some great ideas _____ _____.

※ 다음 우리말에 맞도록 대화를 영어로 쓰시오.

Communicate: Listen - Listen and Answer Dialog 1

G: _____

B: _____

G: _____

B: _____

G: _____

B: _____

G: _____

B: _____

G: Kevin, 올해의 특별한 목표가 있니?
B: 응, 전국 수영 대회에서 금메달을 따고 싶어.
G: 멋지네!
B: 민솔아, 너는?
G: 난 내 시간을 더 잘 관리하고 싶어.
B: 어떻게 네 목표를 달성할 거니?
G: 나는 일일 계획표와 주간 계획표를 만들 계획이야.
B: 좋은 생각이야.

Communicate: Listen - Listen and Answer Dialog 2

G: _____

B: _____

G: _____

B: _____

G: _____

B: _____

G: _____

B: _____

G: _____

B: _____

G: 민수 오빠, 잠깐 얘기 좀 할 수 있을까?
B: 물론. 뭔데?
G: 나는 주간 계획표를 작성하고 있어.
B: 정말? 잘했다, 동생아.
G: 여기 있어. 한번 보고 조언 좀 해 줘.
B: 음, 공부 시간이 많구나.
G: 응, 나는 열심히 공부할 계획이야.
B: '다운타임'을 조금 더 추가하는 게 어때?
G: '다운타임'?
B: 응, 내 말은 넌 가끔 쉬어야 한다는 거야.

Communicate: Listen - Listen More

(The phone rings.)

W: _____

B: _____

W: _____

B: _____

W: _____

B: _____

W: _____

B: _____

W: _____

B: _____

W: _____

(전화기가 울린다.)
W: 안녕, 종하구나.
B: 안녕하세요, 할머니. 이번 주 토요일에 할머니를 방문하고 싶어요.
W: 그거 좋겠다. 우리는 함께 채소를 심을 수 있어.
B: 정말요? 어떤 종류의 채소죠?
W: 이번에는 토마토와 고추를 심을 계획이야.
B: 와! 재미있겠는데요.
W: 이번 토요일에 날씨가 맑을 거라고 들었어. 모자를 가져와야 해.
B: 알았어요, 그럴게요.
W: 떠나기 전에 자외선 차단제를 바르는 게 어때?
B: 그럼요. 토요일에 뵙겠습니다.
W: 알았어. 안녕.

Communicate: Listen - Listen and Complete

M: 1. _____

　　2. _____

My Speaking Portfolio

1. G: _____

　　 _____

2. B1: _____

　　 _____

3. B2: _____

　　 _____

Wrap Up - Listening ❸

B: _____

G: _____

B: _____

G: _____

B: _____

Wrap Up - Listening ❹

G: _____

B: _____

G: _____

B: _____

G: _____

Step1

※ 다음 우리말과 일치하도록 빈칸에 알맞은 것을 골라 쓰시오.

1 _____ a new school year _____ _____ to many students.

A. is   B. stressful   C. beginning

2 _____ can we _____ off _____ a good start?

A. to   B. how   C. get

3 *Teen Today* _____ Raccoon 97, a _____ webtoon artist, _____ ideas.

A. for   B. asked   C. popular

4 _____ think about things that are _____ to change or _____ to change.

A. easy   B. hard   C. let's

5 Things _____ Are _____ to _____

A. Hard   B. Change   C. That

6 Your _____ Room_ You _____ it _____.

A. up   B. Messy   C. clean

7 Then you _____ new _____ into it, and it soon gets _____ again.

A. messy   B. bring   C. stuff

8 But _____ _____.

A. worry   B. don't

9 Your room is _____ cleaner _____ mine.

A. than   B. much

10 Your Family_ There is _____ someone in your family who _____ you _____.

A. crazy   B. drives   C. always

11 Remember _____ he or she is still a _____ of _____ family.

A. your   B. that   C. member

12 You just have _____ live together and _____ for each _____.

A. other   B. to   C. care

13 Your Name _____ Your Teacher's List_ If you are late _____ do not _____, your teacher will _____ your name on his or her list.

A. on   B. behave   C. or   D. put

1 새 학년을 시작하는 것은 많은 학생들에게 스트레스를 준다.

2 어떻게 하면 우리는 좋은 출발을 할 수 있을까?

3 Teen Today는 유명한 웹툰 작가인 Raccoon 97에게 아이디어를 물었다.

4 바꾸기 어렵거나 쉽게 바꿀 수 있는 것들에 대해 생각해 보자.

5 바꾸기 어려운 것들

6 너의 지저분한 방_ 너는 방을 깨끗이 치운다.

7 그런 다음 새로운 물건을 가져오면 곧 다시 지저분해진다.

8 하지만 걱정하지 마.

9 네 방은 내 방보다 훨씬 더 깨끗해.

10 너의 가족_ 너의 가족 중에는 항상 너를 미치게 하는 사람이 있다.

11 그나 그녀가 여전히 너의 가족 구성원이라는 것을 기억하라.

12 너는 함께 살아야 하고 서로 돌봐야 한다.

13 선생님의 명단에 있는 너의 이름_ 만약 네가 늦거나 예의 바르게 행동하지 않는다면, 너의 선생님은 너의 이름을 그나 그녀의 명단에 올릴 것이다.

14 You _____ _____ change the _____.

A. easily   B. list   C. cannot

15 _____ That _____ Easy _____ Change

A. to   B. Are   C. Things

16 Your Underpants_ If you _____ them _____ day, your mom will not tell you one _____ and one times.

A. hundred   B. every   C. change

17 "Life is C _____ B _____ D."

A. and   B. between

18 It _____ "Life is Choice between _____ and _____."

A. Birth   B. means   C. Death

19 Your Friends_ You can _____ _____ friends.

A. change   B. your

20 Does it _____ _____?

A. strange   B. sound

21 You _____ think _____ you have the _____ number of friends.

A. that   B. perfect   C. may

22 If you _____ a new friend to the list, _____, you will feel _____ better than before.

A. even   B. add   C. however

23 Your Mind_ You _____ one thing _____ first, and now you think _____ thing.

A. at   B. another   C. thought

24 That is okay. _____ someone said, "If you can change your _____, you can change your _____."

A. life   B. mind   C. as

25 "Focus _____ the things _____ are easy to change, and _____ to make today _____ than yesterday. Good luck!"

A. try   B. that   C. better   D. on

26 _____ 5 Plans _____ the Year

A. for   B. top

27 We _____ 200 *Teen Today* _____, " What are your plans _____ the year?"

A. for   B. readers   C. asked

14 너는 명단을 쉽게 바꿀 수 없다.

15 바꾸기 쉬운 것들

16 너의 팬티_ 만약 네가 매일 팬티를 갈아입으면, 너의 엄마는 너에게 입이 닳도록 말하지 않을 거야.

17 "인생은 B와 D 사이의 C이다."

18 그것은 "인생은 탄생과 죽음 사이의 선택이다."를 의미한다.

19 너의 친구들_ 너는 네 친구들을 바꿀 수 있다.

20 이상하게 들리는가?

21 너는 네가 완벽한 수의 친구들을 가지고 있다고 생각할지도 모른다.

22 하지만 새로운 친구를 목록에 추가하면 이전보다 훨씬 더 기분이 좋아질 것이다.

23 너의 마음_ 너는 처음에는 이런 것을 생각했고, 지금은 또 다른 것을 생각한다.

24 괜찮다. 누군가 말했듯이, "마음을 바꿀 수 있다면, 인생을 바꿀 수 있어."

25 "바꾸기 쉬운 일에 집중하고, 어제보다 오늘을 더 좋게 만들려고 노력해. 행운을 빌어!"

26 올해의 5대 계획

27 우리는 200명의 Teen Today 독자들에게 "올해의 계획은 무엇인가?"라고 물었다.

※ 다음 우리말과 일치하도록 빈칸에 알맞은 말을 쓰시오.

1 _____ a new school year _____ _____ to many students.

2 How can we _____ _____ to a good _____?

3 *Teen Today* asked Raccoon 97, a _____ webtoon artist, _____ _____.

4 Things That _____ Hard _____ _____

5 _____ think about things _____ are _____ to change or _____ to change.

6 Your _____ Room_ You _____ it _____.

7 Then you bring new _____ into it, and it soon _____ _____ again.

8 But _____ _____.

9 Your room is much _____ _____ mine.

10 Your Family_ There _____ _____ someone in your family who _____ you _____.

11 Remember _____ he or she is still _____ _____ your family.

12 You just _____ _____ live together and _____ _____ each other.

13 Your Name on Your Teacher's List_ If you are _____ or do not _____, your teacher will _____ your name _____ his or her list.

---

1 새 학년을 시작하는 것은 많은 학생들에게 스트레스를 준다.

2 어떻게 하면 우리는 좋은 출발을 할 수 있을까?

3 Teen Today는 유명한 웹툰 작가인 Raccoon 97에게 아이디어를 물었다.

4 바꾸기 어려운 것들

5 바꾸기 어렵거나 쉽게 바꿀 수 있는 것들에 대해 생각해 보자.

6 너의 지저분한 방_ 너는 방을 깨끗이 치운다.

7 그런 다음 새로운 물건을 가져오면 곧 다시 지저분해진다.

8 하지만 걱정하지 마.

9 네 방은 내 방보다 훨씬 더 깨끗해.

10 너의 가족_ 너의 가족 중에는 항상 너를 미치게 하는 사람이 있다.

11 그나 그녀가 여전히 너의 가족 구성원이라는 것을 기억해라.

12 너는 함께 살아야 하고 서로 돌봐야 한다.

13 선생님의 명단에 있는 너의 이름_ 만약 네가 늦거나 예의 바르게 행동하지 않는다면, 너의 선생님은 너의 이름을 그나 그녀의 명단에 올릴 것이다.

14 You cannot _____ _____ the list.

15 Things _____ Are Easy _____ _____

16 Your Underpants_ If you _____ them _____ _____, your mom will not tell you one hundred and one times.

17 "Life is C _____ B _____ D."

18 It means "Life is _____ between _____ and _____."

19 Your Friends_ You _____ _____ your friends.

20 Does it _____ _____?

21 You _____ think _____ you have the _____ number of friends.

22 If you _____ a new friend to the list, _____, you will feel even _____ _____ before.

23 Your Mind_ You _____ one thing _____ _____, and now you think _____ thing.

24 That is okay. _____ someone said, "_____ you can change your _____, you can change your _____."

25 "_____ _____ the things that are easy to change, and _____ _____ make today _____ _____ yesterday. Good luck!"

26 _____ 5 Plans _____ the Year

27 We _____ 200 *Teen Today* _____, " What are your plans _____ the year?"

14	너는 명단을 쉽게 바꿀 수 없다.
15	바꾸기 쉬운 것들
16	너의 팬티_ 만약 네가 매일 팬티를 갈아입으면, 너의 엄마는 너에게 입이 닳도록 말하지 않을 거야.
17	"인생은 B와 D 사이의 C이다."
18	그것은 "인생은 탄생과 죽음 사이의 선택이다."를 의미한다.
19	너의 친구들_ 너는 네 친구들을 바꿀 수 있다.
20	이상하게 들리는가?
21	너는 네가 완벽한 수의 친구들을 가지고 있다고 생각할지도 모른다.
22	하지만 새로운 친구를 목록에 추가하면 이전보다 훨씬 더 기분이 좋아질 것이다.
23	너의 마음_ 너는 처음에는 이런 것을 생각했고, 지금은 또 다른 것을 생각한다.
24	괜찮다. 누군가 말했듯이, "마음을 바꿀 수 있다면, 인생을 바꿀 수 있어."
25	"바꾸기 쉬운 일에 집중하고, 어제보다 오늘을 더 좋게 만들려고 노력해. 행운을 빌어!"
26	올해의 5대 계획
27	우리는 200명의 Teen Today 독자들에게 "올해의 계획은 무엇인가?"라고 물었다.

※ 다음 문장을 우리말로 쓰시오.

1 Beginning a new school year is stressful to many students.

➡ _____

2 How can we get off to a good start?

➡ _____

3 *Teen Today* asked Raccoon 97, a popular webtoon artist, for ideas.

➡ _____

4 Let's think about things that are hard to change or easy to change.

➡ _____

5 Things That Are Hard to Change

➡ _____

6 Your Messy Room_ You clean it up.

➡ _____

7 Then you bring new stuff into it, and it soon gets messy again.

➡ _____

8 But don't worry.

➡ _____

9 Your room is much cleaner than mine.

➡ _____

10 Your Family_ There is always someone in your family who drives you crazy.

➡ _____

11 Remember that he or she is still a member of your family.

➡ _____

12 You just have to live together and care for each other.

➡ _____

13 Your Name on Your Teacher's List_ If you are late or do not behave, your teacher will put your name on his or her list.

➡ _____

_____

14 You cannot easily change the list.

➡ _____

15 Things That Are Easy to Change

➡ _____

16 Your Underpants_ If you change them every day, your mom will not tell you one hundred and one times.

➡ _____

17 "Life is C between B and D."

➡ _____

18 It means "Life is Choice between Birth and Death."

➡ _____

19 Your Friends_ You can change your friends.

➡ _____

20 Does it sound strange?

➡ _____

21 You may think that you have the perfect number of friends.

➡ _____

22 If you add a new friend to the list, however, you will feel even better than before.

➡ _____

23 Your Mind_ You thought one thing at first, and now you think another thing.

➡ _____

24 That is okay. As someone said, "If you can change your mind, you can change your life."

➡ _____

25 "Focus on the things that are easy to change, and try to make today better than yesterday. Good luck!"

➡ _____

26 Top 5 Plans for the Year

➡ _____

27 We asked 200 *Teen Today* readers, "What are your plans for the year?"

➡ _____

※ 다음 괄호 안의 단어들을 우리말에 맞도록 바르게 배열하시오.

1 ▶ (many / a / stressful / to / school / is / year / beginning / students. / new)
➡ _____

2 ▶ (how / to / start? / we / good / get / can / off / a)
➡ _____

3 ▶ (webtoon / Teen / asked / popular / ideas. / Raccoon / a / artist, / for / Today / 97,)
➡ _____

4 ▶ (think / or / change. / things / are / to / change / about / easy / hard / to / let's / that)
➡ _____

5 ▶ (Are / to / That / Hard / Change / Things)
➡ _____

6 ▶ (you / it / up. / Room_ / clean / Messy / Your)
➡ _____

7 ▶ (you / bring / again. / new / stuff / soon / messy / into / then / it, / and / it / gets /)
➡ _____

8 ▶ (worry. / don't / but)
➡ _____

9 ▶ (room / is / than / / much / cleaner / mine. / your)
➡ _____

10 ▶ (Your / Family_ / crazy. / family / is / always / you / someone / there / in / your / drives / who)
➡ _____

11 ▶ (she / remember / still / your / family. / that / or / is / a / member / of / he)
➡ _____

12 ▶ (together / you / other. / just / have / live / each / and / care / for / to)
➡ _____

13 ▶ (on / Your / List_ / Teacher's / Name / Your / you / or / are / late / will / do / if / not / behave, / your / teacher / put / your / name / list. / on / his / or / her)
➡ _____

1 새 학년을 시작하는 것은 많은 학생들에게 스트레스를 준다.

2 어떻게 하면 우리는 좋은 출발을 할 수 있을까?

3 Teen Today는 유명한 웹툰 작가인 Raccoon 97에게 아이디어를 물었다.

4 바꾸기 어렵거나 쉽게 바꿀 수 있는 것들에 대해 생각해 보자.

5 바꾸기 어려운 것들

6 너의 지저분한 방_ 너는 방을 깨끗이 치운다.

7 그런 다음 새로운 물건을 가져오면 곧 다시 지저분해진다.

8 하지만 걱정하지 마.

9 네 방은 내 방보다 훨씬 더 깨끗해.

10 너의 가족_ 너의 가족 중에는 항상 너를 미치게 하는 사람이 있다.

11 그나 그녀가 여전히 너의 가족 구성원이라는 것을 기억해라.

12 너는 함께 살아야 하고 서로 돌봐야 한다.

13 선생님의 명단에 있는 너의 이름_ 만약 네가 늦거나 예의 바르게 행동하지 않는다면, 너의 선생님은 너의 이름을 그나 그녀의 명단에 올릴 것이다.

14 (the / you / list. / change / cannot / easily)

➡ _____

15 (Change / Things / Easy / That / to / Are)

➡ _____

16 (Underpants_ / Your / if / day, / you / them / change / every / your / times. / mom / you / not / tell / one / will / and / one / hundred)

➡ _____

➡ _____

17 (and / is / D." / between / B / "life / C)

➡ _____

18 (means / it / is / Death." / between / Birth / Choice / "Life / and)

➡ _____

19 (change / Friends_ / you / can / friends. / Your / your)

➡ _____

20 (strange? / it / does / sound)

➡ _____

21 (have / you / perfect / may / think / number / friends. / that / you / the / of)

➡ _____

22 (if / to / you / than / add / new / will / before. / friend / the / list, / however, / you / a / even / better / feel)

➡ _____

➡ _____

23 (you / Mind_ / / first, / thought / Your / one / thing. / at / think / and / thing / now / you / another)

➡ _____

24 (okay. / is / that) (as / someone / your / said, / you / can / "If / change / mind, / life." / you / change / can / your)

➡ _____

➡ _____

25 (change, / on / the / to / things / "Focus / that / are / easy / and / try / today / make / yesterday. / better / than / to) (luck!" / good)

➡ _____

➡ _____

26 (Year / the / Top / Plans / 5 / for)

➡ _____

27 (readers, / asked / we / Teen / 200 / Today / are / "What / plans / year?" / for / your / the)

➡ _____

---

14 너는 명단을 쉽게 바꿀 수 없다.

15 바꾸기 쉬운 것들

16 너의 팬티_ 만약 네가 매일 팬티를 갈아입으면, 너의 엄마는 너에게 입이 닳도록 말하지 않을 거야.

17 "인생은 B와 D 사이의 C이다."

18 그것은 "인생은 탄생과 죽음 사이의 선택이다."를 의미한다.

19 너의 친구들_ 너는 네 친구들을 바꿀 수 있다.

20 이상하게 들리는가?

21 너는 네가 완벽한 수의 친구들을 가지고 있다고 생각할지도 모른다.

22 하지만 새로운 친구를 목록에 추가하면 이전보다 훨씬 더 기분이 좋아질 것이다.

23 너의 마음_ 너는 처음에는 이런 것을 생각했고, 지금은 또 다른 것을 생각한다.

24 괜찮다. 누군가 말했듯이, "마음을 바꿀 수 있다면, 인생을 바꿀 수 있어."

25 "바꾸기 쉬운 일에 집중하고, 어제보다 오늘을 더 좋게 만들려고 노력해. 행운을 빌어!"

26 올해의 5대 계획

27 우리는 200명의 Teen Today 독자들에게 "올해의 계획은 무엇인가?"라고 물었다.

※ **다음 우리말을 영어로 쓰시오.**

1 새 학년을 시작하는 것은 많은 학생들에게 스트레스를 준다.

➡ _____

2 어떻게 하면 우리는 좋은 출발을 할 수 있을까?

➡ _____

3 Teen Today는 유명한 웹툰 작가인 Raccoon 97에게 아이디어를 물었다.

➡ _____

4 바꾸기 어렵거나 쉽게 바꿀 수 있는 것들에 대해 생각해 보자.

➡ _____

5 바꾸기 어려운 것들

➡ _____

6 너의 지저분한 방_ 너는 방을 깨끗이 치운다.

➡ _____

7 그런 다음 새로운 물건을 가져오면 곧 다시 지저분해진다.

➡ _____

8 하지만 걱정하지 마.

➡ _____

9 네 방은 내 방보다 훨씬 더 깨끗해.

➡ _____

10 너의 가족_ 너의 가족 중에는 항상 너를 미치게 하는 사람이 있다.

➡ _____

11 그나 그녀가 여전히 너의 가족 구성원이라는 것을 기억해라.

➡ _____

12 너는 함께 살아야 하고 서로 돌봐야 한다.

➡ _____

13 선생님의 명단에 있는 너의 이름_ 만약 네가 늦거나 예의 바르게 행동하지 않는다면, 너의 선생님은 너의 이름을 그나 그녀의 명단에 올릴 것이다.

➡ _____

_____

14 너는 명단을 쉽게 바꿀 수 없다.

➡ _____

15 바꾸기 쉬운 것들

➡ _____

16 너의 팬티_ 만약 네가 매일 팬티를 갈아입으면, 너의 엄마는 너에게 입이 닳도록 말하지 않을 거야.

➡ _____

17 "인생은 B와 D 사이의 C이다."

➡ _____

18 그것은 "인생은 탄생과 죽음 사이의 선택이다."를 의미한다.

➡ _____

19 너의 친구들_ 너는 네 친구들을 바꿀 수 있다.

➡ _____

20 이상하게 들리는가?

➡ _____

21 너는 네가 완벽한 수의 친구들을 가지고 있다고 생각할지도 모른다.

➡ _____

22 하지만 새로운 친구를 목록에 추가하면 이전보다 훨씬 더 기분이 좋아질 것이다.

➡ _____

23 너의 마음_ 너는 처음에는 이런 것을 생각했고, 지금은 또 다른 것을 생각한다.

➡ _____

24 괜찮다. 누군가 말했듯이, "마음을 바꿀 수 있다면, 인생을 바꿀 수 있어."

➡ _____

25 "바꾸기 쉬운 일에 집중하고, 어제보다 오늘을 더 좋게 만들려고 노력해. 행운을 빌어!"

➡ _____

26 올해의 5대 계획

➡ _____

27 우리는 200명의 Teen Today 독자들에게 "올해의 계획은 무엇인가?"라고 물었다.

➡ _____

※ 다음 우리말과 일치하도록 빈칸에 알맞은 말을 쓰시오.

My Speaking Portfolio - Step 3

1. "I have two _____ _____ the year.

2. First, I'd _____ _____ _____ a 10 km marathon.

3. _____ _____ this goal, I'm _____ _____ run _____ _____ _____ every day.

4. Also, I'm going to _____ _____ _____ _____.

5. The _____ goal is ......"

My Writing Portfolio

1. My Phone _____

2. I _____ _____ _____ my phone _____.

3. I use _____ phone _____ I _____ _____.

4. I _____ my friends _____ play games _____ _____ _____.

5. I know _____ it is _____ _____ _____ time.

6. _____ _____ _____, I will do two _____ _____ _____ the habit.

7. I will _____ _____ my phone _____ 10 p.m.

8. I will also _____ a phone control app _____ _____ my phone _____ _____.

9. If I _____ _____, I _____ _____ to my family or _____ comic books.

※ 다음 우리말을 영어로 쓰시오.

My Speaking Portfolio - Step 3

1. "나는 올해 두 가지 목표가 있다.

   ➡ _____

2. 먼저 10킬로미터 마라톤을 완주하고 싶다.

   ➡ _____

3. 이 목표를 달성하기 위해 나는 매일 한 시간씩 달릴 계획이다.

   ➡ _____

4. 또한, 나는 매일 줄넘기를 할 것이다.

   ➡ _____

5. 다른 목표는 ......"

   ➡ _____

My Writing Portfolio

1. 내 전화 습관

   ➡ _____

2. 나는 전화 습관을 바꾸고 싶다.

   ➡ _____

3. 나는 지루할 때 전화기를 사용한다.

   ➡ _____

4. 나는 전화로 친구들에게 문자를 보내거나 게임을 한다.

   ➡ _____

5. 나는 그것이 시간 낭비라는 것을 안다.

   ➡ _____

6. 이제부터 나는 그 습관을 없애기 위해 두 가지 일을 할 거야.

   ➡ _____

7. 나는 오후 10시 이후에 전화기를 끌 것이다.

   ➡ _____

8. 나는 또한 내 전화를 덜 자주 사용하기 위해 전화 제어 앱을 다운로드할 것이다.

   ➡ _____

9. 지루하면 가족과 이야기하거나 만화책을 읽을 것이다.

   ➡ _____

※ 다음 영어를 우리말로 쓰시오.

01 remember   _____

02 save   _____

03 stomach   _____

04 suddenly   _____

05 communicate   _____

06 culture   _____

07 delicious   _____

08 finally   _____

09 important   _____

10 repeat   _____

11 shout   _____

12 follow   _____

13 special   _____

14 landmark   _____

15 different   _____

16 thumping   _____

17 admission fee   _____

18 famous   _____

19 translation   _____

20 fantastic   _____

21 mean   _____

22 growl   _____

23 nervous   _____

24 offer   _____

25 fortune   _____

26 appear   _____

27 meaning   _____

28 however   _____

29 information   _____

30 official language   _____

31 expression   _____

32 opening hour   _____

33 respond   _____

34 work   _____

35 traditional   _____

36 carefully   _____

37 be useful for   _____

38 find out   _____

39 for a while   _____

40 look around   _____

41 right now   _____

42 step onto   _____

43 what kind of   _____

※ 다음 우리말을 영어로 쓰시오.

01 전통의, 전통적인

02 대답[응답]하다

03 유명한

04 번역, 통역

05 환상적인

06 위

07 의사소통하다

08 마침내

09 따라가다

10 중요한

11 반복하다

12 외치다, 소리치다

13 특별한

14 도착하다

15 웃다

16 다른

17 기억하다

18 남겨 두다, 저축하다

19 갑자기

20 쿵쾅거리는

21 충분한

22 입장료

23 나라, 시골

24 문화

25 의미

26 긴장한

27 운, 행운

28 정보

29 표현

30 합격하다

31 이해하다

32 효력이 있다

33 오디션

34 조심스럽게, 신중히

35 나타나다

36 번역기, 번역가

37 ~에 집중을 하다

38 예를 들어

39 잠깐, 잠시 동안

40 서두르다

41 어떤 종류의

42 지금 곧, 당장

43 ~을 둘러보다

※ 다음 영영풀이에 알맞은 단어를 <보기>에서 골라 쓴 후, 우리말 뜻을 쓰시오.

1 _____ : known or recognized by very many people: _____

2 _____ : to have the intended effect or result: _____

3 _____ : to achieve the required standard in an exam, a test, etc.: _____

4 _____ : to say something again: _____

5 _____ : as many or as much as someone needs or wants: _____

6 _____ : chance or luck, especially in the way it affects people's lives: _____

7 _____ : to keep something available for use in the future: _____

8 _____ : facts or details about someone or something: _____

9 _____ : to give someone the opportunity to accept or take something: _____

10 _____ : an object or structure on land that is easy to see and recognize:

_____

11 _____ : anxious about something or afraid of something: _____

12 _____ : to say or write something as an answer to a question or request:

_____

13 _____ : to make your ideas, feelings, thoughts, etc. known to other people so that

they understand them: _____

14 _____ : words that have been changed from one language into a different language:

_____

15 _____ : the customs and beliefs, art, way of life, and social organization of a

particular country or group: _____

16 _____ : things that people say, write, or do in order to show their feelings,

opinions, and ideas: _____

보기			
offer	translation	enough	respond
pass	culture	fortune	expression
nervous	information	save	landmark
famous	work	communicate	repeat

※ 다음 우리말과 일치하도록 빈칸에 알맞은 말을 쓰시오.

Communicate: Listen - Listen and Answer Dialog 1

B: It _____ nice. What _____ you _____, Uncle Abbas?

M: I'm _____ kebab.

B: Kebab? What is it?

M: It's a _____ Turkish food. We have small _____ _____ meat and vegetables on a _____.

B: Oh, it _____ _____.

M: _____ you _____ some?

B: Sure. I'd _____ some.

M: Here _____ are.

B: It _____ great. You _____ _____ your own restaurant!

M: Thanks. I'm _____ you _____ it.

Communicate: Listen - Listen and Answer Dialog 2

W: What _____ you _____ _____ do today, Kevin?

B: I'm going to _____ _____ the city.

W: Do you know _____ _____ _____ your way?

B: Sure. I have a map _____ _____ _____!

W: Okay. _____ _____ _____ landmarks, too.

B: I'm sorry, but _____ do you _____ _____ "landmarks"?

W: I mean _____ places or _____ buildings.

B: All right. I will _____ _____ remember the places _____ I see.

Communicate: Listen - Listen More

G: Hey, Jongha!

B: Hi, Claire. Those cookies _____ _____.

G: _____ you _____ some?

B: No, _____. I'm too _____.

G: _____ are you _____ nervous?

B: I have my _____ _____ the school radio station _____ _____ an hour.

G: Oh, really? Break a leg!

B: *Break a leg*? _____ do you _____?

G: I mean " _____ _____."

B: That's a funny _____. Thanks! _____ some cookies _____ me, okay?

해석

B: 냄새가 좋네요. Abbas 이모부, 무슨 요리를 하고 계세요?
M: 케밥을 만들고 있어.
B: 케밥이요? 그게 뭐죠?
M: 터키 전통 음식이야. 꼬치에 작은 고기와 채소 조각을 끼워서 먹는 거지.
B: 오, 맛있겠어요.
M: 좀 먹어 볼래?
B: 물론이죠. 좀 주세요.
M: 여기 있어.
B: 맛이 좋네요. 이모부는 직접 식당을 차려야 해요!
M: 고마워. 네가 마음에 든다니 기쁘다.

W: Kevin, 오늘 뭐 할 거야?
B: 저는 시내를 둘러볼 거예요.
W: 길 찾는 방법을 아니?
B: 물론이죠. 전화기에 지도가 있어요!
W: 알았어. landmarks도 기억하도록 해라.
B: 죄송하지만, "landmarks"가 무슨 뜻이에요?
W: 중요한 장소나 특별한 건물들을 말하는 거야.
B: 알겠어요. 저는 제가 보는 장소들을 기억하도록 노력할게요.

G: 이봐, 종하야!
B: 안녕, Claire. 저 쿠키들 맛있어 보인다.
G: 좀 먹어 볼래?
B: 아니, 괜찮아. 너무 긴장돼.
G: 왜 그렇게 긴장하니?
B: 30분 후에 학교 라디오 방송국 오디션이 있어.
G: 아, 정말? Break a leg!
B: Break a leg? 무슨 뜻이지?
G: "행운을 빌어."라는 뜻이야.
B: 그거 재미있는 표현이네. 고마워! 쿠키 좀 남겨줘, 알았지?

Communicate: Listen - Listen and Complete

M: 1. The train will leave _____ _____ _____ _____ .

2. I have a _____ _____ this week.

Communicate: Speak 2

A: _____ _____ _____ some *bibimbap*?

B: No, _____ . I don't like _____ .

A: Then _____ _____ pizza?

B: Yes, _____ .

My Writing Portfolio - Step 1

G: Look. The _____ of our _____ is *Enjoy Paris*!

B: *Enjoy Paris*? _____ interesting!

G: This app _____ _____ what _____ _____ in Paris.

B: Does it give _____ on _____ museums and theaters?

G: Yes. You can _____ _____ about _____ hours and _____ fees.

B: Fantastic.

G: It also tells you _____ _____ _____ there.

B: Oh, I'll _____ it _____ _____ !

G: I'm _____ you'll _____ it.

Wrap Up - Listening ❺

B: _____ you _____ some sandwiches?

G: _____ _____ _____ sandwich?

B: Ham and _____ _____ .

G: _____ , _____ . I _____ eat eggs.

B: Then, _____ _____ _____ some apple pie?

G: Okay. Apples are _____ _____ _____ .

Wrap Up - Listening ❻

G: _____ _____ , everyone. Hit the road!

B: I'm sorry, but _____ do you _____ _____ that?

G: I mean _____ time to _____ _____ .

B: Like, "It's _____ _____ _____ "?

G: Yes.

B: Great! _____ _____ the road.

M: 1. 기차는 30분 후에 떠날 것이다.
　　2. 나는 이번 주에 일정이 바빠.

A: 비빔밥 좀 먹을래?
B: 아니, 됐어. 나는 야채를 좋아하지 않아.
A: 그럼 피자는 어때?
B: 응, 부탁해.

G: 봐. 우리 앱의 이름은 '파리를 즐겨라'야!
B: 파리를 즐겨라? 재미있겠다!
G: 이 앱은 파리에서 볼 수 있는 것에 중점을 두고 있어.
B: 유명한 박물관과 극장에 대한 정보를 제공하니?
G: 응. 개장 시간과 입장료에 대해 알 수 있어.
B: 환상적이구나.
G: 그것은 거기에 가는 방법도 알려줘.
B: 오, 지금 바로 그것을 다운로드할게!
G: 난 네가 그것을 좋아할 거라고 확신해.

B: 샌드위치 좀 먹을래?
G: 어떤 종류의 샌드위치?
B: 햄과 달걀 샌드위치.
G: 아니, 괜찮아. 나는 달걀을 먹지 않아.
B: 그럼, 사과 파이 좀 먹을래?
G: 좋아. 사과는 내가 가장 좋아하는 과일이야.

G: 서둘러, 모두들. Hit the road!
B: 미안하지만, 그게 무슨 뜻이야?
G: 내 말은 출발할 시간이라는 거야.
B: "가야 할 시간이야." 같은 뜻인 거야?
G: 응.
B: 좋아! Hit the road(출발하자).

※ 다음 우리말에 맞도록 대화를 영어로 쓰시오.

Communicate: Listen - Listen and Answer Dialog 1

B: _____

M: _____

B: _____

M: _____

B: _____

M: _____

B: _____

M: _____

B: _____

M: _____

Communicate: Listen - Listen and Answer Dialog 2

W: _____

B: _____

W: _____

B: _____

W: _____

B: _____

W: _____

B: _____

Communicate: Listen - Listen More

G: _____

B: _____

G: _____

B: _____

G: _____

B: _____

G: _____

B: _____

G: _____

B: _____

해석

B: 냄새가 좋네요. Abbas 이모부, 무슨 요리를 하고 계세요?
M: 케밥을 만들고 있어.
B: 케밥이요? 그게 뭐죠?
M: 터키 전통 음식이야. 꼬치에 작은 고기와 채소 조각을 끼워서 먹는 거지.
B: 오, 맛있겠어요.
M: 좀 먹어 볼래?
B: 물론이죠. 좀 주세요.
M: 여기 있어.
B: 맛이 좋네요. 이모부는 직접 식당을 차려야 해요!
M: 고마워. 네가 마음에 든다니 기쁘다.

W: Kevin, 오늘 뭐 할 거야?
B: 저는 시내를 둘러볼 거예요.
W: 길 찾는 방법을 아니?
B: 물론이죠. 전화기에 지도가 있어요!
W: 알았어. landmarks도 기억하도록 해라.
B: 죄송하지만, "landmarks"가 무슨 뜻이에요?
W: 중요한 장소나 특별한 건물들을 말하는 거야.
B: 알겠어요. 저는 제가 보는 장소들을 기억하도록 노력할게요.

G: 이봐, 종하야!
B: 안녕, Claire. 저 쿠키들 맛있어 보인다.
G: 좀 먹어 볼래?
B: 아니, 괜찮아. 너무 긴장돼.
G: 왜 그렇게 긴장하니?
B: 30분 후에 학교 라디오 방송국 오디션이 있어.
G: 아, 정말? Break a leg!
B: Break a leg? 무슨 뜻이지?
G: "행운을 빌어."라는 뜻이야.
B: 그거 재미있는 표현이네. 고마워! 쿠키 좀 남겨줘, 알았지?

Communicate: Listen - Listen and Complete

M: 1. _____

   2. _____

Communicate: Speak 2

A: _____

B: _____

A: _____

B: _____

My Writing Portfolio - Step 1

G: _____

B: _____

G: _____

B: _____

G: _____

B: _____

G: _____

B: _____

G: _____

Wrap Up - Listening ❺

B: _____

G: _____

B: _____

G: _____

B: _____

G: _____

Wrap Up - Listening ❻

G: _____

B: _____

G: _____

B: _____

G: _____

B: _____

M: 1. 기차는 30분 후에 떠날 것이다.
   2. 나는 이번 주에 일정이 바빠.

A: 비빔밥 좀 먹을래?
B: 아니, 됐어. 나는 야채를 좋아하지 않아.
A: 그럼 피자는 어때?
B: 응, 부탁해.

G: 봐. 우리 앱의 이름은 '파리를 즐겨라'야!
B: 파리를 즐겨라? 재미있겠다!
G: 이 앱은 파리에서 볼 수 있는 것에 중점을 두고 있어.
B: 유명한 박물관과 극장에 대한 정보를 제공하니?
G: 응. 개장 시간과 입장료에 대해 알 수 있어.
B: 환상적이구나.
G: 그것은 거기에 가는 방법도 알려줘.
B: 오, 지금 바로 그것을 다운로드할게!
G: 난 네가 그것을 좋아할 거라고 확신해.

B: 샌드위치 좀 먹을래?
G: 어떤 종류의 샌드위치?
B: 햄과 달걀 샌드위치.
G: 아니, 괜찮아. 나는 달걀을 먹지 않아.
B: 그럼, 사과 파이 좀 먹을래?
G: 좋아. 사과는 내가 가장 좋아하는 과일이야.

G: 서둘러, 모두들. Hit the road!
B: 미안하지만, 그게 무슨 뜻이야?
G: 내 말은 출발할 시간이라는 거야.
B: "가야 할 시간이야." 같은 뜻인 거야?
G: 응.
B: 좋아! Hit the road(출발하자).

※ 다음 우리말과 일치하도록 빈칸에 알맞은 것을 골라 쓰시오.

1 Jaden's _____ is _____ Florence, Italy.
A. in　　　　　　B. family

2 They _____ _____ Ms. Gambini, _____ mother's friend.
A. his　　　　B. visiting　　C. are

3 Today his parents are _____ to museums, but Jaden _____ to stay _____.
A. wants　　　　B. behind　　　　C. going

4 He _____ the translation app _____ his phone will help him _____.
A. on　　　　　　B. communicate　C. thinks

5 His _____ growls, _____ he enters the kitchen.
A. so　　　　　　B. stomach

6 _____ Ms. Gambini _____ Jaden, she _____ "Buon giorno. Vuoi un pezzo di pane e un bicchiere di latte?"
A. says　　　　B. when　　　　C. sees

7 Jaden does _____ know _____ to _____.
A. respond　　　B. not　　　　C. how

8 Then the app says, "Good morning. _____ you like a _____ of bread and a _____ of milk?"
A. glass　　　　B. would　　　　C. piece

9 Jaden _____, "Yes, _____."
A. please　　　　B. answers

10 There is a _____ on the door, and a woman _____ Ms. Gambini invited _____ in.
A. walks　　　　B. whom　　　　C. knock

11 The two _____ _____ speaking Italian very _____.
A. fast　　　　B. begin　　　　C. women

12 So the _____ does not _____.
A. understand　　B. translator

13 Jaden turns _____ the phone and _____ it _____ the table.
A. on　　　　　　B. off　　　　　C. leaves

14 He goes _____ _____ enjoy the _____ morning.
A. to　　　　　　B. sunny　　　　C. out

15 He follows a _____ sound and finds a girl _____ is kicking a soccer ball _____ a wall.
A. against　　　B. thumping　　C. who

16 She _____ to him and _____, "Buon giono."
A. says　　　　B. turns

17 His phone is _____ the kitchen, _____ Jaden does not know _____ to say.
A. what　　　　B. so　　　　　C. in

18 He just _____ the words _____ the girl _____, "Buon giorno."
A. said　　　　B. that　　　　C. repeats

19 The girl _____ the ball _____ him.
A. to　　　　　　B. kicks

20 Jaden _____ _____ translator for _____.
A. that   B. needs   C. no

21 For a _____, the two play _____ the _____.
A. ball   B. while   C. with

22 _____, the girl points _____ _____ and says, "Mi chiamo Rosabella."
A. herself   B. finally   C. at

23 "_____ name is Jaden," he _____.
A. responds   B. my

24 _____ Rosabella _____, "Arrive l'autobus."
A. says   B. suddenly

25 Jaden _____ the words that _____ _____ *bus* and *arrive*.
A. like   B. understands   C. sound

26 _____ enough, a bus _____.
A. appears   B. sure

27 Kids _____ soccer uniforms _____ _____ the windows, "Ciao, Rosabella!"
A. from   B. in   C. shout

28 _____ Rosabella steps _____ the bus, Jaden says, "Good _____."
A. onto   B. luck   C. as

29 She _____ not _____.
A. understand   B. does

30 So Jaden _____ and _____, "Buon, buon ...."
A. says   B. thinks

31 He points _____ the soccer ball _____ she is _____ in her hand.
A. holding   B. to   C. that

32 Rosabella _____, "Fortuna! Buona _____!"
A. shouts   B. fortuna

33 Fortuna _____ _____ *fortune*.
A. like   B. sounds

34 "Buona fortuna!" _____ _____.
A. shouts   B. he

35 Rosabella and _____ friends shout _____, "Molte grazie!"
A. back   B. her

36 The bus _____ _____.
A. away   B. rolls

37 Jaden _____ _____ to the kitchen.
A. back   B. goes

38 He says _____ the translation app, " Learning from people is _____ fun. Can you _____ me some Italian, Ms. Gambini?"
A. teach   B. into   C. more

39 Ms. Gambini _____, "Si," and _____.
A. laughs   B. says

20 Jaden은 그것 때문에 번역 앱이 필요하지 않다.

21 잠시 동안, 두 사람은 공을 가지고 논다.

22 마침내, 그 소녀는 자신을 가리키며 "Mi chiamo Rosabella." 라고 말한다.

23 "내 이름은 Jaden이야."라고 그가 대답한다.

24 갑자기 Rosabella가 "Arrive l'autobus."라고 말한다.

25 Jaden은 '버스'와 '도착하다'라는 단어와 비슷한 소리가 나는 단어를 알아듣는다.

26 아니나 다를까, 버스 한 대가 나타난다.

27 축구 유니폼을 입은 아이들이 창문에서 "Ciao, Rosabella!"라고 외친다.

28 Rosabella가 버스에 오를 때, Jaden은 "행운을 빌어."라고 말한다.

29 그녀는 이해하지 못한다.

30 그래서 Jaden은 생각하고 "Buon, buon ...."이라고 말한다.

31 그는 그녀가 손에 들고 있는 축구공을 가리킨다.

32 Rosabella가 "Fortuna! Buona fortuna!"라고 소리친다.

33 Fortuna는 '행운'처럼 들린다.

34 "Buona fortuna!"라고 그가 소리친다.

35 Rosabella와 그녀의 친구들은 "Molte grazie!"라고 다시 외친다.

36 버스가 굴러간다.

37 Jaden은 부엌으로 돌아간다.

38 그는 번역 앱에 말한다. "사람들에게서 배우는 것은 더 재미있습니다. 이탈리아어 좀 가르쳐 주실 수 있나요, Gambini 씨?"

39 Gambini 씨는 "Si,"라고 말하고는 웃는다.

※ 다음 우리말과 일치하도록 빈칸에 알맞은 말을 쓰시오.

1 Jaden's _____ is _____ Florence, _____.

2 They _____ _____ Ms. Gambini, _____ _____ friend.

3 Today his parents _____ _____ _____ museums, but Jaden wants to _____ _____.

4 He thinks the _____ app _____ his phone will _____ him _____.

5 His stomach _____, _____ he _____ the kitchen.

6 _____ Ms. Gambini _____ Jaden, she _____ "Buon giorno. Vuoi un pezzo di pane e un bicchiere di latte?"

7 Jaden does not know _____ _____ _____.

8 Then the app says, "Good morning. _____ you _____ a piece of bread and _____ _____ _____ milk?"

9 Jaden _____, "Yes, _____."

10 There is a _____ _____ the door, and a woman _____ Ms. Gambini invited _____ _____.

11 The two _____ begin _____ Italian very _____.

12 So the _____ does not _____.

13 Jaden _____ _____ the phone and _____ it _____ the table.

14 He _____ _____ _____ _____ the sunny morning.

15 He _____ a _____ sound and finds a girl _____ _____ _____ a soccer ball _____ a wall.

16 She _____ _____ him and _____, "Buon giono."

17 His phone is in the kitchen, _____ Jaden does not know _____ _____.

18 He just _____ the words _____ the girl said, "Buon giorno."

19 The girl _____ the ball _____ _____.

1 Jaden의 가족은 이탈리아 플로 렌스에 있다.

2 그들은 그의 어머니의 친구인 Gambini 씨를 방문하고 있다.

3 오늘 그의 부모님은 박물관에 갈 예정이지만, Jaden은 집에 남고 싶어 한다.

4 그는 자신의 전화기에 있는 번역 앱이 의사소통을 하는 데 도움이 될 것이라고 생각한다.

5 그는 배가 꼬르륵거려서 부엌으로 들어간다.

6 Gambini 씨가 Jaden을 보자, 그녀는 "Buon giorno. Vuoi un pezzo di pane e un bicchiere di latte?"라고 말한다.

7 Jaden은 어떻게 대답해야 할지 모른다.

8 그러자 앱이 "좋은 아침입니다. 빵 한 개와 우유 한 잔 드시겠어요?"라고 말한다.

9 Jaden은 "네, 부탁해요."라고 대답한다.

10 문을 두드리는 소리가 들리고 Gambini 씨가 초대한 한 여자가 안으로 들어온다.

11 두 여자는 아주 빨리 이탈리아어를 말하기 시작한다.

12 그래서 번역 앱은 이해하지 못한다.

13 Jaden은 전화기를 끄고 그것을 탁자 위에 둔다.

14 그는 화창한 아침을 즐기기 위해 밖으로 나간다.

15 그는 쿵쾅거리는 소리를 따라가다 벽에 축구공을 차고 있는 소녀를 발견한다.

16 그녀는 그에게 돌아서서 "Buon giorno."라고 말한다.

17 그의 전화기는 부엌에 있어서 Jaden은 뭐라고 말해야 할지 모른다.

18 그는 단지 소녀가 말한 말들인 "Buon giorno"를 반복한다.

19 소녀는 그에게 공을 찬다.

20 Jaden _____ no _____ for that.

21 _____ _____ _____, the two play _____ the ball.

22 Finally, the girl _____ _____ _____ and says, "Mi chiamo Rosabella."

23 "_____ _____ is Jaden," he _____.

24 _____ Rosabella _____, "Arrive l'autobus."

25 Jaden _____ the words that _____ _____ *bus* and *arrive*.

26 Sure _____, a bus _____.

27 Kids _____ soccer uniforms _____ _____ the windows, "Ciao, Rosabella!"

28 _____ Rosabella _____ _____ the bus, Jaden says, "Good luck."

29 She _____ _____ _____.

30 _____ Jaden _____ and _____, "Buon, buon …."

31 He _____ _____ the soccer ball that she _____ _____ in her hand.

32 Rosabella _____, "Fortuna! Buona fortuna!"

33 Fortuna _____ _____ *fortune*.

34 "Buona fortuna!" he _____.

35 Rosabella and her friends _____ _____, "Molte grazie!"

36 The bus _____ _____.

37 Jaden _____ _____ _____ the kitchen.

38 He _____ _____ the translation app, "_____ from people is _____ fun. Can you _____ _____ _____ _____, Ms. Gambini?"

39 Ms. Gambini _____, "Si," and _____.

---

20 Jaden은 그것 때문에 번역 앱이 필요하지 않다.

21 잠시 동안, 두 사람은 공을 가지고 논다.

22 마침내, 그 소녀는 자신을 가리키며 "Mi chiamo Rosabella."라고 말한다.

23 "내 이름은 Jaden이야."라고 그가 대답한다.

24 갑자기 Rosabella가 "Arrive l'autobus."라고 말한다.

25 Jaden은 '버스'와 '도착하다'라는 단어와 비슷한 소리가 나는 단어를 알아듣는다.

26 아니나 다를까, 버스 한 대가 나타난다.

27 축구 유니폼을 입은 아이들이 창문에서 "Ciao, Rosabella!"라고 외친다.

28 Rosabella가 버스에 오를 때, Jaden은 "행운을 빌어."라고 말한다.

29 그녀는 이해하지 못한다.

30 그래서 Jaden은 생각하고 "Buon, buon …."이라고 말한다.

31 그는 그녀가 손에 들고 있는 축구공을 가리킨다.

32 Rosabella가 "Fortuna! Buona fortuna!"라고 소리친다.

33 Fortuna는 '행운'처럼 들린다.

34 "Buona fortuna!"라고 그가 소리친다.

35 Rosabella와 그녀의 친구들은 "Molte grazie!"라고 다시 외친다.

36 버스가 굴러간다.

37 Jaden은 부엌으로 돌아간다.

38 그는 번역 앱에 말한다. "사람들에게서 배우는 것은 더 재미있습니다. 이탈리아어 좀 가르쳐 주실 수 있나요, Gambini 씨?"

39 Gambini 씨는 "Si,"라고 말하고는 웃는다.

※ 다음 문장을 우리말로 쓰시오.

1 Jaden's family is in Florence, Italy.

➡ _____

2 They are visiting Ms. Gambini, his mother's friend.

➡ _____

3 Today his parents are going to museums, but Jaden wants to stay behind.

➡ _____

4 He thinks the translation app on his phone will help him communicate.

➡ _____

5 His stomach growls, so he enters the kitchen.

➡ _____

6 Jaden does not know how to respond.

➡ _____

7 Then the app says, "Good morning. Would you like a piece of bread and a glass of milk?"

➡ _____

8 There is a knock on the door, and a woman whom Ms. Gambini invited walks in.

➡ _____

9 The two women begin speaking Italian very fast.

➡ _____

10 So the translator does not understand.

➡ _____

11 Jaden turns off the phone and leaves it on the table.

➡ _____

12 He goes out to enjoy the sunny morning.

➡ _____

13 He follows a thumping sound and finds a girl who is kicking a soccer ball against a wall.

➡ _____

14 His phone is in the kitchen, so Jaden does not know what to say.

➡ _____

15 He just repeats the words that the girl said, "Buon giorno."

➡ _____

16 The girl kicks the ball to him. Jaden needs no translator for that.

➡ _____

17 For a while, the two play with the ball.

➡ _____

18 Finally, the girl points at herself and says, "Mi chiamo Rosabella."

➡ _____

19 "My name is Jaden," he responds.

➡ _____

20 Jaden understands the words that sound like *bus* and *arrive*.

➡ _____

21 Sure enough, a bus appears.

➡ _____

22 Kids in soccer uniforms shout from the windows, "Ciao, Rosabella!"

➡ _____

23 As Rosabella steps onto the bus, Jaden says, "Good luck." She does not understand.

➡ _____

24 He points to the soccer ball that she is holding in her hand.

➡ _____

25 Fortuna sounds like *fortune*.

➡ _____

26 Rosabella and her friends shout back, "Molte grazie!"

➡ _____

27 The bus rolls away.

➡ _____

28 Jaden goes back to the kitchen.

➡ _____

29 He says into the translation app, "Learning from people is more fun. Can you teach me some Italian, Ms. Gambini?"

➡ _____

30 Ms. Gambini says, "Si," and laughs.

➡ _____

※ 다음 괄호 안의 단어들을 우리말에 맞도록 바르게 배열하시오.

1 (family / Italy. / in / Jaden's / is / Florence,)
➡ _____

2 (are / they / Ms. / Gambini, / visiting / friend. / mother's / his)
➡ _____

3 (his / today / museums, / are / parents / to / going / but / wants / behind. / Jaden / stay / to)
➡ _____

4 (the / thinks / app / he / translation / his / on / phone / him / communicate. / help / will)
➡ _____

5 (growls, / stomach / his / so / the / kitchen, / enters / he)
➡ _____

6 (Ms. / Gambini / when / Jaden, / sees / says / she / "Buon / giorno. / Vuoi / un / pezzo / di / pane / e / un / bicchiere / di / latte?")
➡ _____

7 (not / Jaden / know / does / respond / to / how)
➡ _____

8 (the / then / says, / app / morning. / "good / like / would / you / bread / piece / of / a / and / a / milk?" / of / glass)
➡ _____

9 (answers, / Jaden / please." / "yes,)
➡ _____

10 (a / knock / the / is / there / door, / on / and / whom / woman / a / Ms. / Gambini / in. / walks / invited)
➡ _____

11 (two / begin / the / women / Italian / fast. / speaking / very)
➡ _____

12 (the / translator / so / not / understand. / does)
➡ _____

13 (turns / Jaden / the / phone / off / and / it / leaves / the / table. / on)
➡ _____

14 (goes / to / he / out / enjoy / morning. / the / sunny)
➡ _____

15 (follows / he / a / sound / thumping / and / a / girl / finds / who / kicking / is / ball / a / soccer / wall. / a / against)
➡ _____

16 (turns / him / she / to / and / says, / giorno." / "Buon)
➡ _____

17 (phone / his / the / is / kitchen, / in / so / does / Jaden / know / not / say. / to / what)
➡ _____

18 (just / he / the / repeats / words / the / girl / that / said, / giorno." / "Buon)
➡ _____

19 (the / kicks / girl / ball / the / him. / to)
➡ _____

1 Jaden의 가족은 이탈리아 플로렌스에 있다.

2 그들은 그의 어머니의 친구인 Gambini 씨를 방문하고 있다.

3 오늘 그의 부모님은 박물관에 갈 예정이지만, Jaden은 집에 남고 싶어 한다.

4 그는 자신의 전화기에 있는 번역 앱이 의사소통을 하는 데 도움이 될 것이라고 생각한다.

5 그는 배가 꼬르륵거려서 부엌으로 들어간다.

6 Gambini 씨가 Jaden을 보자, 그녀는 "Buon giorno. Vuoi un pezzo di pane e un bicchiere di latte?"라고 말한다.

7 Jaden은 어떻게 대답해야 할지 모른다.

8 그러자 앱이 "좋은 아침입니다. 빵 한 개와 우유 한 잔 드시겠어요?"라고 말한다.

9 Jaden은 "네, 부탁해요."라고 대답한다.

10 문을 두드리는 소리가 들리고 Gambini 씨가 초대한 한 여자가 안으로 들어온다.

11 두 여자는 아주 빨리 이탈리아어를 말하기 시작한다.

12 그래서 번역 앱은 이해하지 못한다.

13 Jaden은 전화기를 끄고 그것을 탁자 위에 둔다.

14 그는 화창한 아침을 즐기기 위해 밖으로 나간다.

15 그는 쿵쾅거리는 소리를 따라가다 벽에 축구공을 차고 있는 소녀를 발견한다.

16 그녀는 그에게 돌아서서 "Buon giorno."라고 말한다.

17 그의 전화기는 부엌에 있어서 Jaden은 뭐라고 말해야 할지 모른다.

18 그는 단지 소녀가 말한 말들인 "Buon giorno"를 반복한다.

19 소녀는 그에게 공을 찬다.

20 (needs / Jaden / translator / that. / for / no)
➡ _____

21 (a / for / while, / play / two / the / ball. / with)
➡ _____

22 (the / finally, / points / girl / herself / at / says, / and / Rosabella." / "Mi / chiamo)
➡ _____

23 (name / Jaden," / my / is / responds. / he)
➡ _____

24 (Rosabella / suddenly / says, / l'autobus." / "Arrive)
➡ _____

25 (understands / Jaden / words / the / that / like / arrive. / sound / and / bus)
➡ _____

26 (enough, / a / sure / appears. / bus)
➡ _____

27 (soccer / kids / uniforms / in / from / shout / windows, / the / Rosabella!" / "Ciao,)
➡ _____

28 (Rosabella / onto / as / the / bus, / steps / says, / Jaden / luck." / "good)
➡ _____

29 (she / understand. / not / does)
➡ _____

30 (Jaden / thinks / so / says, / and / "Buon, / buon ...."
➡ _____

31 (points / the / he / ball / to / soccer / that / is / she / hand. / in / holding / her)
➡ _____

32 (shouts, / Rosabella / "Fortuna! / Buona / fortuna!")
➡ _____

33 (like / fortuna / fortune. / sounds)
➡ _____

34 ("Buona / fortuna!" / shouts. / he)
➡ _____

35 (and / Rosabella / friends / her / back, / shout / "Molte / grazie!")
➡ _____

36 (bus / rolls / the / away.)
➡ _____

37 (Jaden / back / to / goes / kitchen. / the)
➡ _____

38 (says / he / into / the / app, / translation / from / "learning / people / more / fun. / is / can / teach / some / Italian, / me / you / Ms. / Gambini?")
➡ _____

39 (Gambini / Ms. / says, / and / laughs. / "Si,")
➡ _____

20 Jaden은 그것 때문에 번역 앱은 필요하지 않다.

21 잠시 동안, 두 사람은 공을 가지고 논다.

22 마침내, 그 소녀는 자신을 가리키며 "Mi chiamo Rosabella." 라고 말한다.

23 "내 이름은 Jaden이야."라고 그가 대답한다.

24 갑자기 Rosabella가 "Arrive l'autobus."라고 말한다.

25 Jaden은 '버스'와 '도착하다'라는 단어와 비슷한 소리가 나는 단어를 알아듣는다.

26 아니나 다를까, 버스 한 대가 나타난다.

27 축구 유니폼을 입은 아이들이 창문에서 "Ciao, Rosabella!"라고 외친다.

28 Rosabella가 버스에 오를 때, Jaden은 "행운을 빌어."라고 말한다.

29 그녀는 이해하지 못한다.

30 그래서 Jaden은 생각하고 "Buon, buon ...."이라고 말한다.

31 그는 그녀가 손에 들고 있는 축구공을 가리킨다.

32 Rosabella가 "Fortuna! Buona fortuna!"라고 소리친다.

33 Fortuna는 '행운'처럼 들린다.

34 "Buona fortuna!"라고 그가 소리친다.

35 Rosabella와 그녀의 친구들은 "Molte grazie!"라고 다시 외친다.

36 버스가 굴러간다.

37 Jaden은 부엌으로 돌아간다.

38 그는 번역 앱에 말한다. "사람들에게서 배우는 것은 더 재미있습니다. 이탈리아어 좀 가르쳐 주실 수 있나요, Gambini 씨?"

39 Gambini 씨는 "Si,"라고 말하고는 웃는다.

※ 다음 우리말을 영어로 쓰시오.

1 Jaden의 가족은 이탈리아 플로렌스에 있다.

➡ _____

2 그들은 그의 어머니의 친구인 Gambini 씨를 방문하고 있다.

➡ _____

3 오늘 그의 부모님은 박물관에 갈 예정이지만, Jaden은 집에 남고 싶어 한다.

➡ _____

4 그는 자신의 전화기에 있는 번역 앱이 의사소통을 하는 데 도움이 될 것이라고 생각한다.

➡ _____

5 그는 배가 꼬르륵거려서 부엌으로 들어간다.

➡ _____

6 Gambini 씨가 Jaden을 보자, 그녀는 "Buon giorno. Vuoi un pezzo di pane e un bicchiere di latte?"라고 말한다.

➡ _____

_____

7 Jaden은 어떻게 대답해야 할지 모른다.

➡ _____

8 그러자 앱이 "좋은 아침입니다. 빵 한 개와 우유 한 잔 드시겠어요?"라고 말한다.

➡ _____

9 Jaden은 "네, 부탁해요."라고 대답한다.

➡ _____

10 문을 두드리는 소리가 들리고 Gambini 씨가 초대한 한 여자가 안으로 들어온다.

➡ _____

11 두 여자는 아주 빨리 이탈리아어를 말하기 시작한다.

➡ _____

12 그래서 번역 앱은 이해하지 못한다.

➡ _____

13 Jaden은 전화기를 끄고 그것을 탁자 위에 둔다.

➡ _____

14 그는 화창한 아침을 즐기기 위해 밖으로 나간다.

➡ _____

15 그는 쿵쾅거리는 소리를 따라가다 벽에 축구공을 차고 있는 소녀를 발견한다.

➡ _____

16 그녀는 그에게 돌아서서 "Buon giorno."라고 말한다.

➡ _____

17 그의 전화기는 부엌에 있어서 Jaden은 뭐라고 말해야 할지 모른다.
➡ _____

18 그는 단지 소녀가 말한 말들인 "Buon giorno"를 반복한다.
➡ _____

19 소녀는 그에게 공을 찬다.
➡ _____

20 Jaden은 그것 때문에 번역 앱이 필요하지 않다.
➡ _____

21 잠시 동안, 두 사람은 공을 가지고 논다.
➡ _____

22 마침내, 그 소녀는 자신을 가리키며 "Mi chiamo Rosabella."라고 말한다.
➡ _____

23 "내 이름은 Jaden이야."라고 그가 대답한다.
➡ _____

24 갑자기 Rosabella가 "Arrive l'autobus."라고 말한다.
➡ _____

25 Jaden은 '버스'와 '도착하다'라는 단어와 비슷한 소리가 나는 단어를 알아듣는다.
➡ _____

26 아니나 다를까, 버스 한 대가 나타난다.
➡ _____

27 축구 유니폼을 입은 아이들이 창문에서 "Ciao, Rosabella!"라고 외친다.
➡ _____

28 Rosabella가 버스에 오를 때, Jaden은 "행운을 빌어요."라고 말한다.
➡ _____

29 그녀는 이해하지 못한다.
➡ _____

30 그래서 Jaden은 생각하고 "Buon, buon …."이라고 말한다.
➡ _____

31 그는 그녀가 손에 들고 있는 축구공을 가리킨다.
➡ _____

32 Rosabella가 "Fortuna! Buona fortuna!"라고 소리친다.
➡ _____

33 Fortuna는 '행운'처럼 들린다.
➡ _____

34 "Buona fortuna!"라고 그가 소리친다.
➡ _____

35 Rosabella와 그녀의 친구들은 "Molte grazie!"라고 다시 외친다.
➡ _____

36 버스가 굴러간다
➡ _____

37 Jaden은 부엌으로 돌아간다.
➡ _____

38 그는 번역 앱에 말한다. "사람들에게서 배우는 것이 더 재미있습니다. 이탈리아어 좀 가르쳐 주실 수 있나요, Gambini 씨?"
➡ _____

39 Gambini 씨는 "Si,"라고 말하고는 웃는다.
➡ _____

※ 다음 우리말과 일치하도록 빈칸에 알맞은 말을 쓰시오.

My Writing Portfolio - Step 1

1. _____ _____ App

2. The name _____ our _____ is *Enjoy Paris*.

3. It _____ on what _____ _____ in Paris.

4. It gives information _____ opening hours and _____ _____
   of museums and theaters.

5. It also tells you _____ _____ _____ there.

6. Our app will be _____ _____ travelers.

1. 우리의 여행 앱
2. 우리 앱의 이름은 "파리를 즐겨라"이다.
3. 그것은 파리에서 무엇을 볼 것인가에 초점을 맞추고 있다.
4. 그것은 박물관과 극장의 개장 시간과 입장료에 대한 정보를 제공한다.
5. 그것은 또한 그곳에 가는 방법을 알려 준다.
6. 우리 앱은 여행객들에게 유용할 것이다.

Wrap Up - Reading

1. Gestures can have different _____ in different _____.

2. _____ example, the "OK sign" _____ "okay" or "all _____"
   in many countries.

3. The gesture means _____ _____.

4. It _____ "money" in some _____.

5. That is _____ something _____.

6. The same sign, _____, means "O" _____ France.

7. It means there is _____, so it is not a very happy _____.

8. _____ we travel, we _____ use gestures _____.

1. 제스처는 다른 문화에서 다른 의미를 가질 수 있다.
2. 예를 들어, 'OK 사인'은 많은 나라에서 '좋다' 또는 '괜찮다'를 의미한다.
3. 그 제스처는 좋은 것을 의미한다.
4. 그것은 어떤 문화에서는 '돈'을 의미한다.
5. 그것 또한 좋은 것이다.
6. 그러나 같은 사인이 프랑스에서는 '제로'를 의미한다.
7. 그것은 아무것도 없다는 것을 의미하기 때문에, 그것은 별로 행복한 제스처가 아니다.
8. 우리는 여행할 때, 신중하게 제스처를 사용해야 한다.

※ 다음 우리말을 영어로 쓰시오.

My Writing Portfolio - Step 1

1. 우리의 여행 앱
   ➡ _____

2. 우리 앱의 이름은 "파리를 즐겨라"이다.
   ➡ _____

3. 그것은 파리에서 무엇을 볼 것인가에 초점을 맞추고 있다.
   ➡ _____

4. 그것은 박물관과 극장의 개장 시간과 입장료에 대한 정보를 제공한다.
   ➡ _____

5. 그것은 또한 그곳에 가는 방법을 알려준다.
   ➡ _____

6. 우리 앱은 여행객들에게 유용할 것이다.
   ➡ _____

Wrap Up - Reading

1. 제스처는 다른 문화에서 다른 의미를 가질 수 있다.
   ➡ _____

2. 예를 들어, 'OK 사인'은 많은 나라에서 '좋다' 또는 '괜찮다'를 의미한다.
   ➡ _____

3. 그 제스처는 좋은 것을 의미한다.
   ➡ _____

4. 그것은 어떤 문화에서는 '돈'을 의미한다.
   ➡ _____

5. 그것 또한 좋은 것이다.
   ➡ _____

6. 그러나 같은 사인이 프랑스에서는 '제로'를 의미한다.
   ➡ _____

7. 그것은 아무것도 없다는 것을 의미하기 때문에, 그것은 별로 행복한 제스처가 아니다.
   ➡ _____

8. 우리는 여행할 때, 신중하게 제스처를 사용해야 한다.
   ➡ _____

※ 다음 영어를 우리말로 쓰시오.

01 hard		22 major	
02 appointment		23 skin	
03 attack		24 regularly	
04 bacteria		25 scratch	
05 cell		26 healthy	
06 creature		27 fever	
07 different		28 remember	
08 digest		29 germ	
09 break		30 finally	
10 exercise		31 success	
11 dangerous		32 terrible	
12 antibody		33 luckily	
13 defend		34 necessary	
14 medicine		35 be good for	
15 multiply		36 plenty of	
16 defense		37 such as	
17 impossible		38 at last	
18 invade		39 protect A from B	
19 macrophage		40 by the way	
20 balanced		41 give up	
21 stomachache		42 in a few days	
		43 be famous for	

※ 다음 우리말을 영어로 쓰시오.

01 위통, 복통 _____

02 공격하다; 공격 _____

03 박테리아, 세균 _____

04 실제로, 정말로 _____

05 몇의 _____

06 주사 _____

07 피부 _____

08 항체 _____

09 세포 _____

10 생물 _____

11 다른 _____

12 소화하다 _____

13 운동하다 _____

14 위험한 _____

15 방어하다 _____

16 마지막으로, 마침내 _____

17 약속 _____

18 세균, 미생물 _____

19 불가능한 _____

20 침입하다 _____

21 방어 _____

22 열 _____

23 다행히도 _____

24 대식 세포 _____

25 균형 잡힌, 안정된 _____

26 부러지다 _____

27 주요한, 중대한 _____

28 필요한 _____

29 규칙적으로 _____

30 약 _____

31 바이러스 _____

32 피해자, 희생자 _____

33 증식[번식]하다 _____

34 긁다, 할퀴다 _____

35 성공 _____

36 마침내, 드디어 _____

37 ~으로 유명하다 _____

38 ~할 준비가 되어 있다 _____

39 그런데 _____

40 포기하다 _____

41 많은 _____

42 나타나다 _____

43 조심하다 _____

※ 다음 영영풀이에 알맞은 단어를 <보기>에서 골라 쓴 후, 우리말 뜻을 쓰시오.

1 _____ : the fact of getting or achieving wealth, respect, or fame: _____

2 _____ : to fight in order to keep someone or something safe: _____

3 _____ : an agreement to meet with someone at a particular time: _____

4 _____ : very important: _____

5 _____ : any one of a group of very small living things that often cause disease: _____

6 _____ : any one of the very small parts that together form all living things: _____

7 _____ : to increase in number by reproducing: _____

8 _____ : an act of putting something such as medicine or vaccine into the body with a needle: _____

9 _____ : a very small living thing that causes disease: _____

10 _____ : to enter or be in a place where you are not wanted: _____

11 _____ : having good or equal amounts of all the necessary parts of something: _____

12 _____ : used to say that something good or lucky has happened: _____

13 _____ : to rub your skin with your fingernails because it feels uncomfortable: _____

14 _____ : an infectious disease like a very bad cold, which causes fever, pains, and weakness: _____

15 _____ : a person who has been attacked, injured, robbed, or killed by someone else: _____

16 _____ : to change food that you have eaten by a biological process into simpler forms that can be used by the body: _____

보기			
digest	luckily	major	balanced
invade	bacteria	defend	shot
flu	appointment	victim	cell
multiply	success	germ	scratch

※ 다음 우리말과 일치하도록 빈칸에 알맞은 말을 쓰시오.

Communicate: Listen - Listen and Answer Dialog 1

B: _____ I go home _____, Ms. Song? I _____ _____ so good.

W: What _____ _____ be the _____?

B: I have a _____ _____. It really _____.

W: _____ _____ _____ get some medicine at the _____ _____?

B: I _____ did. But it _____ _____.

W: Okay. You _____ go. _____ _____ a doctor, okay?

B: _____. Thanks.

Communicate: Listen - Listen and Answer Dialog 2

(*The phone rings.*)

B: Hello, Sora.

G: Hi, Jongha. I _____ you were _____. Are you _____ now?

B: Yes, I _____ the doctor, and I _____ _____ now.

G: _____ _____ hear that. _____ _____ _____, I called you _____ _____ about our science project.

B: Yeah, we _____ _____. Can you _____ _____ tomorrow?

G: Okay. _____ _____ at Simpson's Donuts _____ nine.

B: At nine? That's too _____. I _____ _____ on the weekend.

G: _____ _____ 10 then?

B: That _____ fine.

Communicate: Listen - Listen More

M: Hi, Minsol. What's _____ _____ your dog?

G: She _____ _____ herself. Actually, she _____ some hair.

M: When did she first _____ _____ _____?

G: _____ three days _____.

M: _____ me _____. (pause) She _____ _____ _____ on her skin. I'll give _____ _____ _____.

G: Thank you.

M: I _____ _____ check your dog again. _____ you _____ _____ next Monday?

G: That's _____ _____ me.

M: Okay. _____ _____.

B: 송 선생님, 집에 일찍 가도 될까요? 몸이 너무 안 좋아요.
W: 무슨 문제가 있니?
B: 배가 너무 아파요. 정말 아파요.
W: 양호실에서 약을 좀 먹는 게 어떠니?
B: 벌써 먹었어요. 하지만 도움이 되지 않았어요.
W: 알겠다. 가도 돼. 병원에 가봐, 알았지?
B: 물론이죠. 고맙습니다.

(전화벨이 울린다.)
B: 여보세요, 소라야.
G: 안녕, 종하야. 아프다고 들었어. 이제 좀 괜찮니?
B: 응, 병원에 갔었는데, 이제 좀 나아졌어.
G: 다행이구나. 그런데, 우리 과학 프로젝트에 대해 얘기하려고 전화했어.
B: 그래, 우리 만나야겠다. 내일 만날 수 있니?
G: 좋아. 9시에 Simpson's Donuts에서 만나자.
B: 9시? 너무 일러. 난 주말에 늦잠을 자.
G: 그럼 10시는 어때?
B: 괜찮아.

M: 안녕, 민솔. 너의 개에게 무슨 문제가 있니?
G: 계속 자기 몸을 긁어요. 사실, 털이 좀 빠졌어요.
M: 너의 개는 언제 처음으로 문제가 생겼니?
G: 약 3일 전에요.
M: 어디 보자. (잠시 멈춘다) 피부에 바이러스가 있어. 약을 좀 줄게.
G: 감사합니다.
M: 네 개를 다시 확인할 필요가 있어. 다음 주 월요일에 올 수 있니?
G: 좋아요.
M: 알겠다. 나중에 보자.

Communicate: Listen - All Ears

M: 1. Can you _____ _____ next Friday?

    2. What's _____ _____ your cat?

M: 1. 다음 주 금요일에 만날까?
2. 너의 고양이에게 무슨 문제가 있니?

Communicate: Speak 2 - Talk in pairs

A: _____ wrong _____ you?

B: I _____ a _____ _____.

A: That's _____ _____. You _____ _____ some water.

B: Okay, _____ _____.

A: 무슨 일 있니?
B: 목이 아파.
A: 그것 참 안됐구나. 너는 물을 좀 마셔야 해.
B: 알았어, 그럴게.

Communicate: Speak 2 - Talk in groups

A: _____ _____ basketball this Saturday.

B: Sure, _____ _____?

A: Can you _____ _____ _____ ten?

B: That's _____ _____ me. Where _____ we _____?

A: _____ _____ at the school gym.

B: Okay. _____ you _____.

A: 이번 토요일에 농구하자.
B: 물론, 좋고말고.
A: 10시에 만날 수 있니?
B: 난 괜찮아. 우리 어디서 만날까?
A: 학교 체육관에서 만나자.
B: 알았어, 거기서 보자.

Wrap Up - Listening ❺

B: Mom, I _____ _____ well.

W: What _____ _____ _____ the problem?

B: I think I _____ _____ _____.

W: Really? _____ _____ _____. Umm, you do _____ _____ _____. I'll _____ you some _____.

B: _____ _____, Mom.

B: 엄마, 몸이 안 좋아요.
W: 뭐가 문제인 것 같니?
B: 열이 있는 것 같아요.
W: 정말? 어디 보자. 음, 정말 열이 있네. 약을 좀 갖다 줄게.
B: 고마워요, 엄마.

Wrap Up - Listening ❻

G: I'm _____ _____ _____ to the Comics Museum tomorrow. Will you _____ _____ me?

B: I really _____ _____ _____.

G: _____ you _____ it at 11?

B: That's _____ _____ me.

G: Okay. _____ _____ _____ the subway station.

G: 내일 만화 박물관에 갈 생각이야. 나하고 같이 갈래?
B: 정말 가고 싶어.
G: 11시에 만날 수 있니?
B: 난 괜찮아.
G: 좋아. 지하철역에서 만나자.

※ 다음 우리말에 맞도록 대화를 영어로 쓰시오.

Communicate: Listen - Listen and Answer Dialog 1

B: _____

W: _____

B: _____

W: _____

B: _____

W: _____

B: _____

B: 송 선생님, 집에 일찍 가도 될까요? 몸이 너무 안 좋아요.
W: 무슨 문제가 있니?
B: 배가 너무 아파요. 정말 아파요.
W: 양호실에서 약을 좀 먹는 게 어떠니?
B: 벌써 먹었어요. 하지만 도움이 되지 않았어요.
W: 알겠다. 가도 돼. 병원에 가봐, 알았지?
B: 물론이죠. 고맙습니다.

Communicate: Listen - Listen and Answer Dialog 2

(The phone rings.)

B: _____

G: _____

B: _____

G: _____

B: _____

G: _____

B: _____

G: _____

B: _____

(전화벨이 울린다.)
B: 여보세요, 소라야.
G: 안녕, 종하야. 아프다고 들었어. 이제 좀 괜찮니?
B: 응, 병원에 갔었는데, 이제 좀 나아졌어.
G: 다행이구나. 그런데, 우리 과학 프로젝트에 대해 얘기하려고 전화했어.
B: 그래, 우리 만나야겠다. 내일 만날 수 있니?
G: 좋아. 9시에 Simpson's Donuts에서 만나자.
B: 9시? 너무 일러. 난 주말에 늦잠을 자.
G: 그럼 10시는 어때?
B: 괜찮아.

Communicate: Listen - Listen More

M: _____

G: _____

M: _____

G: _____

M: _____

G: _____

M: _____

G: _____

M: _____

M: 안녕, 민솔. 너의 개에게 무슨 문제가 있니?
G: 계속 자기 몸을 긁어요. 사실, 털이 좀 빠졌어요.
M: 너의 개는 언제 처음으로 문제가 생겼니?
G: 약 3일 전에요.
M: 어디 보자. (잠시 멈춘다) 피부에 바이러스가 있어. 약을 좀 줄게.
G: 감사합니다.
M: 네 개를 다시 확인할 필요가 있어. 다음 주 월요일에 올 수 있니?
G: 좋아요.
M: 알겠다. 나중에 보자.

Communicate: Listen - All Ears

M: 1. _____

　　2. _____

Communicate: Speak 2 - Talk in pairs

A: _____

B: _____

A: _____

B: _____

Communicate: Speak 2 - Talk in groups

A: _____

B: _____

A: _____

B: _____

A: _____

B: _____

Wrap Up - Listening ❺

B: _____

W: _____

B: _____

W: _____

B: _____

Wrap Up - Listening ❻

G: _____

B: _____

G: _____

B: _____

G: _____

Step1

※ 다음 우리말과 일치하도록 빈칸에 알맞은 것을 골라 쓰시오.

1 Germs are _____, but _____ is impossible to see them _____ your eyes.
　A. with　　　　B. it　　　　C. everywhere

2 There _____ two major _____ of germs: _____ and viruses.
　A. are　　　　B. bacteria　　C. kinds

3 _____ are very small _____.
　A. creatures　　B. bacteria

4 _____ are _____.
　A. good　　　　B. some

5 They _____ help you _____ the food _____ you eat.
　A. that　　　　B. digest　　C. can

6 _____ are bad and can _____ you sick.
　A. make　　　　B. others

7 Viruses are germs _____ can only live _____ the cells of other _____ bodies.
　A. inside　　　B. living　　C. that

8 They _____ diseases _____ as the flu.
　A. such　　　　B. cause

9 "Bad" germs can _____ your body _____ your _____, mouth, nose, and eyes.
　A. skin　　　　B. through　　C. enter

10 What _____ when they _____?
　A. invade　　　B. happens

11 The germs _____ in the _____.
　A. body　　　　B. multiply

12 Your body _____ a war _____.
　A. zone　　　　B. becomes

13 You start to _____ tired and _____.
　A. weak　　　　B. feel

14 Luckily, your _____ has an army of _____.
　A. defense　　　B. body

15 The T cells _____ the _____!
　A. alarm　　　　B. sound

16 The B cells _____ to fight the _____ _____ antibodies.
　A. with　　　　B. germs　　C.arrive

17 The _____ cells show _____ and _____ the germs.
　A. eat　　　　B. up　　　C. macrophage

18 _____, this army is _____ the white blood _____.
　A. cells　　　　B. together　　C. called

19 If all _____ well, they win the _____.
　A. fight　　　　B. goes

20 _____ a _____ days, you start to _____ better.
　A. few　　　　B. feel　　　C. in

1 세균은 어디에나 있지만 눈으로 세균을 보는 것은 불가능하다.

2 세균에는 두 가지 주요한 종류가 있다: 박테리아와 바이러스이다.

3 박테리아는 매우 작은 생물이다.

4 어떤 것들은 좋다.

5 그것들은 당신이 먹는 음식을 소화하는 데 도움을 줄 수 있다.

6 다른 것들은 나쁘고 당신을 아프게 할 수 있다.

7 바이러스는 다른 살아 있는 몸의 세포 안에서만 살 수 있는 세균이다.

8 그들은 독감과 같은 질병을 일으킨다.

9 '나쁜' 세균은 피부, 입, 코, 눈을 통해 몸에 들어갈 수 있다.

10 그들이 침입하면 어떻게 되는가?

11 세균은 몸속에서 증식한다.

12 당신의 몸은 전쟁 지역이 된다.

13 당신은 피곤하고 약해지기 시작한다.

14 다행히도, 당신의 몸은 방어 부대를 가지고 있다.

15 T세포가 경보를 발한다!

16 B세포는 항체로 세균과 싸우기 위해 도착한다.

17 대식 세포가 나타나서 세균을 먹는다.

18 이 군대는 함께 백혈구라고 부른다.

19 모든 것이 잘되면 싸움에서 이긴다.

20 며칠 후면 당신은 회복되기 시작한다.

21 The body remembers the _____, so it cannot make _____ of _____ again.
A. copies   B. invader   C. itself

22 But the germs are _____, _____.
A. too   B. smart

23 They can _____ form and _____ the body.
A. change   B. trick

24 There are _____ ways to _____ yourself _____ germs.
A. protect   B. from   C. several

25 First, _____ your hands _____ soap and _____ water.
A. with   B. warm   C. wash

26 A balanced _____ will _____ your body strong and _____.
A. healthy   B. keep   C. diet

27 _____ is also important to _____ regularly and get _____ of sleep.
A. exercise   B. plenty   C. it

28 _____, get the necessary _____.
A. shots   B. finally

29 They are the best _____ against _____.
A. germs   B. defense

30 If you _____ these _____, you will not be a _____ of "bad" germs.
A. victim   B. steps   C. follow

31 _____ more _____ of me.
A. copies   B. make

32 It's _____ job to _____ the body.
A. defend   B. my

33 That _____ a nice _____!
A. meal   B. was

34 Are _____ any more germs to _____?
A. eat   B. there

35 _____ year, I'll _____ in my cousin.
A. send   B. next

36 He'll _____ you then for _____ fight!
A. another   B. see

37 _____ _____ I do now?
A. can   B. what

38 I'm _____ to fight _____ germs.
A. any   B. ready

39 We _____ _____.
A. up   B. give

40 We can't _____ you _____.
A. sick   B. make

---

21 몸은 침입자를 기억하므로 침입자는 다시 복제할 수 없다.

22 하지만 세균들도 영리하다.

23 그들은 형태를 바꿀 수 있고 몸을 속일 수 있다.

24 세균으로부터 당신 자신을 보호하는 몇 가지 방법이 있다.

25 먼저 비누와 따뜻한 물로 손을 씻어라.

26 균형 잡힌 식단은 당신의 몸을 튼튼하고 건강하게 해줄 것이다.

27 규칙적으로 운동하고 충분한 잠을 자는 것도 중요하다.

28 마지막으로 필요한 주사를 맞아라.

29 그것들은 세균을 막는 최고의 방어 수단이다.

30 만약 당신이 이 단계를 따른다면, 당신은 "나쁜" 세균의 희생자가 되지 않을 것이다.

31 나를 더 복제해 줘.

32 몸을 지키는 게 내 일이야.

33 정말 맛있는 식사였어!

34 먹을 세균이 더 있니?

35 내년에는 내 사촌을 보낼게.

36 그때 그가 또 싸우려고 널 만나게 될 거야!

37 지금 내가 무엇을 할 수 있을까?

38 나는 어떤 세균과도 싸울 준비가 되어 있어.

39 우리는 포기한다.

40 우리는 널 아프게 할 수 없어.

※ 다음 우리말과 일치하도록 빈칸에 알맞은 말을 쓰시오.

1 Germs are _____, but it is _____ _____ _____ them with your eyes.

2 There are two _____ _____ of germs: _____ and _____.

3 Bacteria _____ very small _____.

4 _____ are _____.

5 They can _____ _____ _____ the food that you eat.

6 _____ are bad and can _____ you _____.

7 Viruses are _____ that can only live _____ the cells of _____ _____ _____.

8 They _____ diseases _____ _____ the flu.

9 "Bad" germs _____ _____ your body _____ your _____, _____, nose, and eyes.

10 What _____ when they _____?

11 The germs _____ in the _____.

12 Your body _____ a war _____.

13 You start to _____ _____ and _____.

14 _____, your body has an _____ _____ _____.

15 The T cells _____ the _____!

16 The B cells arrive _____ _____ the _____ with _____.

17 The _____ cells _____ _____ and eat the germs.

18 Together, this army is called the _____ _____.

19 If all _____ _____, they _____ the fight.

20 In a _____ _____, you start to _____ _____.

1 세균은 어디에나 있지만 눈으로 세균을 보는 것은 불가능하다.

2 세균에는 두 가지 주요한 종류가 있다: 박테리아와 바이러스이다.

3 박테리아는 매우 작은 생물이다.

4 어떤 것들은 좋다.

5 그것들은 당신이 먹는 음식을 소화하는 데 도움을 줄 수 있다.

6 다른 것들은 나쁘고 당신을 아프게 할 수 있다.

7 바이러스는 다른 살아 있는 몸의 세포 안에서만 살 수 있는 세균이다.

8 그들은 독감과 같은 질병을 일으킨다.

9 '나쁜' 세균은 피부, 입, 코, 눈을 통해 몸에 들어갈 수 있다.

10 그들이 침입하면 어떻게 되는가?

11 세균은 몸속에서 증식한다.

12 당신의 몸은 전쟁 지역이 된다.

13 당신은 피곤하고 약해지기 시작한다.

14 다행히도, 당신의 몸은 방어 부대를 가지고 있다.

15 T세포가 경보를 발한다!

16 B세포는 항체로 세균과 싸우기 위해 도착한다.

17 대식 세포가 나타나서 세균을 먹는다.

18 이 군대는 함께 백혈구라고 부른다.

19 모든 것이 잘되면 싸움에서 이긴다.

20 며칠 후면 당신은 회복되기 시작한다.

21 The body remembers the _____, so it _____ _____ _____ of itself again.

22 _____ the germs are _____, _____.

23 They can _____ _____ and trick the body.

24 There are _____ _____ _____ _____ yourself from germs.

25 First, _____ your hands _____ _____ and warm water.

26 A balanced diet will _____ your body _____ and _____.

27 It is also _____ _____ _____ regularly and get _____ _____ sleep.

28 _____, get the _____ _____.

29 They are the best _____ _____ germs.

30 If you follow these _____, you will not _____ _____ _____ of "bad" germs.

31 _____ more _____ _____ me.

32 It's my _____ _____ _____ the body.

33 That was a _____ _____!

34 Are there any _____ _____ _____ _____?

35 Next year, I'll _____ _____ my cousin.

36 He'll see you then _____ _____ _____!

37 _____ can I _____ now?

38 _____ _____ _____ fight any germs.

39 We _____ _____.

40 We can't _____ _____ _____.

21 몸은 침입자를 기억하므로 침입자는 다시 복제할 수 없다.

22 하지만 세균들도 영리하다.

23 그들은 형태를 바꿀 수 있고 몸을 속일 수 있다.

24 세균으로부터 당신 자신을 보호하는 몇 가지 방법이 있다.

25 먼저 비누와 따뜻한 물로 손을 씻어라.

26 균형 잡힌 식단은 당신의 몸을 튼튼하고 건강하게 해줄 것이다.

27 규칙적으로 운동하고 충분한 잠을 자는 것도 중요하다.

28 마지막으로 필요한 주사를 맞아라.

29 그것들은 세균을 막는 최고의 방어 수단이다.

30 만약 당신이 이 단계를 따른다면, 당신은 "나쁜" 세균의 희생자가 되지 않을 것이다.

31 나를 더 복제해 줘.

32 몸을 지키는 게 내 일이야.

33 정말 맛있는 식사였어!

34 먹을 세균이 더 있니?

35 내년에는 내 사촌을 보낼게.

36 그때 그가 또 싸우려고 널 만나게 될 거야!

37 지금 내가 무엇을 할 수 있을까?

38 나는 어떤 세균과도 싸울 준비가 되어 있어.

39 우리는 포기한다.

40 우리는 널 아프게 할 수 없어.

※ 다음 문장을 우리말로 쓰시오.

1   Germs are everywhere, but it is impossible to see them with your eyes.

➡ _____

2   There are two major kinds of germs: bacteria and viruses.

➡ _____

3   Bacteria are very small creatures.

➡ _____

4   Some are good.

➡ _____

5   They can help you digest the food that you eat.

➡ _____

6   Others are bad and can make you sick.

➡ _____

7   Viruses are germs that can only live inside the cells of other living bodies.

➡ _____

8   They cause diseases such as the flu.

➡ _____

9   "Bad" germs can enter your body through your skin, mouth, nose, and eyes.

➡ _____

10   What happens when they invade?

➡ _____

11   The germs multiply in the body.

➡ _____

12   Your body becomes a war zone.

➡ _____

13   You start to feel tired and weak.

➡ _____

14   Luckily, your body has an army of defense.

➡ _____

15   The T eslls sound the alarm!

➡ _____

16   The B cells arrive to fight the germs with antibodies.

➡ _____

17 The macrophage cells show up and eat the germs.

➡ _____

18 Together, this army is called the white blood cells.

➡ _____

19 If all goes well, they win the fight.

➡ _____

20 In a few days, you start to feel better.

➡ _____

21 The body remembers the invader, so it cannot make copies of itself again.

➡ _____

22 But the germs are smart, too.

➡ _____

23 They can change form and trick the body.

➡ _____

24 There are several ways to protect yourself from germs.

➡ _____

25 First, wash your hands with soap and warm water.

➡ _____

26 A balanced diet will keep your body strong and healthy.

➡ _____

27 It is also important to exercise regularly and get plenty of sleep.

➡ _____

28 Finally, get the necessary shots.

➡ _____

29 They are the best defense against germs.

➡ _____

30 If you follow these steps, you will not be a victim of "bad" germs.

➡ _____

31 Make more copies of me.

➡ _____

32 It's my job to defend the body.

➡ _____

33 That was a nice meal!

➡ _____

34 Are there any more germs to eat?

➡ _____

35 Next year, I'll send in my cousin.

➡ _____

36 He'll see you then for another fight!

➡ _____

37 I'm ready to fight any germs.

➡ _____

38 We can't make you sick.

➡ _____

※ 다음 괄호 안의 단어들을 우리말에 맞도록 바르게 배열하시오.

1 (everywhere, / are / germs / but / is / it / impossible / see / to / your / eyes. / with / them)
➡ _____

2 (are / major / there / kinds / two / germs: / of / viruses. / and / bacteria)
➡ _____

3 (very / creatures. / small / bacteria / are)
➡ _____

4 (good. / some / are)
➡ _____

5 (help / they / digest / can / you / the / eat. / you / that / food)
➡ _____

6 (bad / others / and / are / you / can / sick. / make)
➡ _____

7 (germs / that / are / viruses / live / can / inside / only / other / of / living / the / bodies. / cells)
➡ _____

8 (diseases / they / cause / the / such / flu. / as)
➡ _____

9 (your / germs / enter / "bad" / body / can / your / through / mouth, / and / skin, / eyes. / nose,)
➡ _____

10 (happens / they / what / invade? / when)
➡ _____

11 (the / multiply / body. / the / germs / in)
➡ _____

12 (body / a / your / zone / war / becomes)
➡ _____

13 (start / tired / you / feel / to / weak. / and)
➡ _____

14 (luckily, / body / has / army / your / defense. / an / of)
➡ _____

15 (the / cells / T / alarm! / the / sound)
➡ _____

16 (the / cells / to / B / fight / arrive / the / antibodies. / with / germs)
➡ _____

17 (cells / the / macrophage / up / eat / and / show / germs. / the)
➡ _____

18 (together, / is / army / this / called / the / blood / cells. / white)
➡ _____

19 (all / well, / if / goes / win / they / fight. / the)
➡ _____

20 (a / days, / few / in / you / feel / to / better. / start)
➡ _____

1 세균은 어디에나 있지만 눈으로 세균을 보는 것은 불가능하다.

2 세균에는 두 가지 주요한 종류가 있다: 박테리아와 바이러스이다.

3 박테리아는 매우 작은 생물이다.

4 어떤 것들은 좋다.

5 그것들은 당신이 먹는 음식을 소화하는 데 도움을 줄 수 있다.

6 다른 것들은 나쁘고 당신을 아프게 할 수 있다.

7 바이러스는 다른 살아 있는 몸의 세포 안에서만 살 수 있는 세균이다.

8 그들은 독감과 같은 질병을 일으킨다.

9 '나쁜' 세균은 피부, 입, 코, 눈을 통해 몸에 들어갈 수 있다.

10 그들이 침입하면 어떻게 되는가?

11 세균은 몸속에서 증식한다.

12 당신의 몸은 전쟁 지역이 된다.

13 당신은 피곤하고 약해지기 시작한다.

14 다행히, 당신의 몸은 방어 부대를 가지고 있다.

15 T세포가 경보를 발한다!

16 B세포는 항체로 세균과 싸우기 위해 도착한다.

17 대식 세포가 나타나서 세균을 먹는다.

18 이 군대는 함께 백혈구라고 부른다.

19 모든 것이 잘되면 싸움에서 이긴다.

20 며칠 후면 당신은 회복되기 시작한다.

21 (body / the / remembers / invader, / the / so / cannot / it / copies / itself / of / again. / make)
➡ _____

22 (the / but / germs / too. / smart, / are)
➡ _____

23 (can / change / they / and / form / the / body. / trick)
➡ _____

24 (are / there / ways / to / several / protect / germs. / yourself / from)
➡ _____

25 (first, / hands / with / wash / your / soap / water. / and / warm)
➡ _____

26 (diet / balanced / will / a / body / keep / healthy. / your / and / strong)
➡ _____

27 (it / also / important / is / exercise / to / and / plenty / regularly / of / sleep. / get)
➡ _____

28 (finally, / the / shots. / necessary / get)
➡ _____

29 (are / best / they / the / defense / germs. / against)
➡ _____

30 (you / these / follow / steps, / if / you / be / not / will / germs. / a / "bad" / of / victim)
➡ _____

31 (copies / make / me. / of / more)
➡ _____

32 (it's / to / job / my / body. / the / defend)
➡ _____

33 (was / meal! / that / nice / a)
➡ _____

34 (there / more / are / any / eat? / to / germs)
➡ _____

35 (year, / next / send / cousin. / I'll / in / my)
➡ _____

36 (see / then / he'll / for / fight! / another / you)
➡ _____

37 (can / now? / what / do / I)
➡ _____

38 (fight / ready / to / I'm / germs. / any)
➡ _____

39 (give / up. / we)
➡ _____

40 (can't / sick. / we / make / you)
➡ _____

21 몸은 침입자를 기억하므로 침입자는 다시 복제할 수 없다.

22 하지만 세균들도 영리하다.

23 그들은 형태를 바꿀 수 있고 몸을 속일 수 있다.

24 세균으로부터 당신 자신을 보호하는 몇 가지 방법이 있다.

25 먼저 비누와 따뜻한 물로 손을 씻어라.

26 균형 잡힌 식단은 당신의 몸을 튼튼하고 건강하게 해줄 것이다.

27 규칙적으로 운동하고 충분한 잠을 자는 것도 중요하다.

28 마지막으로 필요한 주사를 맞아라.

29 그것들은 세균을 막는 최고의 방어 수단이다.

30 만약 당신이 이 단계를 따른다면, 당신은 "나쁜" 세균의 희생자가 되지 않을 것이다.

31 나를 더 복제해 줘.

32 몸을 지키는 게 내 일이야.

33 정말 맛있는 식사였어!

34 먹을 세균이 더 있니?

35 내년에는 내 사촌을 보낼게.

36 그때 그가 또 싸우려고 널 만나게 될 거야!

37 지금 내가 무엇을 할 수 있을까?

38 나는 어떤 세균과도 싸울 준비가 되어 있어.

39 우리는 포기한다.

40 우리는 널 아프게 할 수 없어.

※ **다음 우리말을 영어로 쓰시오.**

1 세균은 어디에나 있지만 눈으로 세균을 보는 것은 불가능하다.
➡ _____

2 세균에는 두 가지 주요한 종류가 있다: 박테리아와 바이러스이다.
➡ _____

3 박테리아는 매우 작은 생물이다.
➡ _____

4 어떤 것들은 좋다.
➡ _____

5 그것들은 당신이 먹는 음식을 소화하는 데 도움을 줄 수 있다.
➡ _____

6 다른 것들은 나쁘고 당신을 아프게 할 수 있다.
➡ _____

7 바이러스는 다른 살아 있는 몸의 세포 안에서만 살 수 있는 세균이다.
➡ _____

8 그들은 독감과 같은 질병을 일으킨다.
➡ _____

9 '나쁜' 세균은 피부, 입, 코, 눈을 통해 몸에 들어갈 수 있다.
➡ _____

10 그들이 침입하면 어떻게 되는가?
➡ _____

11 세균은 몸속에서 증식한다.
➡ _____

12 당신의 몸은 전쟁 지역이 된다.
➡ _____

13 당신은 피곤하고 약해지는 것을 느끼기 시작한다.
➡ _____

14 다행히도, 당신의 몸은 방어 군대를 가지고 있다.
➡ _____

15 T세포가 경보를 발한다!
➡ _____

16 B세포는 항체로 세균과 싸우기 위해 도착한다.
➡ _____

17 대식 세포가 나타나서 세균을 먹는다.
➡ _____

18 이 군대는 함께 백혈구라고 부른다.
➡ _____

19 모든 것이 잘되면 싸움에서 이긴다.
➡ _____

20 며칠 후면 당신은 회복되기 시작한다.
➡ _____

21 몸은 침입자를 기억하므로 다시 복제할 수 없다.
➡ _____

22 하지만 세균들도 영리하다.
➡ _____

23 그들은 형태를 바꿀 수 있고 몸을 속일 수 있다.
➡ _____

24 세균으로부터 여러분 자신을 보호하는 몇 가지 방법이 있다.
➡ _____

25 먼저 비누와 따뜻한 물로 손을 씻어라.
➡ _____

26 균형 잡힌 식단은 당신의 몸을 튼튼하고 건강하게 해줄 것이다.
➡ _____

27 규칙적으로 운동하고 충분한 잠을 자는 것도 중요하다.
➡ _____

28 마지막으로 필요한 주사를 맞아라.
➡ _____

29 그것들은 세균을 막는 최고의 방어이다.
➡ _____

30 만약 당신이 이 단계를 따른다면, 당신은 "나쁜" 세균의 희생자가 되지 않을 것이다.
➡ _____

31 나를 더 복제해 주세요.
➡ _____

32 몸을 지키는 게 내 일이야.
➡ _____

33 정말 맛있는 식사였어!
➡ _____

34 먹을 세균이 더 있니?
➡ _____

35 내년에는 내 사촌을 보낼게.
➡ _____

36 그때 그가 또 싸우려고 널 보게 될 거야!
➡ _____

37 지금 내가 무엇을 할 수 있을까?
➡ _____

38 나는 어떤 세균과도 싸울 준비가 되어 있어.
➡ _____

39 우리는 포기한다.
➡ _____

40 우리는 널 아프게 할 수 없어.
➡ _____

※ 다음 우리말과 일치하도록 빈칸에 알맞은 말을 쓰시오.

My Writing Portfolio - Step 1

1. Sit _____, Move _____

2. It is _____ to _____ online games too much.

3. It is time _____ go _____ and exercise.

4. Stay _____

5. _____ too many snacks is not _____ for your health.

6. It is _____ to eat _____ fruit and vegetables.

1. 덜 앉고, 더 움직여라
2. 온라인 게임을 너무 많이 하는 것은 위험하다.
3. 이제 외출해서 운동할 시간이다.
4. 건강을 유지해라
5. 과자를 너무 많이 먹는 것은 건강에 좋지 않다.
6. 과일과 채소를 충분히 먹는 것이 중요하다.

Words in Action - B

1. Frida Kahlo was a _____ _____ [artist].

2. She is _____ for her _____ paintings.

3. Charles Schulz was a _____ who created the famous _____ Charlie Brown.

4. Park Gyeongri was a _____ Korean _____.

5. She _____ 25 years _____ *Toji*.

6. James Cameron is the _____ of the movie, *Avatar*.

7. Jang Yeongsil was a(n) _____ [scientist] who _____ water clocks.

1. Frida Kahlo는 멕시코 화가[예술가]였다.
2. 그녀는 독특한 그림으로 유명하다.
3. Charles Schulz는 유명한 캐릭터인 Charlie Brown을 만든 만화가였다.
4. 박경리는 위대한 한국 작가였다.
5. 그녀는 토지를 쓰는 데 25년이 걸렸다.
6. James Cameron은 영화 '아바타'의 감독이다.
7. 장영실은 물시계를 만든 발명가[과학자]였다.

Wrap Up - Reading

1. Every day you _____ your hands _____ _____ different things.

2. You _____ your phone and computer.

3. You open and _____ doors _____ your hands, _____.

4. There _____ germs on everything _____ you touch.

5. If you eat snacks _____ your hands, the germs on your hands can _____ _____ your body.

6. Then _____ _____ you do?

7 _____ your hands _____ soap!

1. 여러분은 매일 다른 것들을 만지기 위해 손을 사용한다.
2. 여러분은 여러분의 전화기와 컴퓨터를 만진다.
3. 여러분은 또한 손으로 문을 열고 닫는다.
4. 여러분이 만지는 모든 것에는 세균이 있다.
5. 만약 여러분이 손으로 과자를 먹는다면, 여러분의 손에 있는 세균은 여러분의 몸으로 들어갈 수 있다.
6. 그럼 어떻게 해야 할까?
7. 비누로 손을 씻어라!

※ 다음 우리말을 영어로 쓰시오.

My Writing Portfolio - Step 1

1. 덜 앉고, 더 움직여라
➡ _____

2. 온라인 게임을 너무 많이 하는 것은 위험하다.
➡ _____

3. 이제 외출해서 운동할 시간이다.
➡ _____

4. 건강을 유지해라
➡ _____

5. 과자를 너무 많이 먹는 것은 건강에 좋지 않다.
➡ _____

6. 과일과 채소를 충분히 먹는 것이 중요하다.
➡ _____

Words in Action - B

1. Frida Kahlo는 멕시코 화가[예술가]였다.
➡ _____

2. 그녀는 독특한 그림으로 유명하다.
➡ _____

3. Charles Schulz는 유명한 캐릭터인 Charlie Brown을 만든 만화가였다.
➡ _____

4. 박경리는 위대한 한국 작가였다.
➡ _____

5. 그녀는 토지를 쓰는 데 25년이 걸렸다.
➡ _____

6. James Cameron은 영화 '아바타'의 감독이다.
➡ _____

7. 장영실은 물시계를 만든 발명가[과학자]였다.
➡ _____

Wrap Up - Reading

1. 여러분은 매일 다른 것들을 만지기 위해 손을 사용한다.
➡ _____

2. 여러분은 여러분의 전화기와 컴퓨터를 만진다.
➡ _____

3. 여러분은 또한 손으로 문을 열고 닫는다.
➡ _____

4. 여러분이 만지는 모든 것에는 세균이 있다.
➡ _____

5. 만약 여러분이 손으로 과자를 먹는다면, 여러분의 손에 있는 세균은 여러분의 몸으로 들어갈 수 있다.
➡ _____

6. 그럼 어떻게 해야 할까?
➡ _____

7. 비누로 손을 씻어라!
➡ _____

MEMO

MEMO

적중100

1학기

정답 및 해설

천재 | 이재영

중
2

영어 기출 문제집

적중'100

1학기

정답 및 해설

천재 | 이재영

중 2

적중'100

Off to a Good Start

핵심 Check   p.10~11

1 (1) are, planning to / planning

(2) What, your plans / I'm planning to

(3) have any plans / thinking of

2 (1) better   (2) Why don't you

(3) What should I do / should study

교과서 대화문 익히기

Check(√) True or False   p.12

1 F   2 T   3 F   4 T

시험대비 실력평가   p.08

01 ④	02 get off	03 ⑤	04 ②
05 ③	06 eco-friendly		
07 (s)trange	08 ①		

01 ④는 유의어 관계이고 나머지는 반의어 관계이다.

02 get off to a good start: 좋은 출발을 하다

03 사람이 규칙적으로 또는 반복적으로 자주 하는 행동: habit(습관)

04 열심히 일해 뭔가를 얻거나 이루다: achieve(성취하다)

05 • clean up: ~를 치우다[청소하다] • care for: ~를 보살피다[돌보다]

06 eco-friendly: 친환경적인, 환경 친화적인

07 일반적인, 정상적인 것과 다른: 이상한 (strange)

08 ①은 '학년'의 의미로 쓰이고, 나머지는 '점수, 성적'의 의미로 쓰였다.

서술형 시험대비   p.09

01 (1) birth   (2) stressful   (3) light

02 (1) once in a while   (2) for an hour   (3) jump rope

03 (1) hard   (2) dish   (3) plant

04 (1) messy   (2) weekly   (3) goal   (4) manage

05 (1) because of   (2) in front of   (3) get some rest

06 (1) (b)ehave   (2) (h)abit   (3) (u)seful   (4) (d)owntime

01 (1) 빠른 : 느린 = 죽음 : 탄생 (2) 놀라움 : 놀라운 = 스트레스 : 스트레스가 많은 (3) 끝 : 시작 = 가벼운 : 무거운

02 (1) once in a while: 가끔 (2) for an hour: 한 시간 동안 (3) jump rope: 줄넘기를 하다

03 (1) hard: 열심히; 어려운 (2) dish: 접시; 요리 (3) plant: 식물; 심다

04 (1) messy: 지저분한 (2) weekly: 주간의 (3) goal: 목표 (4) manage: 관리하다

05 (1) because of: ~ 때문에 (2) in front of: ~ 앞에 (3) get some rest: 약간의 휴식을 취하다

06 (1) behave: 예의 바르게 행동하다 (2) habit: 습관, 버릇 (3) useful: 유용한 (4) downtime: 한가한[휴식] 시간

교과서 확인학습   p.14~15

Communicate: Listen - Listen and Answer Dialog 1

special goal / whin a gold medal / What about / manage, better / How, achieve / planning to, weekly / Sounds

Communicate: Listen - Listen and Answer Dialog 2

for a mimute / What / working on / Good for / Have, give, adivce / a lot of / I'm planning to / Why don't you / once in a while

Communicate: Listen - Listen More

like to / great, can plant / What kind of / planning to plant / be / going to be, should bring / I will / Why don't , put on / No problem, on

Communicate: Listen - Listen and Complete

How, achieve, goal / I'd like to

My Speaking Portfolio

1 eco-friendly, I'm planning to

2 to pass, take, classes, going to watch, on

3 have a goal, planning to review, solve, problems

Wrap Up - Listening ❸

are, going to / planning, with / sounds, have any plans / visit, eat / fun Enjoy

Wrap Up - Listening ❹

look down, problem / don't have / Why don't you / get, ideas

01 ⑤   02 ⑤   03 ④   04 ④

01 You 'd better+동사원형 ~.은 '너는 ~하는 게 좋겠다'라는 의미로 충고하기 표현이다.

02 I'm planning to ~는 '나는 ~할 계획이다'라는 뜻으로, I'm going to ~와 바꿔 쓸 수 있다.

03 ④는 jacket을 왜 입었는지 묻는 문장이고, 나머지는 jacket을 입으라고 충고하는 문장이다.

04 계획을 묻는 표현이 오는 것이 자연스럽다.

01 ②   02 weekly   03 ④   04 going
05 ②   06 in   07 downtime
08 She is planning to study hard.   09 ⑤
10 ①, ③   11 ⑤   12 ④   13 ②
14 도서관에서 과학 잡지를 읽으면
15 he has a science project, and he doesn't any ideas

01 주어진 문장은 '한번 보고 조언 좀 해줘.'라는 의미로 '공부 시간이 많구나.'라는 문장 앞에 오는 것이 가장 적절하다.

02 weekly: 주간의

03 문맥상 칭찬의 표현이 들어가야 한다. ④는 '끔찍한 일이구나'라는 뜻이다.

04 I'm planning to ~.는 I'm going to ~.로 바꿔 쓸 수 있다.

05 ②를 제외한 모든 문장은 휴식 시간을 추가하라고 조언하는 문장이다.

06 once in a while: 가끔, 이따금

07 누군가 일을 멈추고 쉴 수 있는 시간: 휴식 시간(downtime)

08 민수의 여동생은 열심히 공부할 계획이라고 말했다.

09 ⓐ What[How] about you?: 너는 어때? ⓑ how: 어떻게

10 계획을 말할 때에는 I'm planning to ~., I have a plan to ~.,I'm going to ~., I will ~. 등을 쓴다.

11 민솔은 시간을 더 잘 관리하기 위해 매일 그리고 주간 일정표를 만들 계획이다.

12 What's the problem?(무슨 일이야?)은 What's wrong?, What happened (to you)?, What's the matter?, What's up? 등으로 바꿔 쓸 수 있다.

13 Why don't you + 동사원형 ~?은 '~하는 게 어때?'라는 뜻으로 충고하기 표현이다.

14 that way는 부사구로 과학 잡지를 읽는 것에 의해서라는 의미이다.

15 look down은 '우울해 보이다'라는 의미이다. 윤수는 과학 프로젝트가 있는데 아무 생각이 나질 않아서 기분이 우울했다.

01 Why don't you ride a bike?
02 (1) Thank you for your advice.
    (2) Why don't we study together?
    (3) You'd better learn some Chinese words.
03 (1) have any plans   (2) thinking of
    (3) planning to go
04 kind
05 Why don't you
06 She's planning to plant some tomatoes and peppers.
07 It's going to be sunny.

01 충고나 제안을 나타내는 표현으로는 Why don't you+동사원형 ~?이 있다.

03 (1) Do you have any plans ~?: ~에 무슨 계획이 있니?
(2) I'm thinking of ~: 나는 ~할까 생각 중이다 (3) I'm planning to ~: 나는 ~할 계획이다

04 kind: 종류

05 You should ~.는 '너는 ~해야 한다'라고 충고를 나타내는 말로 Why don't you ~? / You'd better ~. 등으로 바꿔 쓸 수 있다.

06 할머니는 토마토와 고추를 심을 계획이다.

07 토요일 날씨는 맑을 것이라고 했다.

[교과서]

Grammar

1 (1) who   (2) which   (3) who   (4) who
2 (1) If   (2) takes   (3) will give   (4) drink

01 (1) who   (2) which   (3) which   (4) who   (5) which
02 (1) If you hurry up, you will catch the bus.
    (2) If it is fine tomorrow, we will go on a picnic.
    (3) If school finishes early today, Kate will read a book at home.
    (4) If you are tired, you can sit here.
03 (1) who   (2) which   (3) who   (4) that   (5) that

01 주격 관계대명사는 선행사가 사람일 경우 who, 사물일 경우 which를 쓴다.

3

02 「If+주어+현재시제, 주어+will[can/may]+동사원형 ~.」의 어순이다.

03 (1) 선행사가 사람(a boy)이므로 who를 쓴다. (2) 선행사가 사물(the pictures)이므로 which 를 쓴다. (3) 선행사가 사람(a friend)이므로 who를 쓴다. (4) 선행사가 사람(the girl)이므로 that을 쓴다. (5) 선행사가 사물(the river)이므로 which 를 쓴다.

시험대비 실력평가
p.23~25

01 ⑤ 02 ① 03 ③
04 (1) who[that] (2) that 05 ④ 06 ②
07 ④ 08 If Susan does not get up now, she will miss the train. 또는 Susan will miss the train if she does not get up now. 09 ① 10 ⑤
11 ⑤ 12 ④ 13 ⑤
14 which → that 15 ② 16 ④
17 What will you do if he visits your home tomorrow?
18 ① 19 ① 20 ⑤

01 첫 번째 문장은 이유, 두 번째 문장은 조건을 나타낸다.

02 ⓐ 선행사가 사람이고 주격이므로 who를 쓴다. ⓑ is의 보어이므로 동명사나 to부정사가 올 수 있다.

03 '~하면'이라는 조건의 접속사가 필요하다.

04 (1) 선행사가 사람(the boy)이므로 which 대신 who나 that을 써야 한다. (2) 선행사 앞에 최상급이 왔으므로 관계 대명사 that을 쓴다.

05 조건을 나타내는 if절은 미래의 의미이더라도 현재 시제로 써야 한다.

06 선행사가 사람이고 주격이므로 관계대명사 who가 들어가야 알맞다.

07 선행사 the building이 사물이고 주격이므로 관계대명사 which가 들어가야 알맞다.

08 첫 문장이 두 번째 문장의 조건이 되므로 접속사 if를 이용하여 연결한다.

09 첫 문장은 선행사가 사람이고 주격이므로 관계대명사 who가 들어가야 알맞다. 두 번째 문장은 선행사가 사물이고 목적격이므로 관계대명사 which가 들어가야 알맞다.

10 ①~④는 내용상 조건을 나타내는 접속사 if가 와야 하고, ⑤는 동사 think의 목적어 역할을 하는 접속사 that이 적절하다.

11 선행사가 사물이고, 관계사절에서 a bag은 주격, the smart phone은 목적격으로 쓰이고 있으므로 관계대명사 which가 알맞다.

12 선행사가 사물이고 주격으로 쓰이는 관계대명사는 which이다.

13 '주말마다'는 반복적인 습관을 나타내므로 현재시제를 사용한다.

14 선행사가 사람과 동물일 때는 that을 사용한다.

15 '만약 ~하면'의 뜻으로 조건절을 이끄는 if와 '~인지 아닌지'의 뜻으로 명사절을 이끄는 접속사 역할을 하는 if가 알맞다.

16 <보기>와 ④는 관계대명사 ①은 지시부사(그렇게), ②는 접속사, ③은 지시대명사, ⑤는 지시형용사로 쓰였다.

17 미래의 일이므로 조건을 나타내는 문장의 주절은 미래 시제를 사용한다.

18 조건의 if절에서는 현재형으로 미래 시제를 나타낸다. ① if I'll have → if I have

19 ① 선행사가 사람이므로 which를 쓸 수 없다.

20 접속사 if가 '~한다면'으로 해석되면 부사절을 이끌고, '~인지 아닌지'로 해석되면 명사절을 이끈다. 주어진 문장과 ⑤의 if는 명사절을 이끄는 접속사이다.

서술형 시험대비
p.26~27

01 that[which
02 (1) I won't be → I'm not / I am not
   (2) you'll pass → you pass
03 that
04 (1) If it rains tomorrow, we won't go hiking.
   (2) Unless you hurry, you will miss the train.
05 (1) The young lady who is sitting on the bench is our music teacher.
   (2) We found a dog which was running toward us.
   (3) This is the firefighter that saved the baby from the burning building.
   (4) This is the only story that is interesting to read.
06 (1) If (2) when (3) Unless
07 (1) I know the woman who[that] is standing by the car.
   (2) Did you see the car which[that] has only two doors?
   (3) This is a restaurant which[that] is famous for its spaghetti.
   (4) Mrs. Brown who[that] lives next door is my English teacher.
08 If she doesn't get up early, she will miss the train.
09 which[that], was
10 (1) If the weather is nice, I always walk to school.
   (2) If it rains on weekends, we watch TV.
   (3) If I am late for class, my teacher gets very angry.
11 I know the[a] doctor who[that] likes baseball.
12 (1) Unless you leave (2) If it doesn't

선행사가 동물(the dog)이므로 which 또는 that을 관계대명사로 쓴다.

02 조건의 if절에서는 미래의 일을 현재형으로 나타낸다.

03 선행사가 사람일 때와 사물일 때 모두 쓸 수 있는 관계대명사는 that이다.

04 (1) if 이하가 조건절이므로, 현재시제가 미래의 내용을 대신한다. (2) unless는 '만약 ~하 지 않으면'의 뜻이므로 not을 붙일 필요가 없다.

05 (1) The young lady를 선행사로 한다. (2) a dog를 선행사로 한다. (3) the firefighter를 선행사로 한다. (4) the only story를 선행사로 한다.

06 when은 때, if는 조건을 나타낸다. unless는 if ~ not의 뜻이다.

07 (1) 선행사가 the woman이므로 주격 관계대명사 who 또는 that으로 연결한다. (2) 선행사가 the car이므로 주격 관계대명사 which 또는 that으로 연결한다. (3) 선행사가 a restaurant이므로 주격 관계대명사 which 또는 that으로 연결한다. (4) 선행사가 Mrs. Brown이므로 주격 관계대명사 who 또는 that으로 연결한다.

08 콤마가 있으므로 if절을 주절 앞에 둔다.

09 선행사가 the traffic accident이므로 관계대명사는 which 또는 that이다. 또, 단수이므로 was가 알맞다.

10 if는 종속절을 이끄는 접속사이다.

11 선행사가 사람이고 주격이므로 who나 that을 쓴다.

12 unless는 if ~ not과 같은 뜻이다.

Reading

확인문제 p.28

1 T 2 F 3 F

확인문제 p.29

1 T 2 F 3 T 4 F

교과서 확인학습 A p.30~31

01 Beginning   02 How, to   03 asked, for
04 Let's, hare, easy   05 That, Change
06 it up   07 bring, into, gets
08 worry   09 cleaner, than 10 drives, crazy
11 Remember, member
12 have to, care for   13 behave, put, on

14 change, list   15 That, to
16 change, tell, hundred   17 between, and
18 means, Birth, Death   19 change, friends
20 sound   21 may, perfect
22 add, to, even, before
23 one, first, another
24 okay, mind, life
25 on, easy, better, luck   26 Plans
27 asked, readers, What, for

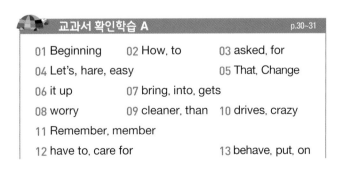

교과서 확인학습 B p.32~33

1 Beginning a new school year is stressful to many students.

2 How can we get off to a good start?

3 Teen Today asked Raccoon 97, a popular webtoon artist, for ideas.

4 Let's think about things that are hard to change or easy to change.

5 Things That Are Hard to Change

6 Your Messy Room_ You clean it up.

7 Then you bring new stuff into it, and it soon gets messy again.

8 But don't worry

9 Your room is much cleaner than mine.

10 Your Family_ There is always someone in your family who drives you crazy.

11 Remember that he or she is still a member of your family.

12 You just have to live together and care for each other.

13 Your Name on Your Teacher's List_ If you are late or do not behave, your teacher will put your name on his or her list.

14 You cannot easily change the list.

15 Things That Are Easy to Change

16 Your Underpants_ If you change them every day, your mom will not tell you one hundred and one times.

17 "Life is C between B and D."

18 It means "Life is Choice between Birth and Death."

19 Your Friends_ You can change your friends.

20 Does it sound strange?

21 You may think that you have the perfect number of friends.

22 If you add a new friend to the list, however, you

23 Your Mind_ You thought one thing at first, and now you think another thing.

24 That is okay. As someone said, "If you can change your mind, you can change your life."

25 "Focus on the things that are easy to change, and try to make today better than yesterday. Good luck!"

26 Top 5 Plans for the Year

27 We asked 200 Teen Today readers, "What are your plans for the year?"

16 That은 지시대명사로 앞 문장의 내용을 받을 수 있다.

17 ⓒ, ① 명사적 용법 ②, ⑤ 부사적 용법 ③, ④ 형용사적 용법

18 plans for the year: 올해의 계획

19 ④의 내용은 본문에 언급되지 않았다.

20 ⓑ, ⑤ 형용사를 수식하는 부사적 용법 ①, ③ 명사적 용법 ②, ④ 형용사적 용법

21 선행사가 사물이고 주격이므로 that이나 which가 알맞다.

22 clean up은 '타동사+부사'의 이어동사이므로 목적어 it은 부사 앞에 위치해야 한다.

23 문맥상 걱정하지 말라는 말이 알맞다.

24 주어진 문장의 it은 전화기로 친구들에게 문자를 보내거나 게임 하는 것을 가리키므로 그것을 서술하는 문장 다음에 와야 한다.

25 때를 나타내는 접속사 when이 알맞다.

26 from now on: 앞으로 계속해서

27 turn off: ~을 끄다

28 ④ 글쓴이가 주로 어떤 앱들을 다운받는지는 언급되지 않았다.

시험대비 실력평가　　　　　　　　　　p.34~37

01 ②　　02 어떻게 하면 우리는 좋은 출발을 할 수 있을까?　　03 ③　　04 ①, ⑤　　05 ⑤

06 ②　　07 ③　　08 easily　　09 ①

지각하는 경우 ② 예의 바르게 행동하지 않을 때 10 ①

11 네가 친구들을 바꿀 수 있는 것　　12 ③

13 add　　14 ①, ④　　15 ④　　16 처음에는 한 가지 것을 생각하고 지금은 또 다른 것을 생각하는 것

17 ①　　18 What are your plans for the year?

19 ④　　20 ⑤　　21 ⑤　　22 You clean it up.　　23 ②　　24 ③　　25 ④

26 앞으로는 그 습관을 깨뜨리기 위해 두 가지 일을 하겠다.

27 ②　　28 ④

01 be stressful to: ~에게 스트레스가 되다

02 get off to a good start: 좋은 출발을 하다

03 ⓒ, ③ 관계대명사 주격 ①, ②, ⑤ 접속사 ④ It was ~ that 강조구문

04 비교급 강조 부사(구)는 much, far, even, a lot 등이 있다.

05 ⑤ Raccoon 97은 여러분의 방은 내 방보다 더 깨끗하다고 말하고 있다.

06 너의 가족 중에는 너를 화나게 하는 사람이 있다는 말 다음에 와야 한다.

07 care for: ~을 돌보다

08 동사를 수식하므로 부사형으로 바꾼다.

10 조건을 나타내는 접속사 if가 알맞다.

11 it은 인칭대명사로 앞에 나온 문장을 받을 수 있다.

12 ⓑ와 ③의 may는 '~일지도 모르다'의 뜻으로 약한 추측을 나타낸다.

13 어떤 것을 늘리거나 완성하거나 개선시키기 위해 다른 것에 넣거나 덧붙이다: add(더하다, 첨가하다)

14 비교급 강조 부사(구)는 much, far, even, a lot 등이 있다.

15 문맥상 '또 다른 것'의 의미인 another가 알맞다.

서술형 시험대비　　　　　　　　　　p.38~39

01 who[that]　　02 after　　03 If　　04 We can't[cannot] easily change the list.　　05 팬티

06 strangely → strange　　07 that　　08 better

09 other → another　　10 If　　11 on

12 luck　　13 readers　　14 weekends → weekend

15 like　　16 with　　17 have[take]　　18 She will visit the art center to enjoy a free concert.

01 선행사가 사람이고 주격이므로 who나 that을 쓴다.

02 care for=look after: ~을 돌보다

03 문맥상 조건을 나타내는 접속사 if를 쓴다.

04 리스트를 쉽게 바꿀 수 없다.

05 them은 앞 문장의 your underpants를 받는다.

06 sound+형용사: ~하게 들리다

07 think의 목적어가 되는 명사절을 이끄는 접속사 that이 온다.

08 good의 비교급 better로 고친다.

09 other 뒤에는 복수명사, another 뒤에는 단수명사가 온다.

10 문맥상 조건을 나타내는 접속사 if를 쓴다.

11 focus on: ~에 집중하다

12 여러분 자신의 능력이나 노력에서 오는 것이 아닌 것으로 여러분에게 일어나는 성공이나 좋은 일들: luck(운)

13 read의 행위자를 나타내는 명사 reader로 고친다.

14 every 뒤에는 단수명사가 온다.

15 like: ~와 같은 / alike: 비슷한

16 with: ~와 함께

17 get[have, take] some rest: 휴식을 좀 취하다

01 ④	02 in front	03 ②	04 ④
05 ②	06 ④	07 (m)essy	08 ⑤
09 ④	10 ⑤	11 ④	12 ③
13 ⑤	14 I'm planning to study hard.		
15 better	16 ①	17 ③	18 ②
19 am	20 ①	21 ①	22 ①
23 If, are	24 ⑤	25 ①	26 What is
the name of the tallest boy that[who] just came in?			
27 ②	28 artist	29 바꾸기 어렵거나 바꾸기	
쉬운 일들에 대해 생각해 보자.		30 ③	31 ③
32 I text my friends or play games on the phone.			
33 ②	34 ④	35 having → to have	
36 ⑤	37 free	38 ①	

01 ④는 유의어 관계이고 나머지는 반의어 관계이다.

02 in front of: ~의 앞에

03 많은 사람이 좋아하거나 즐기는: 인기 있는(popular)

04 ④는 '접시, 그릇'의 뜻으로 쓰였고, 나머지는 '요리, 음식'의 뜻으로 쓰였다.

05 focus on: ~에 집중하다, ~에 주력하다

06 stand in line: 일렬로 나란히 서다 / drive ~ crazy: ~를 화나게 하다

07 더럽고 깨끗하지 않은: messy(지저분한)

08 「You'd better+동사원형 ~」은 상대방에게 충고를 할 때 사용하는 표현이다.

09 계획을 묻는 표현이 오는 것이 자연스럽다.

10 You should+동사원형 ~.과 유사한 표현에는 You had better+동사원형 ~. / I advise you to+동사원형 ~. / I suggest you+동사원형 ~. / Why don't you+동사원형 ~? / How[What] about ~? 등이 있다.

11 ⑤ 다음 주말의 계획에 대한 물음에 대해, 특별한 것이 없다고 대답한 다음 그것이 기대된다고 말하는 것은 어색하다.

12 for a minute: 잠깐 / Good for you.: 잘했다.

13 have a look: 보다

14 I'm planning to+동사원형 ~: 나는 ~할 계획이다.

15 Why don't you+동사원형 ~?은 You should+동사원형 ~. / You'd better+동사원형 ~. 등으로 바꿔 쓸 수 있다.

16 선행사가 사람(the girl)이고 주격이므로 who가 적절하다.

17 if가 이끄는 절이 부사절이면 미래의 일이라도 현재시제가 미래시제를 대신한다.

18 선행사가 동물일 경우에는 관계대명사 which나 that 둘 다 쓸 수 있는데, 둘 중 어느 것을 더 좋아하냐고 물을 때는 의문사 which로 시작해야 하므로 ②가 정답이다.

19 unless는 부정의 의미를 포함하고 있다. unless = If ~ not

20 관계대명사 that 다음에 be동사 were가 왔으므로 선행사로 복수

명사가 와야 한다.

21 '만약 ~하면'의 조건절을 이끄는 접속사와 '~인지 아닌지'의 명사절을 이끄는 접속사 역할을 하는 if가 적절하다.

22 ①은 의문대명사이고, 나머지는 사물을 선행사로 하는 관계대명사 주격이다.

23 if는 '만일 ~라면, ~한다면'이라는 뜻으로 조건을 나타내는 접속사이다.

24 ⑤ 선행사 The men이 복수이므로 who 다음의 동사도 복수형 are로 바꾼다.

25 ① unless에 이미 부정의 의미가 들어가 있으므로 Unless를 If로 바꿔야 한다.

26 선행사가 사람이고 주격이므로 관계대명사 that이나 who를 써서 한 문장으로 만든다.

27 get off to a good start: 좋은 출발을 하다

28 art: 미술 / artist: 미술가

29 that 이하가 이끄는 절은 형용사절로 선행사 things를 수식한다.

30 역접의 접속사 but이 알맞다.

31 ③ 10시 이후에는 전화기를 꺼야겠다는 말이 되어야 한다. turn on → turn off

32 text: 문자를 보내다 / or: 또는, ~이나

33 break the habit: 습관을 버리다

34 ⓒ, ④ 부사적 용법 ①, ⑤ 형용사적 용법 ②, ③ 명사적 용법

35 decide는 to부정사를 목적어로 취한다.

36 ⓑ와 ⑤는 전치사로, 나머지는 모두 동사로 쓰였다.

37 어떤 것에 대해 대가를 지불하지 않는: free(무료의)

38 ① 앞으로 주말마다 한가한 시간을 가지기로 결정했다.

01 waste	02 ⑤	03 ③	
04 (d)owntime		05 ③, ④	06 ④
07 (D) - (B) - (A) - (C)		08 ①, ⑤	09 ⑤
10 ③	11 ③	12 ②	13 ①
14 ②	15 ①	16 ③	17 ①, ④
18 ②	19 ④	20 ①	21 ⑤
22 ②, ④	23 like	24 ①	25 ②
26 ①, ②, ④	27 ②		

01 반의어 관계이다. 가벼운 : 무거운 = 낭비하다 : 저축하다

02 열심히 일해 뭔가를 얻거나 이루다: achieve(성취하다)

03 once in a while: 가끔 / stand in line: 줄을 서다

04 downtime: 휴식 시간

05 미래의 의도나 계획을 나타내는 표현으로 be planning to+동사원형 / be going to+동사원형 / be thinking of -ing / will 등을 쓸 수 있다.

06 상대방에게 충고하는 표현을 찾는다. ③은 전치사 about 뒤에

7

동명사가 오지 않아 잘못된 표현이다.

07 (D) 안 좋아 보인다. 무슨 일이니? – (B) 키가 더 크면 좋겠는데. 어떻게 하죠? – (A) 매일 줄넘기를 해 봐. – (C) 좋아요. 한 번 해 볼게요.

08 계획이나 의도를 말할 때에는 I will ~., I'm going to ~., I'm planning to ~. 등을 쓴다.

09 ⑤는 '너는 왜 너의 모자를 가져 오지 않았니?'라는 의미로 과거의 일에 대한 이유를 묻는 말이고 나머지는 상대방에게 충고를 하는 표현들이다.

10 Why don't you+동사원형 ~?은 충고를 할 때 쓰는 표현이다.

11 좋하는 어떤 스타일의 모자를 가지고 있는지는 알 수 없다.

12 if 가 있는 조건절에서는 현재시제가 미래를 대신한다.

13 신행사가 사람(a girl)이고 주격이므로 관계대명사 who가 들어가야 알맞다.

14 if ~ not = unless: 만약 ~하지 않으면

15 who는 관계대명사로 쓰일 수도 있지만 의문사로 쓰여 '누구'의 의미를 나타낸다. ①은 의문사로 쓰였고, 나머지는 관계대명사로 쓰였다.

16 조건을 나타내는 if절에서는 현재시제가 미래를 대신한다.

17 선행사가 사람이고 주격이므로 who나 that을 쓸 수 있다.

18 ⓑ, ② 동사의 목적어가 되는 명사절을 이끄는 접속사이다. ① 진주어 ③, ⑤ 관계대명사 ④ It ~ that 강조구문

19 care for: ~을 돌보다, 좋아하다

20 문맥상 조건을 나타내는 접속사가 알맞다.

21 ⑤ 선생님의 리스트를 쉽게 바꿀 수 없다고 하였으므로 잘못에 관대하지 않다고 유추할 수 있다.

22 ⓐ, ②, ④ 명사적 용법 ①,③ 형용사적 용법 ⑤ 부사적 용법

23 such as=like: ~와 같은

24 ⓒ, ① ~와 함께 ② ~을 가진, ~이 있는 ③ ~으로 ④ ~에게 ⑤ ~에, ~에 관하여

25 on+요일

26 have[get, take] some rest: 휴식을 좀 취하다

27 ② 알 수 없음

서술형 실전문제 p.50~51

01 should

02 Why don't you take your baseball glove?

03 should

04 You should go to bed early. / Why don't you go to bed early? / I advise you to go to bed early. / How[What] about going to bed early? 등

05 (1) What are you planning to do
   (2) I'm thinking of playing

06 (1) Dad cooks me a fried egg which[that] is my favorite.

---

(2) I have an uncle who[that] is a math teacher.

(3) She has a bird which[that] speaks English.

07 (1) If you have a fever, you should see a doctor.

(2) If it rains tomorrow, I will go to a movie.

(3) If you add yellow to blue, it becomes green.

08 (1) is → are

(2) who → which[that]

(3) who → that

09 친구들을 바꿀 수 있는 것

10 You may think that you have the perfect number of friends.

11 to

12 very → much/even/far/a lot

13 처음에는 한 가지 것을 생각하고 지금은 다른 것을 생각하는 것

14 ⓑ mind ⓒ life

15 thought, change, try, today, yesterday

01 상대방에게 조언할 때 '~해야 한다'라는 의미의 조동사 should가 알맞다.

02 Why don't you+동사원형 ~?: ~하는 게 어때?

03 상대방에게 조언을 구할 때 What should I do?라고 물을 수 있다.

04 You 'd better+동사원형 ~.은 '~하는 게 좋겠다'라는 의미로 충고를 말하는 표현이다.

05 미래의 일이나 앞으로의 계획을 나타낼 때는 be going to ~ / be planning to ~ / think of -ing 등의 표현을 이용한다.

06 (1) 선행사가 사물(a fried egg)이므로 which나 that을 쓴다.
   (2) 선행사가 사람이므로 who나 that을 쓴다. (3) 선행사가 동물(a bird)이므로 which나 that을 쓴다.

07 (1) see a doctor: 진찰을 받다 (2) go to a movie: 영화 보러 가다 (3) add A to B: B에 A를 추가하다[더하다]

08 (3) 선행사가 사람과 동물이므로 관계대명사는 that을 쓴다.

09 it은 인칭대명사로 앞에 나온 문장을 받을 수 있다.

10 접속사 that은 think의 목적어가 되는 명사절을 이끈다

11 add A to B: B에 A를 더하다

12 very는 원급을 수식한다.

13 that은 지시대명사로 앞에 나온 문장을 받을 수 있다.

14 문맥상 '마음을 바꾸면 인생을 바꿀 수 있다'는 뜻이 되어야 한다.

창의사고력 서술형 문제 p.52

|모범답안|

01 (1) A waiter is someone who serves food in a restaurant.

(2) A zookeeper is someone who looks after animals in the zoo.

(3) Dessert is sweet food which is served after a meal.

02 (1) If Andy is free next Sunday, I'll go to a movie with him.

(2) If my brother doesn't get any better, I'll take him to the hospital.

(3) If I win the first prize on the test, my mom will buy me an i-Pad.

03 (1) If I go to China, I can see the Great Wall.

(2) If it is sunny tomorrow, I will go hiking with my friends.

(3) If I find an abandoned dog on the street, I will bring it to my house.

03 '만약 ~이라면'의 뜻의 if를 활용하여 조건절을 만든다. if가 이끄는 절이 부사절일 때는 미래시제 대신 현재시제를 쓰는 것에 유의한다.

단원별 모의고사

p.53~56

01 ③	02 ④	03 ④	04 ⑤
05 on	06 ③	07 ⑤	08 ⑤
09 Why don't you add some downtime		10 ⑤	
11 ③	12 ③	13 ④	14 tells →
tell	15 ①	16 you stop	17 ③
18 ⑤	19 ④	20 ②	21 ③
22 ⑤	23 ③	24 ⑤	25 ③
26 She will visit it on the third Saturday of the month.			
27 ①	28 ⑤	29 life	30 ②

01 ③은 유의어 관계이고 나머지는 반의어 관계이다.

02 ④는 save(절약하다)의 영영풀이이다.

03 focus on: ~에 집중하다 / care for: ~을 좋아하다

04 light: 가벼운; 날이 밝은

05 from now on: 이제부터

06 be planning to: ~할 계획이다

07 충고를 하는 표현이므로 How about -ing?로 바꿔 쓸 수 있다.

08 빈칸에는 요청에 승낙하는 표현이 들어가야 한다. Not at all. (천만에.)은 감사하다는 말에 답하는 표현이다.

09 Why don't you + 동사원형 ~?: ~하는 게 어때?

10 once in a while: 가끔(=now and then)

11 소녀가 몇 시간 동안 공부하는지는 알 수 없다.

12 조건을 나타내는 if 부사절에서는 미래의 일이라도 현재시제를 사용한다.

13 unless: 만약 ~하지 않으면

14 선행사가 three books로 복수이므로 that절의 동사는 복수형

tell이 되어야 한다.

15 앞 문장의 빈칸에는 the famous singer를 선행사로 하는 주격 관계대명사 who가, 뒤 문장에는 a chair를 선행사로 하는 주격 관계대명사 which가 들어가야 알맞다.

16 if ~ not = unless

17 ③ 조건을 나타내는 if절에서는 현재시제가 미래를 대신한다. will leave → leave

18 ⑤ 문장의 주어는 The man이고 who is sitting on the box는 The man을 수식하는 관계대명사절이다. 따라서 동사는 have가 아니라 단수형인 has가 알맞다.

19 if ~ not = unless: 만약 ~하지 않으면

20 on the phone: 전화기로 / from now on: 지금부터 계속해서

21 turn off: ~을 끄다

22 less often: 덜 자주

23 ③ 필자가 전화기를 유용하다고 생각하는지는 알 수 없다.

24 주어진 문장은 집에서 쉬겠다는 뜻이므로 집밖에서의 활동을 서술하는 문장들 다음에 와야 한다.

25 ⓑ, ③ 무료의 ①, ⑤ 한가한 ②, ④ 자유로운

27 at first: 처음에는

28 ① (자격·기능 등이) ~로(서), ② 이유, ③ ~한 대로, ④ ~ 함에 따라, ~할수록, ⑤ ~처럼, ~하듯이

29 live의 명사형을 쓴다.

30 focus on: ~에 집중하다

9

Lesson 2

Connecting with the World

시험대비 실력평가 p.60

01 ⑤ 02 admission 03 ④
04 German 05 ④ 06 look around
07 (e)nough 08 ②

01 ⑤는 유의어 관계이고 나머지는 반의어 관계이다.

02 admission fee: 입장료

03 사람들이 자신의 감정, 의견, 생각을 보여주기 위해 말하거나, 글을 쓰거나 또는 하는 것들: 표현(expression)

04 '국가명 : 언어명'의 관계이다. 러시아 : 러시아어 = 독일 : 독일어

05 • 쿠키들은 맛있어 보인다. • 사과는 내가 아주 좋아하는 과일이다. • 우리의 앱은 관광객들에게 유용할 것이다. • 케밥은 전통적인 터키 음식이다.

06 look around: ~을 둘러보다

07 누군가 필요하거나 원하는 만큼 많은: 충분한(enough)

08 what kind of: 어떤 종류의 / focus on: ~에 집중을 하다

서술형 시험대비 p.61

01 (1) special (2) different (3) Spanish (4) Turkish
02 (1) half an hour (2) useful for (3) up (4) out
03 (1) audition (2) meaning (3) landmark
04 (1) way (2) works (3) save
05 (1) right now (2) for example (3) mean by
06 (1) (f)ortune (2) (n)ervous (3) (t)ranslation

01 (1) 가벼운 : 무거운 = 일반적인 : 특별한 (2) 배부른 : 배고픈 = 같은 : 다른 (3), (4) 국가명 : 그 국가의 언어

02 (1) in half an hour: 30분 후에 (2) be useful for: ~에 유용하다 (3) hurry up: 서두르다. (4) find out: ~에 대해 알아내다[알게 되다]

03 (1) audition: 오디션 (2) meaning: 의미 (3) landmark: 랜드마크, 주요 지형지물

04 (1) way: 길, 방법, 방식 (2) work: 일하다, 효과가 있다 (3) save: 저축하다, 절약하다

05 (1) right now: 지금 곧, 당장 (2) for example: 예를 들면 (3) mean by: 의미하다, 뜻하다

06 (1) fortune: 운, 행운 (2) nervous: 긴장한 (3) translation: 번역

Conversation

핵심 Check p.62~63

1 (1) Would / please (2) like some / No thanks
  (3) Do you want / full
2 (1) Hurry up / but, mean / I mean, moving
  (2) mean / It means (3) What do you / Good luck

교과서 대화문 익히기

Check(√) True or False p.64

1 T 2 F 3 T 4 F

교과서 확인학습 p.66~67

Communicate: Listen - Listen and Answer Dialog 1
smells, cooking / making / What / traditional, pieces of / sounds / Would, like / love / you / tastes, should open / like

Communicate: Listen - Listen and Answer Dialog 2
are, going to / look around / how to / map, my / Try to / but, mean by / important, special / try to, that

Communicate: Listen - Listen More
look delicious / Would, like / thanks / Why, so / audition, in half an hour / Break / What, mean / Good luck, expression, Save, for

Communicate: Listen - All Ears
half an hour / have schedule

Communicate: Speak 2
Would you like / No, thanks / how about

My Writing Portfolio - Step 1
our app / Sounds / what to see / give information on / find out, admission fees / how to get / right now / I'm sure

Wrap Up - Listening ⑤
Would, like / What kind of / egg sandwich / thanks / would you like / favorite

Wrap Up - Listening ⑥
Hurry up / what, mean by / time to start / time to go / Let's

시험대비 기본평가   p.68

01 ④   02 ⑤   03 ⑤   04 ⑤

01 음식을 권할 때는 Would you like some ~?의 표현을 쓴다.

02 What do you mean?: 무슨 뜻이야?

03 No, thanks.는 음식 권유에 거절할 때 쓰인다.

04 빈칸 뒤의 말 '그녀는 모든 것에 대해 알아.'로 보아 빈칸에는 A가 한 말의 의미를 물어보는 표현이 와야 한다.

시험대비 실력평가   p.69~70

01 ③   02 ⑤   03 ④   04 ④

05 ①   06 ③   07 ⑤   08 ⑤

09 ②   10 행운을 빌어! 11 she has her audition for the school radio station in half an hour 12 ③

13 ②   14 ②

01 주어진 문장은 '그것은 전통적인 터키 음식이야.'라는 뜻으로 What is it?(그것은 뭐니?)라는 질문의 대답으로 오는 것이 적절하다.

02 음식에 대한 묘사로 문맥상 맛있다는 표현이 들어가야 한다.

03 소년의 응답이 '물론. 나는 좀 먹고 싶어.'라고 한 것으로 보아 빈칸에는 음식을 권유하는 말이 알맞다.

04 ④ 소년이 Abbas에게 식당을 오픈해야 한다고 말한 것이며 Abbas가 새 식당을 열 것인지는 알 수 없다.

05 소녀의 첫 말에 대해 소년이 미안하지만 무슨 뜻이냐고 묻자, 소녀가 '이제 움직이기 시작할 시간이야.'라고 말한 것으로 보아 '출발해.'라는 의미이다.

06 What do you mean by that?: 그게 무슨 뜻이니? = What is the meaning of that?: 그것의 의미가 무엇이니?

07 주어진 문장은 '그것은 재미있는 표현이구나.'라는 의미로, Claire의 마지막 말인 I mean "Good luck." 다음에 오는 것이 자연스럽다.

08 '나는 너무 긴장돼.'라고 말한 것으로 보아 음식 권유에 거절하는 표현이 들어가는 것이 적절하다.

09 in half an hour: 30분 후에

10 Claire는 Break a leg!의 의미가 "Good luck!"이라고 설명해 주고 있다.

11 Claire는 30분 후에 학교 라디오 방송국의 오디션이 있기 때문에 너무 긴장된다고 했다.

12 주어진 문장은 'landmarks도 기억하도록 해라.'라는 의미로 소년이 landmarks가 무슨 뜻인지 묻는 문장 앞에 와야 한다.

13 how to+동사원형: ~하는 방법

14 landmarks가 무슨 의미인지 묻고 그것의 의미에 대해 정의하는 내용이므로 빈칸에는 '의미하다'라는 뜻의 mean이 와야 한다.

서술형시험대비   p.71

01 What do you mean (by that)?

02 (1) Would you like some pizza?

    (2) No, thanks. / No, thank you.

03 (B)reak, (l)eg

04 (D) – (B) – (C) – (A)

05 He's going to look around the city.

06 (A) to find   (B) to remember   (C) that

07 그것은 중요한 장소들 또는 특별한 건물들을 의미한다.

08 He will use a map on his phone.

01 상대방이 한 말을 이해하지 못했을 때 '그게 무슨 뜻이니?'라고 묻는 표현이 알맞다.

02 음식을 권유할 때 사양하는 표현으로 No, thanks. / No, thank you.를 쓴다.

03 Break a leg!: 행운을 빌어!

04 (D) 비빔밥 좀 먹을래? - (B) 아니, 괜찮아. 나는 야채를 좋아하지 않아. - (C) 그럼 피자는 어때? - (A) 응, 부탁해.

05 Kevin은 오늘 도시를 둘러 볼 것이라고 했다.

06 (A) how to+동사원형: ~하는 방법 (B) try -ing: 시험삼아 ~해 보다, try to+동사원형: ~하려고 노력하다 (C) 선행사가 장소를 나타내므로 관계대명사 that이 와야 한다.

07 여자가 I mean important places or special buildings.라고 말했다.

08 전화기에 지도가 있다고 했으므로 전화기의 지도를 이용할 것이다.

교과서

Grammar

핵심 Check   p.72~73

1 (1) that   (2) that   (3) whom   (4) which   (5) which

2 (1) where   (2) when   (3) where   (4) how   (5) which

시험대비 기본평가   p.74

01 (1) when   (2) how   (3) whom   (4) which

02 (1) how to make   (2) want to eat

    (3) how to get   (4) where to go

03 (1) who   (2) whom   (3) which   (4) that

01 (1) when+to부정사: 언제 ~할지 (2) how +to부정사: ~하는 방법 (3) 선행사가 사람이고 목적격이므로 관계대명사 whom으로 연결한다. (4) 선행사가 사물이고 목적격이므로 관계대명사 which로 연결한다.

02 (1) how+to부정사: ~하는 방법 (2) what+to부정사: 무엇을

~할지 (3) how+to부정사: ~하는 방법 (4) where+to부정사: 어디로 ~할지

03 (1) 주격 관계대명사 who가 필요하다. (2) 전치사 다음에는 that을 쓸 수 없다. (3) 사물이 선행사 (a knife)이므로 전치사의 목적어 역할을 하는 목적격 관계대명사 which가 와야 한다. (4) the only가 선행사를 수식하므로 목적격 관계대명사 that이 온다.

시험대비 실력평가 p.75~77

01 ②　　02 ①　　03 ②

04 (1) which → who(m)[that]　(2) that → which

05 to　　06 ④　　07 ②　　08 they should　　09 ⑤　　10 that　　11 ①

12 The man gave me all the money that he had.

13 ⑤　　14 ④　　15 ③

16 should begin

17 (1) which → who(m)[that]　(2) were → was

18 ②　　19 ③　　20 ①　　21 ②

01 선행사가 사람(the gentleman)이고 동사 met의 목적어 역할을 하므로 who(m)나 that이 와야 한다.

02 '~하는 방법'은 how to ~로 나타낸다.

03 「의문사+to부정사」는 조동사 should를 써서 명사절로 바꿔 쓸 수 있다.

04 (1) 선행사가 사람이므로 knows의 목적어 역할을 하는 who(m) 또는 that을 쓴다.
(2) 관계대명사 that은 전치사 뒤에 올 수 없다.

05 to부정사는 의문사와 함께 쓰여 '~해야 하는지'의 뜻을 나타낸다.

06 ④에서 listened는 자동사이므로 목적어를 취할 때는 전치사 to가 필요하다. (which → to which)

07 ② 동사 eat의 목적어로 what이 왔으므로 뒤에 lunch가 또 올 수 없다. (what → where 또는 lunch → for lunch)

08 「의문사+to부정사」=「의문사+주어+ should+동사원형」

09 목적격 관계대명사는 생략할 수 있다. that은 사물과 사람에 모두 쓸 수 있다.

10 선행사가 사람일 때와 사물일 때 모두 쓸 수 있는 관계대명사는 that이다.

11 how+to부정사: ~하는 방법, what+to부정사: 무엇을 ~ 할지

12 선행사 all the money를 목적격 관계대명사 that이 이끄는 절이 수식한다.

13 ⑤ 「의문사+to부정사」 또는 「의문사+주어+ should+동사원형」 (where should go → where to go 또는 where thay should go)

14 ④ 전치사 다음에는 that을 쓸 수 없다.

15 「의문사+to부정사」 구문으로 첫 번째 문장은 문맥상 '무엇을 입

어야 할지'가 되어야 하므로 what이 알맞고, 두 번째 문장은 '~하는 방법'이라는 의미가 되어야 하므로 how가 알맞다.

16 「의문사+to부정사」 구문은 「의문사+주어+ should+동사원형」으로 바꿔 쓸 수 있다.

17 (1) 선행사가 사람이므로 목적격 관계대명사 who(m)나 that이 와야 한다.
(2) 문장의 주어(The knife)는 단수 명사이므로 be동사는 was가 되어야 한다.

18 목적격 관계대명사는 생략할 수 있다. ②의 who는 앞에 나온 The boy를 수식하는 주격 관계대명사이므로 생략할 수 없다.

19 ⓓ 「who+to부정사」는 어색한 표현이므로, Do you know who will tell me about it?으로 바꿔 쓴다. ⓔ when to finish it은 언제 끝낼지 때에 관한 물음인데, tomorrow와 쓰이면, 때를 나타내는 부사가 중복되어 어색한 문장이 된다.

20 ①의 that은 명사절을 이끄는 접속사로 쓰였고, 나머지는 관계대명사로 쓰였다.

21 ②의 what to read는 동사 is의 보어로 쓰였고, 나머지 「의문사+to부정사」는 모두 목적어로 쓰였다.

서술형 시험대비 p.78~79

01 (1) I know the man who(m)[that] you are looking for.
(2) This is the bag which[that] I got from Nancy.
(3) He is the boy who(m)[that] I meet at the bus stop every morning.

02 (1) how　(2) what　(3) which　(4) where

03 that

04 (1) My brother doesn't know where he should go.
(2) Alice doesn't know what she should cook.
(3) Please tell me when I should help you.

05 W(w)hen

06 (1) I bought my sister a blouse (which[that] was) made in France.
(2) Do you know the boy (whom) I met on the street yesterday?
(3) This is the city that is famous for its beautiful buildings.

07 (1) I can't decide what to buy[what I should buy] for my mother's birthday.
(2) Bill didn't tell us where to stay.

08 (1) who(m) [that]　(2) which[that]

09 (1) I didn't know when to leave.
(2) Do you know how to play the guitar?
(3) I don't know where to meet her.

10 (1) I saw a man and his dog that looked very tired.

(2) John with whom I played tennis yesterday is the best player in this town.

(3) This bike which[that] my father bought (for) me last year is my treasure.

(4) My sister ate the ice cream that[which] my mother bought for me.

(5) The house in which we lived two years ago was in Incheon.

11 (1) where to practice (2) when to visit
(3) who(m) to go (4) what to buy

01 목적격 관계대명사는 접속사와 대명사의 역할을 하며, 선행사가 사람일 경우 who(m)나 that, 사물일 경우 which나 that을 쓴다.

02 (1) 방법을 나타낼 때는 「how+to부정사」를 쓴다. (2) '몇시'는 what time을 쓴다. (3) '어느 책'은 which book으로 나타낸다. (4) '이름을 적을 곳'은 장소를 나타내므로 where가 알맞다.

03 선행사가 사람일 때와 사물일 때 모두 쓸 수 있는 관계대명사는 that이다.

04 「의문사+to부정사」 구문을 「의문사+주어+should+동사원형」 구문으로 바꿔 쓸 수 있다.

05 때를 묻는 의문부사 when: 언제 / when to meet: 언제 만날지

06 (1) which was나 that was은 생략할 수 있다. (2) whom은 생략할 수 있다. (3) that이 이끄는 절의 선행사가 단수명사이므로 동사는 is가 되어야 한다

07 (1) '무엇을 사야 할지'의 의미이므로 「의문사+to부정사」 또는 「의문사+주어+ should+동사원형」의 형태로 고쳐야 한다. (2) 「의문사+to부정사」 구문이므로, to 다음에 동사원형 stay가 와야 한다.

08 (1) 선행사가 사람이고 목적격이므로 관계대명사는 who, whom 또는 that을 쓸 수 있다. (2) 선행사가 사물이고 목적격이므로 관계대명사는 which나 that을 쓸 수 있다.

09 (1) 의문사(when)+to leave (2) 의문사(how)+to play the guitar (3) 의문사(where)+to meet her

10 (1) 선행사가 사람과 동물(a man and his dog)이므로 관계대명사 that을 쓴다. (4) 선행사가 사물이므로 관계대명사 that이나 which를 쓴다. (5) 선행사가 사물(the house)이므로, 전치사 in의 목적어 역할을 하는 목적격 관계대명사 which를 쓴다.

11 (3) 목적격 whom 대신 주격 who를 써도 좋다.

[교과서]
Reading

[확인문제]   p.80

1 F 2 T 3 T 4 F 5 T

[확인문제]   p.82

1 F 2 T 3 F 4 T

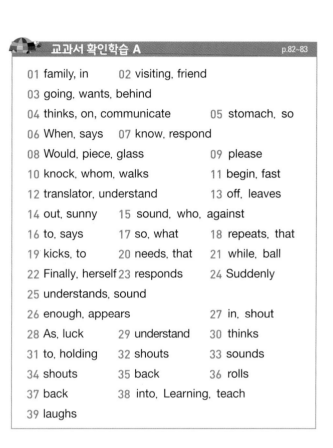

교과서 확인학습 A   p.82~83

01 family, in   02 visiting, friend
03 going, wants, behind
04 thinks, on, communicate   05 stomach, so
06 When, says   07 know, respond
08 Would, piece, glass   09 please
10 knock, whom, walks   11 begin, fast
12 translator, understand   13 off, leaves
14 out, sunny   15 sound, who, against
16 to, says   17 so, what   18 repeats, that
19 kicks, to   20 needs, that 21 while, ball
22 Finally, herself 23 responds 24 Suddenly
25 understands, sound
26 enough, appears   27 in, shout
28 As, luck   29 understand   30 thinks
31 to, holding   32 shouts   33 sounds
34 shouts   35 back   36 rolls
37 back   38 into, Learning, teach
39 laughs

교과서 확인학습 B   p.84~85

1 Jaden's family is in Florence, Italy.

2 They are visiting Ms. Gambini, his mother's friend.

3 Today his parents are going to museums, but Jaden wants to stay behind.

4 He thinks the translation app on his phone will help him communicate.

5 His stomach growls, so he enters the kitchen.

6 When Ms. Gambini sees Jaden, she says "Buon giorno. Vuoi un pezzo di pane e un bicchiere di latte?"

7 Jaden does not know how to respond.

8 Then the app says, "Good morning. Would you like a piece of bread and a glass of milk?"

9 Jaden answers, "Yes, please."

10 There is a knock on the door, and a woman whom Ms. Gambini invited walks in.

11 The two women begin speaking Italian very fast.

12 So the translator does not understand.

13 Jaden turns off the phone and leaves it on the table.

14 He goes out to enjoy the sunny morning.

15 He follows a thumping sound and finds a girl who is kicking a soccer ball against a wall.

16 She turns to him and says, "Buon giono."

17 His phone is in the kitchen, so Jaden does not know what to say.

18 He just repeats the words that the girl said, "Buon giorno."

19 The girl kicks the ball to him.

20 Jaden needs no translator for that.

21 For a while, the two play with the ball.

22 Finally, the girl points at herself and says, "Mi chiamo Rosabella."

23 "My name is Jaden," he responds.

24 Suddenly Rosabella says, "Arrive l'autobus."

25 Jaden understands the words that sound like bus and arrive.

26 Sure enough, a bus appears.

27 Kids in soccer uniforms shout from the windows, "Ciao, Rosabella!"

28 As Rosabella steps onto the bus, Jaden says, "Good luck."

29 She does not understand.

30 So Jaden thinks and says, "Buon, buon ...."

31 He points to the soccer ball that she is holding in her hand.

32 Rosabella shouts, "Fortuna! Buona fortuna!"

33 Fortuna sounds like fortune.

34 "Buona fortuna!" he shouts.

35 Rosabella and her friends shout back, "Molte grazie!"

36 The bus rolls away.

37 Jaden goes back to the kitchen.

38 He says into the translation app, "Learning from people is more fun. Can you teach me some Italian, Ms.Gambini?"

39 Ms. Gambini says, "Si," and laughs.

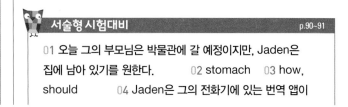

시험대비 실력평가　　　　　　　　　　p.86~89

01 ②	02 ①	03 Will → Would	
04 ③	05 ③	06 ①, ③, ④	07 ②
08 ④	09 He goes out to enjoy the sunny		
morning.	10 ③	11 ④, ⑤	12 소녀가
자기에게 공을 차는 것		13 herself	14 ④
15 like	16 ⑤	17 ⑤	18 ③
19 ⑤	20 ②	21 rolls	22 to

---

23 사람에게서 배우는 것이 더 재미있기 때문이다.

24 ④	25 ②	26 그 제스처는 무엇인가
좋은 것을 의미한다.		27 money 　28 ①
29 ⑤		

01 ⓐ 역접의 접속사가 필요하다. ⓑ 결과를 나타내는 접속사가 필요하다.

02 '어떻게 응답해야 할지'의 뜻이 되어야 자연스럽다.

03 Would you like ~?: ~을 드시겠어요?

04 ③ Jaden이 왜 박물관에 가지 않으려 하는지는 알 수 없다.

05 두 여인이 이탈리아어를 아주 빨리 말하기 시작했다는 말 다음에 와야 한다.

06 선행사가 사람으로 목적격이므로 who, whom, that을 쓸 수 있다.

07 turn off: ~을 끄다

08 ⓒ, ④ ~에, ~에 붙여 ① ~에 맞서, ~에 대항하여 ②, ③ ~에 반대하여 ⑤ ~와 대조적으로

10 ⓐ의 is는 완전자동사로 1문형을 만든다. ③ 1문형 ① 3문형 ② 2문형 ④ 5문형 ⑤ 4문형

11 선행사가 사물이고 목적격이므로 which나 that을 쓸 수 있다.

12 that은 지시대명사로 앞에 언급된 내용을 받는다.

13 목적어가 자기 자신이므로 재귀대명사를 써야 한다.

14 ④ Jaden은 소녀와 공을 가지고 놀아서 번역 앱이 필요하지 않다.

15 like: ~와 같이, ~처럼 / alike: 아주 비슷한

16 문맥상 '나타나다'가 알맞다.

17 ⓒ, ⑤ ~할 때 ① ~한 대로 ② ~함에 따라 ③ ~이기 때문에 ④ ~이듯이, ~인 것 처럼

18 point to: ~을 가리키다

19 ⑤의 내용은 본문에 언급되지 않았다.

20 ⓑ와 ②는 전치사로 쓰였고, 나머지는 모두 동사로 쓰였다.

21 표면을 따라 움직이다: roll(구르다)

22 teach는 간접목적어를 직접목적어 뒤로 보낼 때 전치사 to를 붙인다.

24 주어진 문장은 같은 사인이 0을 의미한다는 뜻이므로 그것은 아무것도 없음을 의미한다는 문장 앞에 와야 한다.

25 for example: 예를 들면

26 something good: 무엇인가 좋은 것

27 That은 지시대명사로 앞에 나온 명사를 받는다.

28 so: 그래서

서술형 시험대비　　　　　　　　　　p.90~91

01 오늘 그의 부모님은 박물관에 갈 예정이지만, Jaden은 집에 남아 있기를 원한다.　　02 stomach　03 how, should　　04 Jaden은 그의 전화기에 있는 번역 앱이

05 knocks on[at]　　06 speaking[to speak]

07 that　　08 그의 전화기는 부엌에 있다. 그래서 Jaden은 무슨 말을 해야 할지 모른다.　　09 which

10 For　　11 Jaden understands the words that sound like bus and arrive.　　12 Because the girl kicks the ball to him.　　13 in　　14 steps

15 He points to the soccer ball that she is holding in her hand.　　16 like

01 are going to=are going to go to

02 음식이 장으로 옮겨지기 전에 소화되는 신체의 기관: stomach(위)

03 의문사+to부정사는 조동사 should를 써서 바꿔 쓸 수 있다.

05 knock on[at]: ~을 노크하다

06 begin은 목적어로 동명사나 to부정사를 취한다.

07 선행사가 사람이고 주격이므로 who나 that을 쓸 수 있다.

08 what to say=what he should say

09 선행사가 사물이므로 which나 that을 쓸 수 있다.

10 for a while: 잠시 동안

11 sound like: ~처럼 들리다

13 in: ~을 입은

14 발걸음을 어떤 것에 디디거나 어떤 특정한 방향으로 옮기다: step(발걸음을 떼어놓다)

15 point to: ~을 가리키다

16 sound like: ~처럼 들리다

영역별 핵심문제　　p.93~97

01 Turkish　　02 ②　　03 For example[instance]

04 ④　　05 official language　　06 ②

07 (t)ranslation　　08 ④　　09 ②

10 (D) – (B) – (A) – (C)　　11 ③　　12 ④

13 up　　14 ⑤　　15 ④　　16 ⑤

17 출발하자.　　18 ④　　19 ②　　20 whom

21 ④　　22 ④　　23 where to go

24 ④　　25 whether to　　26 ③　　27 ③

28 ①, ⑤　　29 ①, ④　　30 His stomach growls, so he enters the kitchen.　　31 how he should

32 audition　　33 ②　　34 ④　　35 Our app　　36 ③　　37 admission　　38 useful

39 ⑤

01 프랑스 : 프랑스어 = 터키 : 터키어

02 ②는 유의어 관계이고 나머지는 반의어 관계이다.

03 for example[instance]: 예를 들어

04 ④는 waste(낭비하다)의 영영풀이이다.

05 official language: 공용어

06 in half an hour: 30분 후에 / walk in: 안으로 들어가다

07 한 언어에서 다른 언어로 옮겨진 글[말]: 번역, 통역 (translation)

08 Would you like some ~?은 How about having some ~?, Why don't you have some ~?으로 바꿔 쓸 수 있다.

09 a busy bee는 '분주한 일꾼, 바쁘게 일하는 사람'이라는 뜻이다.

10 (D) 비빔밥 좀 먹을래? - (B) 응, 부탁해. - (A) 맛이 어때? - (C) 오, 맛있어.

11 'A.S.A.P'가 무슨 의미인지를 묻고 그것의 의미에 대해 정의하는 내용이므로 빈칸에는 '의미하다'라는 뜻의 mean이 적절하다.

12 주어진 질문은 '케이크 좀 먹을래?'라는 뜻으로 ④번을 제외한 나머지는 상대방의 권유를 거절하는 표현이다.

13 hurry up: 서두르다

14 빈칸 뒤의 말 '움직이기 시작할 시간이야라는 의미야'로 보아 빈칸에는 Hit the road가 무슨 뜻인지 묻는 질문이 와야 한다.

15 like: (예를 들어) ~처럼

16 명암, 날씨, 거리, 시간 등을 나타내는 비인칭 주어 it이다. ⑤는 the room을 받는 인칭대명사 it이다.

17 hit the road: 출발하다

18 선행사 the ring이 사물이고 목적격이므로 관계대명사 which[that]가 들어가야 알맞다.

19 '어떻게 ~하는지, ~하는 방법'은 「how+to부정사」를 써서 나타낸다.

20 선행사가 사람(friend)이고 앞에 전치사 to가 있으므로 목적격 관계대명사 whom을 쓴다.

21 ④ 「who+to부정사」 구문은 사용하지 않는다. 대신 Will you tell me who will invite Jack?으로 나타낸다.

22 동사 work는 자동사이므로 목적격 whom을 취하기 위해서는 '~와 함께'라는 의미의 전치사 with가 필요하다.

23 '어디로 가야 할지'는 「의문사 where+to부정사」로 나타낼 수 있다.

24 <보기>와 나머지는 목적격 관계대명사로 쓰였고, ④는 명사절을 이끄는 접속사로 쓰였다.

25 맨 마지막의 or not에 유의한다. '~할 것인지 말 것인지'를 나타내는 말은 whether이고 뒤에 dye(염색하다)라는 동사가 이어지므로 「whether+to부정사」 구문임을 알 수 있다.

26 ③ 관계대명사 that은 전치사(in)의 목적어가 될 수 없다. (that → which)

27 ③은 문맥으로 보아 who가 동사 take의 주어 역할을 하므로 조동사 should가 들어가야 한다. 나머지는 모두 to가 적절하다.

28 ⓐ, ①, ⑤ 명사적 용법 ② 형용사적 용법 ③, ④ 부사적 용법

29 'help+목적어+원형부정사/to부정사'의 형을 취한다.

30 enter는 타동사이므로 전치사 없이 목적어를 취한다.

31 '의문사+to부정사'는 should를 써서 바꿔 쓸 수 있다.

32 감독이나 지휘자가 배우, 댄서, 뮤지션이 연극, 영화, 오케스트

라에 출연할 자질이 있는 지를 결정하기 위해 주어지는 짧은 공연: audition(오디션)

33 문맥상 역접의 접속사 but이 알맞다.

34 뒤에 이어지는 말로 보아 좋은 일이 있기를 바라는 말임을 알 수 있다.

35 It은 인칭대명사로 앞에 나온 단수 명사를 받는다.

36 문맥상 '무엇을 보아야 하는지'가 알맞다.

37 어떤 장소에 들어가는 행위: admission(입장)

38 use: 이용, 유용 / useful: 유용한

39 ⑤ 우리의 앱은 여행자들에게 유용할 것이라고 언급되었다.

단원별 예상문제　　p.98~101

01 ④	02 ⑤	03 ②	04 for[For]
05 ⑤	06 ⑤	07 ②	08 Why don't
09 ⑤		10 Here you are.[Here it is.]	
11 traditional	12 ③	13 ⑤	
14 know them → know	15 ②	16 ③	
17 ①	18 ⑤	19 ①, ⑤	20 There is a knock on the door
21 ②, ④			
22 speaking 또는 to speak	23 ④	24 ③	
25 off	26 that	27 ⑤	28 her → herself
29 ④			

01 ④는 국가명이고 나머지는 언어명이다.

02 step onto: ~에 올라타다

03 의도하는 효과나 결과를 갖다: 효과가 있다(work)

04 for a while: 잠깐 / for example: 예를 들면

05 • 출발합시다. • 나는 그곳에 가는 방법을 안다. • 그게 무슨 뜻이니? • 그 소년은 벽에 공을 차고 있다.

07 음식을 권유하고 있다. ②번은 거절을 한 후 '비빔밥을 좀 먹어 보겠다'고 말하고 있으므로 어색하다.

08 Would you like some?은 Why don't you have some?으로 바꿔 쓸 수 있다.

09 Sure.라고 했으므로 음식 권유에 승낙의 표현이 들어가야 한다.

10 Here you are.[Here it is.]는 물건을 건네줄 때 사용하는 표현이다.

11 오랜 시간 동안 변하지 않은 특정 집단의 믿음, 관습 또는 삶의 부분인: 전통적인(traditional)

12 소년이 케밥에 대해서 물어봤으므로, 소년은 케밥을 먹어 본 적이 없다.

13 앞 문장에는 the doll을 선행사로 하는 목적격 관계대명사 which나 that이 들어가고, 뒤 문장에는 the man을 선행사로 하는 목적격 관계대명사 who(m)이나 that이 들어간다.

14 know의 목적어 them은 관계대명사로 바뀌고, 목적격 관계대명사이기 때문에 생략된 형태이다.

15 ②에서 '카메라를 사용하는 방법'은 「의문사+to부정사」 구문으로 나타내야 한다.

16 ③ 선행사가 사람이고 목적격으로 쓰였으므로 관계대명사 who(m) 또는 that이 알맞다.

17 「의문사+to부정사」 구문을 이용한다.

18 관계대명사 목적격은 생략할 수 있다. ⑤의 who는 주격 관계대명사이므로 생략할 수 없다.

19 a piece[slice] of bread: 빵 한 개 / a glass of milk: 우유 한 잔

20 There is 구문을 이용한다.

21 선행사가 사람이고 목적격이므로 who, whom, that을 쓸 수 있다.

22 begin은 목적어로 동명사나 to부정사를 취한다.

23 ④ Gambini 씨가 초대한 여인이 누구인지는 본문에 언급되지 않았다.

24 주어진 문장은 Jaden needs no translator for that.의 that의 내용이므로 ③에 와야 한다.

25 turn off: ~을 끄다

26 관계대명사 who 대신 that을 쓸 수 있다.

27 접속사 so는 이유를 나타내는 접속사 because나 as를 써서 바꿔 쓸 수 있다.

28 동사의 목적어가 주어 자신이므로 재귀대명사를 써야 한다.

29 ④ Jaden은 소녀가 자기에게 축구공을 차서 대화를 할 필요가 없다.

서술형 실전문제　　p.102~103

01 What does that mean?

02 Why don't you have some juice?
How[What] about drinking some juice? 등

03 What do you mean by that?
What's the meaning of it? 등

04 How do you say

05 (1) whom everyone in my class
(2) which I want to watch

06 (1) I couldn't make up my mind which to choose.
(2) He doesn't know when to study/play and when to play/study.

07 what → which[that]

08 (1) where　(2) when　(3) what

09 Suddenly　10 that/which

11 in　　　　12 understand

13 She is holding a soccer ball (in her hand).

14 like　　　15 to

16 She can teach him Italian. / She can teach Italian to him.

01 What does that mean?: 그게 무슨 의미니?

02 음식을 권유하는 표현에는 Do you want ~? / Why don't you have ~? / How[What] about -ing ~? / Would you like ~? 등이 있다.

03 A의 말 Hit the road!에 대해 그게 무슨 뜻이냐고 묻는 상황이다.

04 how do you say ~?는 해당 언어로 어떻게 말하는지 물어볼 때 사용하는 표현이다.

05 (1) 목적격 관계대명사 whom이 이끄는 절이 선행사 a teacher를 수식한다. (2) 목적격 관계대명사 which가 이끄는 절이 선행사 The movie를 수식한다.

06 (1) '어느 것을 ~할 것인지'는 which to ~로 쓴다. make up one's mind: 결심하다 (2) '언제 공부해야/놀아야 하는지'는 when to study/play로 나타낸다.

07 a pen이 선행사이므로 관계대명사는 which나 that을 쓴다.

08 (1) 뒤에 compass가 나왔으므로, 방향에 관한 내용이 와야 한다. 따라서 where to fly가 어울린다. (2) 때에 관한 질문이 뒤따르므로 when to go가 오는 것이 자연스럽다. (3) what to do: 무엇을 할지

09 sudden: 갑작스러운 / suddenly: 갑자기

10 선행사가 사물이고 주격이므로 which나 that을 쓸 수 있다.

11 전치사 in은 '~을 입은, ~을 입고'의 뜻으로 착용을 나타낸다.

12 어떤 사람이 의도하는 것을 알다: understand(이해하다)

14 sound like: ~처럼 들리다

15 go back to: ~으로 돌아가다

창의사고력 서술형 문제 p.104

|모범답안|

01 Enjoy Paris, what to see, opening hours, admission fees, how to get

02 (1) I want to know how to go to the hospital.
(2) I didn't know what to choose.
(3) I didn't decide where to stay during my trip.
(4) I told him when to leave.

03 a new T-shirt, Mission Impossible Ⅲ, pizza, Chu Shinsu
(1) a new T-shirt
(2) want to watch is Mission Impossible Ⅲ
(3) that I want to eat is pizza
(4) I want to meet is Chu Shinsu

단원별 모의고사 p.105~108

01 disappear 02 ④ 03 ④
04 (c)ommunicate 05 ① 06 ⑤

07 ① 08 around 09 ⑤ 10 ⑤
11 (A) too (B) that 12 ③ 13 ④
14 ③ 15 how to cook 16 ④, ⑤
17 ④ 18 ② 19 ④ 20 which
→ that 21 ③ 22 ①, ④ 23 sunny
24 ①, ④ 25 ⑤ 26 ④ 27 ④
28 ③ 29 carefully 30 ④

01 반의어 관계이다. 중요한 : 중요하지 않은 = 나타나다 : 사라지다

02 눈에 잘 띄고 알아보기 쉬운 지상의 물체나 구조물: landmark(주요 지형지물)

03 work: 작동하다, 효과가 있다

04 당신의 아이디어, 감정, 생각 등을 다른 사람들에게 알리고 그들이 그것들을 이해할 수 있도록 하다: 의사소통하다 (communicate)

05 step onto: ~에 올라타다

06 ⑤ 무엇을 먹고 싶은지 묻는 말에 '나는 피자를 먹었다'고 대답하는 것은 어색하다.

07 (A) 이봐, Kate, 떡 좀 먹을래? (C) 그래, 줘. 오! 맛있다. (D) 좀 더 먹을래? (B) 응, 고마워.

08 look around: ~을 둘러보다

09 how to+동사원형: ~하는 방법 /
what do you mean by ~?: ~은 무슨 뜻이니?

10 landmark는 중요한 장소 또는 특별한 건물들을 가리킨다.

11 (A) too: (긍정문에서) ~도(또한/역시) / either: (부정문에서) ~도(또한/역시) (B) 선행사가 the places이므로 관계대명사 that[which]이 알맞다.

12 앞 문장은 선행사가 사물이고 주격이므로 which나 that이 알맞고, 뒤 문장은 선행사가 사람이고 목적격이므로 who(m)나 that이 알맞다.

13 ④ make의 목적어가 될 수 있는 말이 있어야 한다.

14 ③은 주격 관계대명사로 쓰인 that이고, 나머지는 모두 목적격 관계대명사로 쓰였다.

15 '요리하는 방법'을 배우고 싶다는 뜻이므로 「how+to부정사」로 나타낼 수 있다.

16 선행사가 the writings로 사물이므로 목적격 관계대명사 that 또는 which가 알맞다.

17 모두 「의문사+to부정사」 구문으로 to가 빈칸에 들어가고, ④는 too ~ to부정사 구문으로 빈칸에 too가 들어간다.

18 ② 소녀의 이름이 Nancy이므로 a girl을 선행사로 하는 소유격 관계대명사 whose가 필요하다.

19 관계대명사 목적격은 생략할 수 있다.

20 선행사 movie를 최상급 형용사가 수식하고 있으므로 관계대명사 that을 써야 한다.

21 두 여인이 이탈리아어를 아주 빨리 말하기 시작했다는 문장 다음에 와야 한다.

17

22 선행사가 사람으로 목적격일 때는 whom, who, that을 쓸 수 있다.

23 sun: 해, 태양 /
   sunny: 화창한

24 선행사가 사람으로 주격일 때는 who나 that을 쓸 수 있다.

25 ⑤ 축구공을 차고 있는 소녀가 누구인지는 언급되지 않았다.

26 ①, ②, ③, ⑤는 모두 the OK sign을 가리키고, ④는 money를 받는다.

27 for example: 예를 들면

28 so: 그래서 / when: ~할 때

29 care의 부사형으로 바꾼다.

30 ④ OK 사인은 프랑스에서는 좋은 의미로 쓰이지 않는다.

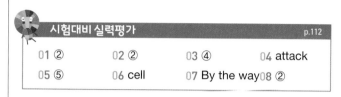

Lesson 3

Healthy Life, Happy Life

시험대비 실력평가   p.112

| 01 ② | 02 ② | 03 ④ | 04 attack |
| 05 ⑤ | 06 cell | 07 By the way | 08 ② |

01 나머지는 모두 동사의 행위자를 나타내는 말이고, ②는 '위험'을 뜻하는 단어이다.

02 show up: 나타나다 / be good for: ~에 좋다

03 번식해서 수가 증가하다: 증식하다(multiply)

04 반의어 관계이다. 어려운 : 쉬운 = 방어하다 : 공격하다

05 make it: (모임 등에) 가다, 참석하다

06 모든 생물을 구성하는 아주 작은 부분들의 어느 하나: cell(세포)

07 by the way: 그런데(화제를 바꿀 때 쓰는 표현)

08 plenty of: 많은 / think of: ~을 생각하다

서술형 시험대비   p.113

01 (1) actor   (2) cartoonist   (3) inventor
02 (1) such as   (2) is famous for   (3) few days
03 (1) germs   (2) digest   (3) multiply   (4) balanced
04 (1) healthy   (2) Luckily   (3) dangerous
05 (1) show up   (2) good for
   (3) plenty of   (4) catch a cold
06 (1) (s)cratch   (2) (v)ictim   (3) (b)acteria

01 (1), (3)은 '동사 : 행위자' 관계이고, (2)는 '명사 - 행위자' 관계이다.

02 (1) such as: ~과 같은 (2) be famous for: ~으로 유명하다 (3) in a few days: 며칠 후에

03 (1) germ: 세균 (2) digest: 소화시키다 (3) multiply: 증식[번식]하다 (4) balanced: 균형 잡힌

04 (1) healthy: 건강한 (2) luckily: 다행히도 (3) dangerous: 위험한

05 (1) show up: 나타나다 (2) be good for: ~에 좋다 (3) plenty of: 많은 (4) catch a cold: 감기에 걸리다

06 (1) scratch: 긁다 (2) victim: 피해자, 희생자 (3) bacteria: 박테리아

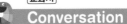

Conversation

핵심 Check p.114~115

1 (1) wrong / stomachache (2) matter / runny nose

  (3) What, problem / have a toothache

2 (1) make it / Sure, then (2) How about going /

  problem (3) Let's play / Sorry, I can't

교과서 대화문 익히기

Check(√) True or False p.116

1 T 2 F 3 T 4 F

교과서 확인학습 p.118~119

Communicate: Listen - Listen and Answer Dialog 1

Can, early, don't feel / seems to / have, stomachache, hurts / Why don't, medicine / already, didn't help / can, Go see / Sure

Communicate: Listen - Listen and Answer Dialog 2

heard, okay / the doctor, feel better / to hear, By the way, to talk / should meet, make it / Let's meet, at / early, late / How about / sounds

Communicate: Listen - Listen More

wrong with / scratching, lost, hair / have the problem / About, ago / Let, see, have a virus / need to check, Can, make / fine with / See

Communicate: Listen - All Ears

make / wrong

Communicate: Speak 2 - Talk in pairs

What's wrong / have, sore throat / bad, should drink / will

Communicate: Speak 2 - Talk in group

Let's / why not / Can you make / with, should, meet / Let's, at / See you

Wrap Up - Listening ⑤

don't feel / What, problem / have a fever / Let me see, do / get you some medicine / Thank

Wrap Up - Listening ⑥

thinking of, come with / to go / make it at / fine with / Let's, at

시험대비 기본평가 p.120

01 ③	02 ④	03 ④	04 ②

01 Can you make it at ~?은 약속 시간을 정할 때 쓰는 표현이다.

02 What's wrong?은 What's the problem?과 바꾸어 쓸 수 있다.

03 B가 동의하고 5시에 만나자고 말했으므로 약속 시간을 정하는 표현인 ④가 알맞다.

04 이어지는 대답으로 보아 상태를 묻는 질문이 알맞다.

시험대비 실력평가 p.121~122

01 ⑤	02 How[What] about getting	03 ④
04 stomachache	05 ②	06 ④
07 meet	08 ②	09 They will meet at the
school gym at ten.	10 ③	11 By the
way	12 ④	13 ②	14 late
15 ⑤		

01 What seems to be the problem?과 What's the matter with you?는 '어디가 안 좋으니?'라는 의미이다.

02 Why don't you + 동사원형 ~?은 How[What] about -ing ~?로 바꿔 쓸 수 있다.

03 ⓒ와 ④는 '허가', ①, ②, ⑤는 '가능, 능력', ③은 '추측'을 나타낸다.

04 위의 또는 위 부근의 통증: 위통, 복통(stomachache)

05 ② 소년은 배가 몹시 아프다고 했다.

06 A가 10시에 만날 수 있는지 묻고 있으므로 빈칸에는 제안을 수락하는 표현이 알맞다. ④는 제안을 거절하는 표현이다.

07 Can you make it at ten?은 Can we meet at ten?으로 바꿔 쓸 수 있다.

08 A가 체육관에서 만나자고 했으므로 만날 장소를 정하는 표현인 ②가 알맞다.

09 A와 B는 10시에 학교 체육관에서 만날 것이다.

10 종하가 지금은 몸이 나아졌다고 했으므로 몸이 괜찮은지를 묻는 ③이 알맞다.

11 by the way: 그런데

12 ④를 제외하고 나머지는 모두 내일 만나자고 제안하는 표현이다.

13 '~하자'고 제안하는 표현은 Let's ~.이다.

14 평소보다 또는 예상되는 때보다 늦게: late(늦게)

15 그들의 과학 과제를 언제까지 끝내야 하는지는 위 대화를 통해 알 수 없다.

01 [모범답안] What's wrong? / What's the problem? / What seems to be the problem? 등

02 Why don't you get some rest?

03 meeting

04 Where should we meet?

05 at the school gym

06 matter[problem]

07 Can you make it next Monday?

08 (A) scratching (B) ago

09 계속해서 자기의 몸을 긁는다. / 털이 빠졌다.

---

01 증상을 묻는 표현에는 What's wrong? / What's the problem? / What's the matter? / What seems to be the problem? 등이 있다.

02 Why don't you + 동사원형 ~?: ~하는 게 어때?

03 10시에 만날 수 있느냐는 의미이다.

04 Where should we meet?: 우리 어디서 만날까?

05 there는 앞에 나온 at the school gym을 가리킨다.

06 What's wrong with ~?는 어떤 증상이 있는지 물어보는 표현으로 What's the matter with ~? / What's the problem with ~? 등으로 바꿔 쓸 수 있다.

07 make it은 시간이나 장소의 표현과 함께 쓰여 '시간에 맞춰 가다, 도착하다'라는 의미를 갖는다.

08 (A) keep -ing: 계속해서 ~하다 (b) ~ ago: ~ 전에(과거 시제에 쓰임)

09 She keeps scratching herself. Actually, she lost some hair.를 통해서 알 수 있다.

[교과서]
Grammar

핵심 Check   p.124~125

1 (1) to understand (2) It (3) to exercise (4) of (5) for
2 (1) to go (2) to help (3) to write with (4) cold to drink

시험대비 기본평가   p.126

01 (1) It (2) to do (3) to visit (4) for (5) of
02 (1) to change (2) to visit (3) to offer
03 (1) exercise → to exercise (2) finish → to finish
　 (3) That → It (4) for → of (5) of → for

---

01 (1) 가주어 it이 필요하다. (2), (3) 형용사적 용법의 to부정사가 필요하다. (4) 형용사가 hard이므로 의미상의 주어는 'for+목적격'을 쓴다. (5) 형용사가 kind이므로 의미상의 주어는 'of+목적격'을 쓴다.

02 형용사적 용법의 to부정사를 이용한다.

03 (1), (2) 가주어 It이 있는 구문이므로 동사원형을 to부정사로 바꾼다. (3) 가주어는 It으로 나타낸다. (4) 형용사가 brave이므로 의미상의 주어는 'of+목적격'을 쓴다. (5) 형용사가 easy이므로 의미상의 주어는 'for+목적격'을 쓴다.

시험대비 실력평가   p.127~129

01 ③   02 ③   03 ④   04 to write
05 It, to change   06 ①   07 ①
08 Do you want anything to eat? [Do you want to eat anything?]   09 ④   10 ④   11 It is difficult to fix the machine.   12 ②   13 ①
14 ①   15 to   16 ⑤   17 sit → sit on[in]   18 ①   19 ③   20 ③
21 It is pleasant to listen to music.   22 ⑤
23 going → to go

---

01 ③은 부사적 용법의 to부정사이다. '~하기 위해'로 해석한다. 나머지는 모두 형용사적 용법이다.

02 가주어 It의 진주어로 to부정사가 필요하다.

03 부정대명사 anything을 수식하는 형용사적 용법의 to부정사가 와야 한다.

04 '써야 할 편지들'이라는 뜻으로 명사 letters를 수식하는 to부정사의 형용사적 용법이다.

05 주어로 쓰인 to부정사가 긴 경우, 이를 뒤로 보내고 그 자리에 가주어 it을 쓴다.

06 <보기>의 to read는 앞에 나온 명사 books를 수식하는 형용사적 용법의 to부정사이다. ① 형용사적 용법 ② 명사적 용법 ③ 부사적 용법 ④ 명사적 용법 ⑤ 부사적 용법

07 가주어 – 진주어 구문으로 「It is+형용사+to부정사」 형태가 적절하다.

08 부정대명사를 수식하는 to부정사의 형용사적 용법을 쓴다.

09 ④의 it은 인칭대명사이고 나머지는 가주어 it[It]이다.

10 ④ to going 대신 time을 수식하는 형용사적 용법의 to부정사가 필요하다.

11 '그 기계를 고치는 것은'은 to fix the machine으로 나타낸다.

12 첫 문장은 형용사가 kind이므로 의미상의 주어는 'of+목적격'을 쓴다. 두 번째 문장은 형용사가 natural이므로 의미상의 주어는 'for+목적격'을 쓴다.

13 honest와 wise는 의미상의 주어로 'of+목적격'을 쓴다.

14 It이 가주어이므로 진주어인 to부정사가 와야 한다.

15 don't have to: ~할 필요가 없다 / reason to be angry at: ~에게 화낸 이유

16 ①, ④ 진주어로 쓰인 to부정사 ② hopes는 to부정사를 목적어로 취한다. ③ enough to+동사원형: ~하기에 충분히 …한 ⑤ 사역동사의 목적격보어는 동사원형이 와야 한다.

17 to부정사의 수식을 받는 명사가 전치사의 목적어일 경우 뒤에 전치사가 온다.

18 ①은 '때'를 나타내는 비인칭 주어이다. 나머지는 가주어 it으로 쓰였따.

19 to부정사의 수식을 받는 명사가 전치사의 목적어일 경우 to부정사 뒤에 전치사를 쓴다. ③은 to talk with라고 해야 옳다.

20 ③은 형용사적 용법의 to부정사이고, 나머지는 모두 명사적 용법으로 쓰였다.

21 to부정사로 쓰인 주어가 길거나 의미를 강조하고 싶을 때 가주어 it을 주어 자리에 쓰고 진주어인 to부정사를 문장 뒤로 보낸다.

22 time을 수식하는 to부정사와 「don't have to+동사원형」의 형태가 필요하다.

23 진주어로 to부정사가 와야 한다.

---

01 to   02 It to

03 (1) It is difficult to learn English.

   (2) He bought a magazine to read on the train.

04 to receive

05 (1) It wasn't easy to visit him every weekend.

   (2) It is an exciting experience to live in another country.

06 (1) She has a strong desire to be a singer.

   (2) We had something to talk about.

   (3) I want a sheet[piece] of paper to write on.

   (4) Please give me something hot to drink.

07 (1) play → to play   (2) of → for

08 (1) It   (2) on   (3) with   (4) to

09 to play with   10 to

11 It, to learn

12 (1) for → of   (2) of → for

13 It's a place to sell many things for 24 hours.

01 앞의 명사를 수식하는 형용사적 용법의 to부정사가 필요하다.

02 가주어 it을 문장 앞에 두고 진주어 to부정사구를 뒤로 보낸다.

03 (1) 가주어 it, 진주어 to부정사 구문이다. (2) '읽을 잡지'이므로 to부정사의 형용사적 용법을 쓴다.

04 가주어인 It의 진주어에 해당하는 to부정사구가 되어야 하므로 to receive로 쓴다.

---

05 (1) '주말마다 그를 방문하는 것'은 to visit him every weekend로 나타낸다. (2) '다른 나라에서 사는 것'은 to live in another country로 나타낸다.

06 (1), (2) to부정사의 형용사적 용법을 이용해 「명사+to부정사」의 형태로 쓴다. (3) to부정사의 목적어가 있고 to부정사의 동사가 자동사일 때는 전치사가 필요하다. (4) -thing으로 끝나는 부정대명사는 「-thing+형용사+to부정사」의 어순을 따른다.

07 (1) time을 수식하는 to부정사로 바꾼다. (2) important는 의미상의 주어로 'for+목적격'을 쓴다.

08 (1) 가주어 it이 필요하다. (2) '~ 위에' 쓰는 것이므로 전치사 on이 필요하다. (3) '칼을 가지고 로프를 자르는' 것이므로 전치사 with가 필요하다. (4) 형용사적 용법의 to부정사가 온다.

09 '같이 놀 친한 친구가 필요하다.'이므로 my best friend를 꾸며주는 to부정사는 전치사 with와 함께 써야 한다.

10 time을 수식하는 to부정사와 「don't have to+동사원형」의 형태가 필요하다.

11 to learn to ride a bike가 주어인 문장으로, 가주어 it이 앞에 온다. to ride는 learn의 목적어로 쓰인 to부정사이다.

12 (1) 형용사가 stupid이므로 의미상의 주어는 'of+목적격'을 쓴다. (2) 형용사가 necessary이므로 의미상의 주어는 'for+목적격'을 쓴다.

13 to부정사의 형용사적 용법 (a place to sell ~)을 이용한다.

1 F   2 T   3 F   4 T   5 T

1 F   2 T   3 T   4 F

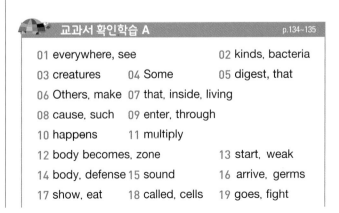

01 everywhere, see   02 kinds, bacteria

03 creatures   04 Some   05 digest, that

06 Others, make   07 that, inside, living

08 cause, such   09 enter, through

10 happens   11 multiply

12 body becomes, zone   13 start, weak

14 body, defense 15 sound   16 arrive, germs

17 show, eat   18 called, cells   19 goes, fight

20 few, feel　　21 invader, copies, itself

22 smart　　　　23 change, trick

24 several, protect　　　　25 wash, warm

26 diet, healthy　27 exercise, plenty

28 Finally, shots　29 defense, germs

30 steps, victim　31 copies　　　32 defend

33 meal　　　　34 there, eat　　35 Next, send

36 see, another　37 can　　　　38 ready, any

39 up　　　　　40 make

1 Germs are everywhere, but it is impossible to see them with your eyes.

2 There are two major kinds of germs: bacteria and viruses.

3 Bacteria are very small creatures.

4 Some are good.

5 They can help you digest the food that you eat.

6 Others are bad and can make you sick.

7 Viruses are germs that can only live inside the cells of other living bodies.

8 They cause diseases such as the flu.

9 "Bad" germs can enter your body through your skin, mouth, nose, and eyes.

10 What happens when they invade?

11 The germs multiply in the body.

12 Your body becomes a war zone.

13 You start to feel tired and weak.

14 Luckily, your body has an army of defense.

15 The T cells sound the alarm!

16 The B cells arrive to fight the germs with antibodies.

17 The macrophage cells show up and eat the germs.

18 Together, this army is called the white blood cells.

19 If all goes well, they win the fight.

20 In a few days, you start to feel better.

21 The body remembers the invader, so it cannot make copies of itself again.

22 But the germs are smart, too.

23 They can change form and trick the body.

24 There are several ways to protect yourself from germs.

25 First, wash your hands with soap and warm water.

26 A balanced diet will keep your body strong and healthy.

27 It is also important to exercise regularly and get plenty of sleep.

28 Finally, get the necessary shots.

29 They are the best defense against germs.

30 If you follow these steps, you will not be a victim of "bad" germs.

31 Make more copies of me.

32 It's my job to defend the body.

33 That was a nice meal!

34 Are there any more germs to eat?

35 Next year, I'll send in my cousin.

36 He'll see you then for another fight!

37 What can I do now?

38 I'm ready to fight any germs.

39 We give up.

40 We can't make you sick.

01 ④	02 ②	03 손대지 마라!	
04 ③	05 ⑤	06 ⑤	07 ①
08 ②, ⑤	09 like	10 multiply	11 invader
12 ①	13 ⑤	14 ②	15 ④
16 ③	17 ④	18 another	19 it →
itself	20 그들은 형태를 바꿔서 몸을 속일 수 있다		
21 ③	22 to protect	23 ②	24 ③
25 ③	26 덤벼.	27 ②	28 규칙적
으로 운동하고 잠을 충분히 자는 것			29 나의
사촌들도 게임 오버라고?		30 ④	31 Finally
32 ⑤	33 ①		

01 주어진 문장은 좋은 박테리아가 있다는 뜻이므로 박테리아가 좋은 일을 하는 문장 앞인 ④에 와야 한다.

02 watch out: 조심하다

03 Hands off!: 손 떼!, 손대지 마!

04 앞뒤 절의 내용이 상반되므로 역접의 접속사 but이 필요하다.

05 선행사가 사물이고 목적격이므로 관계대명사 which나 that을 쓸 수 있다.

06 ⑤ 박테리아는 유익한 것과 해로운 것이 있다.

07 문맥상 '공격하다'가 알맞다.

08 선행사가 사물이고 주격이므로 관계대명사 which나 that을 쓸 수 있다.

09 such as: ~와 같은

10 수나 양이 크게 증가하다: multiply(증식하다, 번식하다)

11 invade: 침략하다 / invader: 침략자, 침입자

12 문맥상 '몸을 방어하다'가 알맞다.

13 ⓒ, ⑤ 부사적 용법 ①, ③, ④ 명사적 용법 ② 형용사적 용법

14 show up: 나타나다

15 T 세포가 어떻게 경보를 발하는지는 언급되지 않았다.

16 game over: 게임 오버, 경기 종료

17 send in: ~을 파견하다

18 뒤에 단수명사가 오므로 another가 알맞다.

19 주어 it의 목적어가 주어 자신이므로 재귀대명사 itself를 써야 한다.

20 change form: 형태를 바꾸다 / trick: 속이다

21 ③ 몸이 자신을 침입한 균을 기억한다고 언급되었다.

22 명사 ways을 수식하는 형용사적 용법의 to부정사이다.

23 protect A from B: B로부터 A를 보호하다

24 ⓒ와 ③은 '~으로'의 뜻으로 수단을 나타낸다. ①, ② ~에게(는) ④ ~에게 ⑤ ~으로(원인)

25 문맥상 '균들과 싸우다'가 알맞다.

26 Bring it on.: 덤벼.

27 ⓒ, ② 5문형 ① 2문형 ③ 1문형 ④ 4문형 ⑤ 3문형

28 It은 가주어로 진주어인 to exercise 이하를 받는다.

29 game over: 게임 오버, 경기 종료.

30 give up: 포기하다

31 final의 부사형 finally로 고친다.

32 against: ~에 대항하여

33 조건의 접속사 if가 알맞다

01 Watch   02 cannot[can't]   03 Others
04 좋은 박테리아는 우리가 먹는 음식을 소화시키는 데 도움이 된다.   05 of   06 enter into → enter
07 나쁜 균들   08 Because the germs multiply in the body.   09 Are there any more germs to eat?
10 defense   11 calling → called   12 며칠 후에 여러분은 기분이 더 좋아지기 시작한다.   13 They sound the alarm.   14 different   15 that
16 snacks   17 with   18 손에 있는 균이 우리의 몸속으로 들어올 수 있기 때문이다.

01 watch out: 조심하다

02 impossible: 불가능한

03 some ~, others ...: 어떤 것들은 ~하고, 또 어떤 것들은 …하다

05 make copies of: ~을 복사[복제]하다

06 enter는 타동사이므로 전치사 없이 목적어를 취한다.

07 they는 앞 문장에 나온 Bad germs를 받는다.

09 Are there ~?의 구문을 쓴다.

10 defend의 명사형으로 고친다.

11 문맥상 진행형이 아니라 수동태가 되어야 한다.

12 in a few days: 며칠 후에 / start to: ~하기 시작하다

14 differ: 다르다 / different: 다른, 여러 가지의

15 선행사가 everything이므로 which보다 that을 더 자주 쓴다.

16 요리하고 먹기에 빠른 간단한 식사: snack(간식)

17 with: ~으로

01 ④   02 ③   03 dangerous 04 ③
05 ②   06 ②   07 give up   08 ④
09 problem   10 ⑤   11 (C) – (A) – (D) – (B)
12 ①   13 ④   14 약을 먹은 것 15 ③
16 He has a terrible stomachache.   17 ④
18 ①   19 ②   20 it is   21 ③
22 ②   23 ②   24 write → write with
25 ⑤   26 It, to   27 I will do anything to make myself look slimmer. 28 ⑤   29 ②
30 living   31 ③   32 ①   33 그는 그때 또 다른 싸움을 위해 널 만날 거야!   34 ②
35 ③   36 ②   37 ①   38 soap
39 They are on everything that we touch.

01 ④는 '명사 - 명사' 관계인데, 나머지는 '동사 - 행위자' 관계이다.

02 • 이것은 매우 어려운 문제이다. • 성공의 비결은 열심히 일하는 데 있다. • 옛날 지폐는 복제하기 너무 쉽다. • 그녀는 피부에 바이러스가 있다.

03 반의어 관계이다. 쉬운 : 어려운 = 안전한 : 위험한

04 by the way: 그런데 / watch out: 조심하다

05 모든 생물들을 구성하는 아주 작은 부분들의 어느 하나: 세포(cell)

06 at last: 마침내(=finally)

07 give up: 포기하다

08 상대방의 증상을 묻는 표현이 쓰여야 한다.

09 No problem.: 문제없어.(제안에 승낙하는 표현)

10 제안에 거절하는 표현이 와야 한다.

11 (C) 무슨 일 있니? - (A) 목이 아파. - (D) 안됐구나. 너는 물을 좀 마셔야 해. - (B) 알았어, 그럴게.

12 문맥상 약속 정하기 표현이 알맞다. Can you make it at 5?: 5시에 만날 수 있니?

13 What seems to be the problem?은 어떤 증상이 있는지 물어보는 표현으로 What's the matter (with ~)? / What's the problem (with ~)? / Is something wrong (with ~)? 등으로 바꿔 쓸 수 있다.

14 인칭대명사 it은 앞에 나온 get some medicine을 가리킨다.

15 위통이 있는 사람에게 해 줄 수 있는 말은 ③이 알맞다.

16 소년은 배가 몹시 아프다고 했다.

17 -thing으로 끝나는 부정대명사를 수식하는 to부정사가 필요하다.

18 가주어 It을 설명하는 진주어 to부정사가 필요하다.

19 형용사가 stupid와 clever이므로 의미상의 주어는 'of+목적격'을 쓴다.

20 뒤에 진주어인 to부정사구가 왔으므로 빈칸에는 가주어인 it과 be동사가 와야 한다.

21 -thing으로 끝나는 부정대명사는 「-thing+형용사+to부정사」의 어순을 취한다.

22 ②는 날씨를 나타내는 비인칭 주어 it이고, 나머지는 to부정사구를 진주어로 하는 가주어 it이다.

23 <보기>와 나머지는 모두 형용사적 용법이고 ②는 부사적 용법이다.

24 to부정사의 수식을 받는 명사가 전치사의 목적어일 경우 뒤에 전치사가 온다.

25 형용사적 용법의 to부정사는 명사나 대명사를 뒤에서 수식하여 형용사처럼 쓰인다. 또한, food는 보통 단수로 쓰인다.

26 To read this book이 주어인 문장으로, 가주어 it이 앞에 온다.

27 anything: 어떤 것이든

28 주어진 문장은 여러분의 몸이 전쟁 지역이 된다는 뜻이므로 피곤하고 약해지는 것을 느낀다는 문장 앞에 와야 한다.

29 균들이 몸을 공격하는 상황이므로 attack이 알맞다.

30 한정적 용법으로 쓰이고 있으므로 living이 와야 한다.

31 때를 나타내는 접속사 when이 알맞다.

32 ① 균은 자신을 복제할 수 있다.

33 another: 또 다른, 다른 하나의

34 so: 그래서

35 문맥으로 보아 '몸을 속이다'가 알맞다.

36 주어진 문장의 too로 보아 전화기와 컴퓨터에 손을 댄다는 말 다음에 와야 한다.

37 접촉해서 '~ 위에'는 on을 쓴다.

38 여러분 자신을 씻거나 또는 때때로 옷을 세탁하기 위해 물과 함께 사용하는 물질: soap(비누)

단원별 예상문제
p.150~153

01 ④ 02 ② 03 inventor 04 ⑤
05 (1) be ready to (2) runny nose, sore throat
06 ① 07 ⑤ 08 ② 09 Can
you make it tomorrow? 10 Why don't we
11 ④ 12 ② 13 write → write on
14 It, to 15 ① 16 ③ 17 ⑤
18 ① 19 나는 어떤 균들과도 싸울 준비가 되어
있어. 20 ② 21 regularly 22 ⑤
23 open 24 There are germs on everything that
you touch. 25 ② 26 ③ 27 Germ 1
의 사촌들도 싸움에 져서 놀랐기 때문이다. 28 ①
29 주사는 균들에 대한 가장 좋은 방어이다. 30 victim

01 ④는 유의어 관계이고 나머지는 반의어 관계이다.

02 give up: 포기하다 / show up: 나타나다

03 그림을 그리다 : 화가 = 발명하다 : 발명가

04 ⑤는 dangerous(위험한)의 영영풀이이다.

05 (1) be ready to: ~할 준비가 되어 있다
(2) have a runny nose: 콧물이 나다 / have a sore throat: 목이 아프다

06 감기에 걸렸을 때 병원에 가보라고 하는 충고가 어울린다.

07 콘서트에 가자는 A의 제안에 B가 동의를 했으므로, 뒤에는 만나는 시간 약속을 하는 내용이 이어지는 것이 자연스럽다.

08 주어진 문장은 '그 말을 들으니 기쁘다.'는 뜻으로 지금은 나아졌다는 문장 다음에 와야 한다.

09 '시간에 맞춰 가다'는 make it이다. '너는 내일 올 수 있니?'라는 뜻의 의문문을 만든다.

10 Let's ~.는 Why don't we ~?로 바꿔 쓸 수 있다.

11 it이 가주어이므로 진주어인 to부정사가 와야 한다.

12 첫 문장은 형용사가 wise이므로 의미상의 주어는 'of+목적격'을 쓴다. 두 번째 문장은 형용사가 impossible이므로 의미상의 주어는 'for+목적격'을 쓴다.

13 to부정사의 수식을 받는 명사가 전치사의 목적어일 경우 뒤에 전치사가 온다.

14 To finish this homework이 주어인 문장으로 가주어 it이 앞에 온다.

15 ①에서 sit은 자동사이므로 chair를 목적어로 취하기 위해서는 전치사 in이나 on이 필요하다.

16 <보기>와 ③의 It은 가주어이다.
①, ④ 비인칭 주어 ②, ⑤ 인칭대명사

17 many places to visit(방문할 많은 장소)에서 to visit은 형용사적 용법의 to부정사로 명사인 many places를 수식한다.

18 ①은 to부정사의 형용사적 용법이고, 나머지는 모두 '~하기 위해서'라는 목적을 나타내는 부사적 용법이다.

19 be ready to: ~할 준비가 되다 / any: (긍정문에서) 어떤 ~이라도

20 Bring it on.: 덤벼라.

21 동사 exercise를 수식하는 부사로 고쳐야 한다.

22 ⓐ, ⑤ 부사적 용법
①, ③, ④ 명사적 용법
② 형용사적 용법

23 open: 열다 / close: 닫다

24 관계대명사는 선행사가 everything이므로 that을 쓴다.

25 조건을 나타내는 접속사 if가 알맞다.

26 get into: ~으로 들어가다

27 game over: 게임 오버, 경기 종료

28 'make+목적어+목적보어' 구문이다.

29 They는 앞 문장의 the necessary shots를 받는다.

30 다치거나 살해당한 사람: victim(희생자)

01 |모범답안| What's the matter[problem] with you? / Is (there) something wrong with you? / What seems to be the problem? 등

02 I have a sore throat.

03 Let's / make it / afraid, How[What] / See

04 (B)-(C)-(D)-(A)

05 (1) It isn't easy to go down the hill.
   (2) I like the photographs which my little[younger] brother takes.

06 (1) It is difficult for me to park a car.
   (2) It is safe to ride a bike with a helmet.
   (3) It is an exciting experience to live in another country.

07 (1) to go to school
   (2) to have[eat] lunch
   (3) to play on the playground
   (4) to do my homework

08 What   09 yourself   10 with

11 여러분이 비누와 따뜻한 물로 손을 씻고 있기 때문이다.

12 up   13 the necessary shots   14 defense

15 여러분이 이 조치들을 따른다면, 나쁜 균들의 희생자가 되 지 않을 것이다.

01 어떤 증상이 있는지 물을 때 사용하는 표현에는 What's wrong with ~? / What's the matter[problem] with ~? / Is (there) something wrong with ~? / What seems to be the problem? 등이 있다.

02 have a sore throat: 목이 아프다

03 Let's ~: ~하자 / make it: 시간에 대다 / I'm afraid I can't.: 나는 할 수 없을 것 같다. / How about ~?: ~은 어떠니? / See you then.: 그때 보자.

04 (B) 무슨 문제 있니? - (C) 음, 이가 아파. - (D) 그것 참 안 됐구 나. 치과에 가 보는 게 어때? - (A) 알았어. 그럴게.

05 (1) 「It ~ to부정사」 구문을 이용하여 문장을 완성한다. (2) 관계 대명사 which를 이용하여 선행사 the photographs를 수식하 도록 한다.

06 to부정사가 이끄는 구가 주어로 오는 경우, to부정사 주어를 문장 뒤로 보내고 그 자리에 It을 쓴다.

07 to부정사의 형용사적 용법을 이용하여 문장을 완성한다.

08 '내가 지금 무엇을 할 수 있는가?'의 뜻이 되어여 자연스럽다.

09 목적어가 주어 자신이므로 재귀대명사를 써야 한다.

10 수단을 나타내는 전치사 with가 알맞다.

12 give up: 포기하다

13 They는 인칭대명사로 앞에 나온 복수명사를 받는다.

14 defend: 방어하다 / defense: 방어

15 follow: 따르다 / step: 단계, 조치

|모범답안|

01 (1) I need something to drink.
   (2) I need a chair to sit on[in].
   (3) He needs friends to talk with.

02 (1) It is kind of her to help the poor.
   (2) It is exciting for us to play the game.
   (3) It is boring for me to watch basketball games.
   (4) It is possible for you to finish the work on time.
   (5) It is difficult for foreigners to learn Korean.

03 (1) a movie to watch
   (2) a baseball game to watch
   (3) a piano lesson to take
   (4) four comic books to read

01 ④	02 ④	03 ④	
04 cartoonist	05 of	06 ④	07 ②
08 the school gym, ten, play basketball			09 ③
10 make	11 How[What] about		12 ④
13 ③	14 ③	15 ③	16 to finish
17 ②	18 ⑤		
19 ⓐ to find ⓑ to find		20 ⑤	
21 impossible	22 ③	23 ①, ④	24 ⑤
25 ④	26 ③	27 ⑤	28 called
29 ②	30 ④		
31 Because the body remembers the invader.			

01 섭취한 음식물을 신체가 사용할 수 있도록 생리 과정을 거쳐 더 단순한 형태로 변화시키다: 소화시키다(digest)

02 watch out for: ~을 조심하다

03 shot: 주사, (농구나 축구 같은 구기에서) 슛

04 '명사 : 행위자' 관계이다. 예술, 미술 : 예술가, 미술가 / 만화 : 만화가

05 plenty of: 많은 / think of -ing: ~할 생각이다

06 A가 10시에 만날 수 있는지 묻고 있으므로 빈칸에는 제안에 승 낙하는 표현인 ④가 알맞다.

07 ②를 제외하고 나머지는 모두 10시에 만나자고 제안하는 표현 이다.

08 A와 B는 농구를 하기 위해 이번 토요일 10시에 학교 체육관에 서 만날 것이다.

09 ⓐ be thinking of: ~할 생각 중이다 ⓒ be fine with: ~에

게는 괜찮다

10 make it: 시간에 대다, 만나다

11 Let's ~.는 How[What] about -ing? / Why don't we ~? 등으로 바꿔 쓸 수 있다.

12 명사 things를 수식하는 형용사적 용법의 to부정사가 와야 한다.

13 문맥상 '함께 여행할 친구를 찾고 있다'는 흐름이 자연스러우므로, 빈칸에는 '~와 함께'에 해당하는 with가 알맞다.

14 기숙사를 사는 것이 아니라, 기숙사에서 사는 것이므로 live 다음에 전치사 in이 필요하다.

15 <보기>의 to eat는 형용사적 용법의 to부정사이다. ①, ②, ⑤ 부사적 용법 ③ 형용사적 용법 ④ 명사적 용법

16 it은 가주어이고, 진주어는 형용사 뒤에 to부정사 형태로 와야 한다.

17 ②의 경우, 두 개의 동사(is, skate)가 같이 쓰일 수는 없다. 가주어 it과 진주어 to부정사구(to skate ~)의 구문으로 만든다.

18 ⑤ -thing이나 -body로 끝나는 부정대명사의 경우 형용사와 to부정사의 수식을 동시에 받으면 「대명사+형용사+to부정사」의 순서로 써야 한다. something important to tell이 올바르다.

19 가주어 It의 진주어로 to부정사 형태가 필요하다.

20 to부정사의 형용사적 용법이다.

21 possible: 가능한 / impossible: 불가능한

22 some ~, others ...: 어떤 것들은 ~하고, 또 어떤 것들은 …하다

23 help는 목적보어로 원형부정사나 to부정사를 취한다.

24 ⑤ 바이러스가 박테리아보다 더 해롭다는 말은 언급되지 않았다.

25 주어진 문장의 they는 the white blood cells를 받는다.

26 germs를 수식하는 형용사적 용법의 to부정사가 와야 한다.

27 show up: 나타나다(=appear)

28 수동태이므로 'be동사+과거분사'의 형을 취한다.

29 other 뒤에는 복수명사, another 뒤에는 단수명사가 온다.

30 ④ 몸이 기억하는 것은 균의 사촌이 아니라 이번에 침입한 균이다.

교과서 다시보기

Lesson
1

01 성적	02 백, 100	03 추가하다
04 한가한[휴식] 시간	05 다른, 또 다른	06 휴식을 취하다
07 매주의, 주간의	08 초(반), 시작	
09 예의 바르게 행동하다		10 낭비; 낭비하다
11 탄생, 출생	12 달성하다, 성취하다	
13 지루한	14 하지만, 그러나	15 통제, 규제
16 이상한	17 다운로드하다, 내려받다	
18 친환경적인, 환경 친화적인		19 운동하다
20 ~사이에, ~중간에		21 관리하다
22 배부른	23 목표	24 습관
25 스트레스가 많은	26 인기있는	27 무거운
28 죽음, 사망	29 역사적인, 역사상의	
30 문자메세지를 보내다		31 어려운; 열심히
32 잡지	33 유용한	34 지저분한
35 무료의; 자유로운	36 완벽한, 완전하	37 기술
38 가끔	39 일렬로 서다	40 우울해 보이다
41 ~에 주력하다, ~에 집중하다		
42 이제부터, 지금부터는		43 잠깐, 잠시동안
44 ~를 미치게 하다	45 약간의 휴식을 취하다	
46 시작하다, 출발을 하다		

01 heavy	02 historical	03 behave
04 relax	05 text	06 messy
07 magazine	08 useful	09 perfect
10 skill	11 popular	12 death
13 hard	14 underpants	15 another
16 weekly	17 app	18 beginning
19 hundred	20 birth	21 downtime
22 achieve	23 bored	24 however
25 control	26 strange	27 download
28 eco-friendly	29 exercise	30 between
31 manage	32 full	33 grade
34 goal	35 habit	36 stressful

37 waste 38 get some rest

39 care for 40 for an hour 41 jump rope

42 because of 43 each other 44 from now on

45 in front of 46 clean up

1 achieve, 달성하다, 성취하다 2 useful, 유용한

3 eco-friendly, 환경 친화적인 4 relax, 휴식을 취하다

5 beginning, 초(반), 시작 6 messy, 지저분한

7 death, 죽음, 사망 8 strange, 이상한

9 downtime, 한가한[휴식] 시간 10 waste, 낭비하다

11 popular, 인기 있는 12 goal, 목표

13 text, 문자메시지를 보내다

14 behave, 예의 바르게 행동하다 15 habit, 습관

16 stressful, 스트레스가 많은

Communicate: Listen - Listen and Answer Dialog 1

special goal for / win, national / What about / like to manage / achieve your goal / planning, daily, weekly / Sounds

Communicate: Listen - Listen and Answer Dialog 2

for a mimute / Sure / working on, weekly / Good for, little / Have a look, advice / a lot of / planning to / Why don't, downtime / relax, while

Communicate: Listen - Listen More

like to visit / plant, together / What kind / I'm planning to / be fun / heard, going, should bring / will / put on, before / problem, on

Communicate: Listen - Listen and Complete

How, goal / like to visit

My Speaking Portfolio

1 be an eco-friendly / walk to school

2 to pass, take online classes, going, a lot of

3 have a goal, grades, planning to, regularly, solve

Wrap Up - Listening ❸

are going to / planning to, with / sounds, any plans / visit, seafood / be fun Enjoy

Wrap Up - Listening ❹

look down, problem / science, don't have / Why don't you read / magazines / can get, that way

Communicate: Listen - Listen and Answer Dialog 1

G: Kevin, do you have a special goal for the year?

B: Yeah, I want to win a gold medal in the national swimming contest.

G: Cool!

B: What about you, Minsol?

G: I'd like to manage my time better.

B: How would you achieve your goal?

G: I'm planning to make a daily and weekly schedule.

B: Sounds good.

Communicate: Listen - Listen and Answer Dialog 2

G: Can I talk with you for a minute, Minsu?

B: Sure. What is it?

G: I'm working on my weekly schedule.

B: Really? Good for you, little sister.

G: Here. Have a look and give me some advice.

B: Hmm, you have a lot of study time.

G: Yeah, I'm planning to study hard.

B: Why don't you add some downtime?

G: Downtime?

B: Yeah, I mean you need to relax once in a while.

Communicate: Listen - Listen More

W: Hi, Jongha.

B: Hello, Grandma. I'd like to visit you this Saturday.

W: That'll be great. We can plant some vegetables together.

B: Really? What kind of vegetables?

W: This time, I'm planning to plant some tomatoes and peppers.

B: Wow! That'll be fun.

W: What kind of books do you read?

B: I heard it's going to be sunny this Saturday. You should bring your cap.

W: Why don't you put on sunscreen before you leave?

B: No problem. I'll see you on Saturday.

W: Okay. Bye.

Communicate: Listen - Listen and Complete

M: 1 How would you achieve your goal?

 2 I'd like to visit you this Saturday.

My Speaking Portfolio

1 G: Hello, I'm Nayeon. I'd like to be an eco-friendly person. I'm planning to walk to school every day.

2 B1: Hi, I'm Junho. My goal for the year is to pass the Korean History Test. I'm planning to take online classes. I'm also going to watch a lot of historical

dramas on TV.

3 Hi, I'm Hojin. I have a goal for the year. I want to get good grades in math. I'm planning to review math lessons regularly. I'm also going to solve 20 math problems every day.

Wrap Up - Listening ❸

B: What are you going to do this weekend, Mina?

G: I'm planning to visit Yeosu with my aunt.

B: That sounds great. Do you have any plans in Yeosu?

G: Well, we'll visit Yeosu Expo Park and eat some seafood.

B: That'll be fun. Enjoy your weekend.

Wrap Up - Listening ❹

G: You look down, Yunsu. What's the problem?

B: I have a science project, and I don't have any ideas.

G: Why don't you read science magazines in the library?

B: Science magazines?

G: Sure. You can get some great ideas that way.

본문 TEST Step 1 p.09~10

01 Beginning, is stressful
02 How, get, to
03 asked, popular, for
04 Let's, hard, easy
05 That, Hard, Change
06 Messy, clean up
07 bring, stuff, messy
08 don't worry
09 much, than
10 always, drives, crazy
11 that, member, your
12 to, care, other
13 on, or, behave, put
14 cannot easily, list
15 Things, Are, to
16 change, every, hundred
17 between, and
18 means, Birth, Death
19 change your
20 sound strange
21 may, that, perfect
22 add, however, even
23 thought, at, another
24 As, mind, life
25 on, that, try, better
26 Top, for
27 asked, readers, for

본문 TEST Step 2 p.11~12

01 Beginning, is stressful
02 get off, start
03 popular, for ideas
04 Are, to change
05 Let's, that, hard, easy
06 Messy, clean, up

---

07 stuff, gets messy
08 don't worry
09 cleaner than
10 is always, drives, crazy
11 that, a member of
12 have to, care for
13 late, behave, put, on
14 easily change
15 That, to Change
16 change, every, day
17 between, and
18 Choice, Birth, Death
19 can change
20 sound strange
21 may, that, perfect
22 add, however, better than
23 thought, at first, another
24 As, If, mind, life
25 Focus on, try to, better than
26 Top, for
27 asked, readers, for

본문 TEST Step 3 p.13~14

1 새 학년을 시작하는 것은 많은 학생들에게 스트레스를 준다.

2 어떻게 하면 우리는 좋은 출발을 할 수 있을까?

3 Teen Today는 유명한 웹툰 작가인 Raccoon 97에게 아이디어를 물었다.

4 바꾸기 어렵거나 쉽게 바꿀 수 있는 것들에 대해 생각해 보자.

5 바꾸기 어려운 것들

6 너의 지저분한 방_ 너는 방을 깨끗이 치운다.

7 그런 다음 새로운 물건을 가져오면 곧 다시 지저분해진다.

8 하지만 걱정하지 마.

9 네 방은 내 방보다 훨씬 더 깨끗해.

10 너의 가족_ 너의 가족 중에는 항상 너를 미치게 하는 사람이 있다.

11 그나 그녀가 여전히 너의 가족 구성원이라는 것을 기억해라.

12 너는 함께 살아야 하고 서로 돌봐야 한다.

13 선생님의 명단에 있는 너의 이름_ 만약 네가 늦거나 예의 바르게 행동하지 않는다면, 너의 선생님은 너의 이름을 그나 그녀의 명단에 올릴 것이다.

14 너는 명단을 쉽게 바꿀 수 없다.

15 바꾸기 쉬운 것들

16 너의 팬티_ 만약 네가 매일 팬티를 갈아입으면, 너의 엄마는 너에게 입이 닳도록 말하지 않을 거야.

17 "인생은 B와 D 사이의 C이다."

18 그것은 "인생은 탄생과 죽음 사이의 선택이다."를 의미한다.

19 너의 친구들_ 너는 네 친구들을 바꿀 수 있다.

20 이상하게 들리는가?

21 너는 네가 완벽한 수의 친구들을 가지고 있다고 생각할지도 모른다.

22 하지만 새로운 친구를 목록에 추가하면 이전보다 훨씬 더 기분이 좋아질 것이다.

23 너의 마음_ 너는 처음에는 이런 것을 생각했고, 지금은 또 다른 것을 생각한다.

24 괜찮다. 누군가 말했듯이, "마음을 바꿀 수 있다면, 인생을 바꿀 수 있어."

25 "바꾸기 쉬운 일에 집중하고, 어제보다 오늘을 더 좋게 만들려고 노력해. 행운을 빌어!"

26 올해의 5대 계획

27 우리는 200명의 Teen Today 독자들에게 "올해의 계획은 무엇인가?"라고 물었다.

본문 TEST Step 4~Step 5   p.15~18

1 Beginning a new school year is stressful to many students.

2 How can we get off to a good start?

3 Teen Today asked Raccoon 97, a popular webtoon artist, for ideas.

4 Let's think about things that are hard to change or easy to change.

5 Things That Are Hard to Change

6 Your Messy Room_ You clean it up.

7 Then you bring new stuff into it, and it soon gets messy again.

8 But don't worry

9 Your room is much cleaner than mine.

10 Your Family_ There is always someone in your family who drives you crazy.

11 Remember that he or she is still a member of your family.

12 You just have to live together and care for each other.

13 Your Name on Your Teacher's List_ If you are late or do not behave, your teacher will put your name on his or her list.

14 You cannot easily change the list.

15 Things That Are Easy to Change

16 Your Underpants_ If you change them every day, your mom will not tell you one hundred and one times.

17 "Life is C between B and D."

18 It means "Life is Choice between Birth and Death."

19 Your Friends_ You can change your friends.

20 Does it sound strange?

21 You may think that you have the perfect number of friends.

22 If you add a new friend to the list, however, you

will feel even better than before.

23 Your Mind_ You thought one thing at first, and now you think another thing.

24 That is okay. As someone said, "If you can change your mind, you can change your life."

25 "Focus on the things that are easy to change, and try to make today better than yesterday. Good luck!"

26 Top 5 Plans for the Year

27 We asked 200 Teen Today readers, "What are your plans for the year?"

구석구석지문 TEST Step 1   p.19

My Speaking Portfolio - Step 3

1. goals for

2. like to finish

3. To achieve, planning to, for an hour

4. jump rope every day

5. other

My Writing Portfolio

1. Habit

2. want to change, habit

3. my, when, feel bored

4. text, or, on the phone

5. that, a waste of

6. From now on, things to break

7. turn off, after

8. download, to use, less often

9. feel bored, will talk, read

구석구석지문 TEST Step 2   p.20

My Speaking Portfolio - Step 3

1. "I have two goals for the year.

2. First, I'd like to finish a 10 km marathon.

3. To achieve this goal, I'm planning to run for an hour every day.

4. Also, I'm going to jump rope every day.

5. The other goal is ……"

My Writing Portfolio

1. My Phone Habit

2. I want to change my phone habit.

3. I use my phone when I feel bored.

4. I text my friends or play games on the phone.

5. I know that it is a waste of time.

6. From now on, I will do two things to break the habit.

7. I will turn off my phone after 10 p.m.

8. I will also download a phone control app to use my phone less often.

9. If I feel bored, I will talk to my family or read comic books.

단어 TEST Step 1   p.21

01 기억하다	02 남겨 두다, 저축하다	
03 위	04 갑자기	05 의사소통하다
06 문화	07 맛있는	08 마침내
09 중요한	10 반복하다	11 외치다, 소리치다
12 따라가다	13 특별한	
14 주요 지형지물, 랜드마크		15 다른
16 쿵쾅거리는	17 입장료	18 유명한
19 번역, 통역	20 환상직인	
21 ~을 뜻하다[의미하다]		22 꼬르륵거리다
23 긴장한	24 제의하다, 권하다	25 운, 행운
26 나타나다	27 의미	28 그러나
29 정보	30 공용어	31 표현
32 개장 시간	33 대답[응답]하다	34 효력이 있다
35 전통의, 전통적인		
36 조심스럽게, 신중히		37 ~에 유용하다
38 ~에 대해 알아내다[알게 되다]		39 잠깐, 잠시 동안
40 ~을 둘러보다	41 지금 곧, 당장	42 ~에 올라타다
43 어떤 종류의		

단어 TEST Step 2   p.22

01 traditional	02 respond	03 famous
04 translation	05 fantastic	06 stomach
07 communicate	08 finally	09 follow
10 important	11 repeat	12 shout
13 special	14 arrive	15 laugh
16 different	17 remember	18 save
19 suddenly	20 thumping	21 enough
22 admission fee	23 country	24 culture
25 meaning	26 nervous	27 fortune
28 information	29 expression	30 pass
31 understand	32 work	33 audition
34 carefully	35 appear	36 translator
37 focus on	38 for example	39 for a while
40 hurry up	41 what kind of	42 right now
43 look around		

1 famous, 유명한   2 work, 효력이 있다   3 pass, 합격하다

4 repeat, 반복하다   5 enough, 충분한   6 fortune, 운, 행운

7 save, 남겨 두다, 저축하다   8 information, 정보

9 offer, 제의하다   10 landmark, 주요 지형물, 랜드마크

11 nervous, 긴장한   12 respond, 대답[응답]하다

13 communicate, 의사소통하다   14 translation, 번역

15 culture, 문화   16 expression, 표현

Communicate: Listen - Listen and Answer Dialog 1

smells, are, cooking / making / traditional, pieces of, stick / sounds, delicious / Would, like / love / you / tastes, should open / glad, like

Communicate: Listen - Listen and Answer Dialog 2

are, going to / look around / how to find / on my phone / Try to remember / what, mean by / important, special / try to, that

Communicate: Listen - Listen More

look delicious / Would, like / thanks, nervous / Why, so / audition for, in half / What, mean / Good luck, expression, Save, for

Communicate: Listen - All Ears

in half an hour / busy schedule

Communicate: Speak 2

Would you like / thanks, vegetables / how about, please

My Writing Portfolio - Step 1

name, app / Sounds / focuses on, to see / information, famous / find out, opening, admission / how to get / download, right now / sure, like

Wrap Up - Listening ❺

Would, like / What kind of / egg sandwich / No, thanks, don't / would you like / my favorite fruit

Wrap Up - Listening ❻

Hurry up / what, mean by / it's, start moving / time to go / Let's hit

Communicate: Listen - Listen and Answer Dialog 1

B: It smells nice. What are you cooking, Uncle Abbas?

M: I'm making kebab.

B: Kebab? What is it?

M: It's a traditional Turkish food. We have small pieces of meat and vegetables on a stick.

B: Oh, it sounds delicious.

M: Would you like some?

B: Sure. I'd love some.

M: Here you are.

B: It tastes great. You should open your own restaurant!

M: Thanks. I'm glad you like it.

Communicate: Listen - Listen and Answer Dialog 2

W: What are you going to do today, Kevin?

B: I'm going to look around the city.

W: Do you know how to find your way?

B: Sure. I have a map on my phone!

W: Okay. Try to remember landmarks, too.

B: I'm sorry, but what do you mean by "landmarks"?

W: I mean important places or special buildings.

B: All right. I will try to remember the places that I see.

Communicate: Listen - Listen More

G: Hey, Jongha!

B: Hi, Claire. Those cookies look delicious.

G: Would you like some?

B: No, thanks. I'm too nervous.

G: Why are you so nervous?

B: I have my audition for the school radio station in half an hour.

G: Oh, really? Break a leg!

B: Break a leg? What do you mean?

G: I mean "Good luck."

B: That's a funny expression. Thanks! Save some cookies for me, okay?

Communicate: Listen - All Ears

M: 1 The train will leave in half an hour.

    2 I have a busy schedule this week.

Communicate: Speak 2

A: Would you like some bibimbap

B: No, thanks. I don't like vegetables.

A: Then how about pizza?

B: Yes, please.

My Writing Portfolio - Step 1

G: Look. The name of our app is Enjoy Paris !

B: Enjoy Paris ? Sounds interesting!

G: This app focuses on what to see in Paris.

B: Does it give information on famous museums and theaters?

G: Yes. You can find out about opening hours and admission fees.

B: Fantastic.

G: It also tells you how to get there.

B: Oh, I'll download it right now!

G: I'm sure you'll like it.

Wrap Up - Listening ❺

B: Would you like some sandwiches?

G: What kind of sandwich?

B: Ham and egg sandwich.

G: No, thanks. I don't eat eggs.

B: Then, would you like some apple pie?

G: Okay. Apples are my favorite fruit.

Wrap Up - Listening ❻

G: Hurry up, everyone. Hit the road!

B: I'm sorry, but what do you mean by that?

G: I mean it's time to start moving.

B: Like, "It's time to go"?

G: Yes.

B: Great! Let's hit the road.

본문 TEST Step 1 · p.28~29

01 family, in 02 are visiting, his

03 going, wants, behind

04 thinks, on, communicate 05 stomach, so

06 When, sees, says

07 not, how, respond

08 Would, piece, glass

09 answers, please

10 knock, whom, walks

11 women begin, fast

12 translator, understand 13 off, leaves on

14 out to, sunny 15 thumping, who, against

16 turns, says 17 in, so, what

18 repeats, that, said 19 kicks, to

20 needs no, that

21 while, with, ball

22 Finally, at herself 23 My, responds

24 Suddenly, says

25 understands, sound like 26 Sure, appears

27 in, shout from 28 As, onto, luck

29 does, understand 30 thinks, says

---

31 to, that, holding

32 shouts, fortuna 33 sounds like

34 he shouts 35 her, back 36 rolls away

37 goes back 38 into, more, teach

39 says, laughs

본문 TEST Step 2 · p.30~31

01 family, in, Italy 02 are visiting, his mother's

03 are going to, stay behind

04 translation, on, help, communicate

05 growls, so, enters

06 When, sees, says 07 how to respond

08 Would, like, a lot of 09 answers, please

10 knock on, whom, walks in

11 women, speaking, fast

12 translator, understand.

13 turns off, leaves, on 14 goes out to enjoy

15 follows, thumping, who is kicking, against

16 turns to, says 17 so, what to say

18 repeats, that 19 kicks, to him

20 needs, translator

21 For a while, with 22 points at herself

23 My name responds 24 Suddenly, says

25 understands, sound like

26 enough, appears 27 in, shout from

28 As, steps onto

29 does not understand

30 So, thinks, says

31 points to , is holding 32 shouts

33 sounds like 34 shouts 35 shout back

36 rolls away 37 goes back to

38 says into, Learning, more, teach me some Italian

39 says, laughs

본문 TEST Step 3 · p.32~33

1 Jaden의 가족은 이탈리아 플로렌스에 있다.

2 그들은 그의 어머니의 친구인 Gambini 씨를 방문하고 있다.

3 오늘 그의 부모님은 박물관에 갈 예정이지만, Jaden은 집에 남고 싶어 한다.

4 그는 자신의 전화기에 있는 번역 앱이 의사소통을 하는 데 도움이 될 것이라고 생각한다.

5 그는 배가 꼬르륵거려서 부엌으로 들어간다.

6 Jaden은 어떻게 대답해야 할지 모른다.

7 그러자 앱이 "좋은 아침입니다. 빵 한 개와 우유 한 잔 드시겠어요?"

라고 말한다.

8 문을 두드리는 소리가 들리고 Gambini 씨가 초대한 한 여자가 안으로 들어온다.

9 두 여자는 아주 빨리 이탈리아어를 말하기 시작한다.

10 그래서 번역 앱은 이해하지 못한다.

11 Jaden은 전화기를 끄고 그것을 탁자 위에 둔다.

12 그는 화창한 아침을 즐기기 위해 밖으로 나간다.

13 그는 쿵쾅거리는 소리를 따라가다 벽에 축구공을 차고 있는 소녀를 발견한다.

14 그의 전화기는 부엌에 있어서 Jaden은 뭐라고 말해야 할지 모른다.

15 그는 단지 소녀가 말한 말들인 "Buon giorno"를 반복한다.

16 소녀는 그에게 공을 찬다. Jaden은 그것 때문에 번역 앱이 필요하지 않다.

17 잠시 동안, 두 사람은 공을 가지고 논다.

18 마침내, 그 소녀는 자신을 가리키며 "Mi chiamo Rosabella."라고 말한다.

19 "내 이름은 Jaden이야."라고 그가 대답한다.

20 Jaden은 '버스'와 '도착하다'라는 단어와 비슷한 소리가 나는 단어를 알아듣는다.

21 아니나 다를까, 버스 한 대가 나타난다.

22 축구 유니폼을 입은 아이들이 창문에서 "Ciao, Rosabella!" 라고 외친다

23 Rosabella가 버스에 오를 때, Jaden은 "행운을 빌어요." 라고 말한다. 그녀는 이해하지 못한다.

24 그는 그녀가 손에 들고 있는 축구공을 가리킨다.

25 Fortuna는 '행운'처럼 들린다.

26 Rosabella와 그녀의 친구들은 "Molte grazie!"라고 다시 외친다.

27 버스가 굴러간다

28 Jaden은 부엌으로 돌아간다.

29 그는 번역 앱에 말한다. "사람들에게서 배우는 것은 더 재미있습니다. 이탈리아어 좀 가르쳐 주실 수 있나요, Gambini 씨?"

30 Gambini 씨는 "Si,"라고 말하고는 웃는다

1 Jaden's family is in Florence, Italy.

2 They are visiting Ms. Gambini, his mother's friend.

3 Today his parents are going to museums, but Jaden wants to stay behind.

4 He thinks the translation app on his phone will help him communicate.

5 His stomach growls, so he enters the kitchen.

6 When Ms. Gambini sees Jaden, she says "Buon giorno. Vuoi un pezzo di pane e un bicchiere di latte?"

7 Jaden does not know how to respond.

8 Then the app says, "Good morning. Would you like a piece of bread and a glass of milk?"

9 Jaden answers, "Yes, please."

10 There is a knock on the door, and a woman whom Ms. Gambini invited walks in.

11 The two women begin speaking Italian very fast.

12 So the translator does not understand.

13 Jaden turns off the phone and leaves it on the table.

14 He goes out to enjoy the sunny morning.

15 He follows a thumping sound and finds a girl who is kicking a soccer ball against a wall.

16 She turns to him and says, "Buon giono."

17 His phone is in the kitchen, so Jaden does not know what to say.

18 He just repeats the words that the girl said, "Buon giorno."

19 The girl kicks the ball to him.

20 Jaden needs no translator for that.

21 For a while, the two play with the ball.

22 Finally, the girl points at herself and says, "Mi chiamo Rosabella."

23 "My name is Jaden," he responds.

24 Suddenly Rosabella says, "Arrive l'autobus."

25 Jaden understands the words that sound like bus and arrive.

26 Sure enough, a bus appears.

27 Kids in soccer uniforms shout from the windows, "Ciao, Rosabella!"

28 As Rosabella steps onto the bus, Jaden says, "Good luck."

29 She does not understand.

30 So Jaden thinks and says, "Buon, buon …."

31 He points to the soccer ball that she is holding in her hand.

32 Rosabella shouts, "Fortuna! Buona fortuna!"

33 Fortuna sounds like fortune.

34 "Buona fortuna!" he shouts.

35 Rosabella and her friends shout back, "Molte grazie!"

36 The bus rolls away.

37 Jaden goes back to the kitchen.

38 He says into the translation app, "Learning from people is more fun. Can you teach me some Italian, Ms.Gambini?"

39 Ms. Gambini says, "Si," and laughs.

My Speaking Portfolio - Step 1

1. Our Travel
2. of, app
3. focuses, to see
4. on, admission fees
5. how to get
6. usueful for

Wrap Up - Reading

1. meanings, cultures
2. For, means, right
3. something good
4. means, cultures
5. also, good
6. however, in
7. nothing, gesture
8. When, should, carefully

My Speaking Portfolio - Step 1

1. Our Travel App
2. The name of our app is Enjoy Paris.
3. It focuses on what to see in Paris.
4. It gives information on opening hours and admission fees of museums and theaters.
5. It also tells you how to get there.
6. Our app will be useful for travelers.

Wrap Up - Reading

1. Gestures can have different meanings in different cultures.
2. For example, the "OK sign" means "okay" or "all right" in many countries.
3. The gesture means something good.
4. It means "money" in some cultures.
5. That is also something good.
6. The same sign, however, means "0" in France.
7. It means there is nothing, so it is not a very happy gesture.
8. When we travel, we should use gestures carefully.

01 어려운
02 약속
03 공격하다, 공격
04 박테리아, 세균
05 세포
06 생물
07 다른
08 소화하다, 소화시키다
09 부러지다
10 운동하다
11 위험한
12 항체
13 방어하다
14 약
15 증식[번식]하다
16 방어
17 불가능한
18 침입하다
19 대식 세포
20 균형 잡힌, 안정된
21 위통, 복통
22 주요한, 중대한
23 피부
24 규칙적으로
25 긁다, 할퀴다
26 건강한
27 열
28 기억하다
29 세균, 미생물
30 마지막으로, 마침내
31 성공
32 끔찍한, 소름끼치는
33 다행이도
34 필요한
35 ~에 좋다
36 많은
37 ~와 같은
38 마침내, 드디어
39 A를 B로부터 보호하다
40 그런데
41 포기하다
42 며칠 후에
43 ~으로 유명하다

01 stomachache
02 attack
03 bacteria
04 actually
05 several
06 shot
07 skin
08 antibody
09 cell
10 creature
11 different
12 digest
13 exercise
14 dangerous
15 defend
16 finally
17 appointment
18 germ
19 impossible
20 invade
21 defense
22 fever
23 luckily
24 macrophage
25 balanced
26 break
27 major
28 necessary
29 regularly
30 medicine
31 virus
32 victim
33 multiply
34 scratch
35 success
36 at last
37 be famous for
38 be ready to
39 by the way
40 give up
41 plenty of
42 show up
43 watch out

1 successc, 성공
2 defend, 방어하다
3 appointment, 약속
4 major, 주요한, 중대한
5 bacteria, 박테리아, 세균
6 cell, 세포

7 multiply, 증식[번식]하다   8 shot, 주사

9 germ, 세균, 미생물   10 invade, 침입하다

11 balanced, 균형잡힌, 안정된   12 luckily, 다행히도

13 scratch, 긁다, 할퀴다   14 flu, 독감

15 victim, 피해자, 희생자   16 digest, 소화하다, 소화시키다

Communicate: Listen - Listen and Answer Dialog 1

Can, early, don't feel / seems to, problem / terrible stomachache, hurts / Why don't you, nurse's office / already, didn't help / can, Go see / Sure

Communicate: Listen - Listen and Answer Dialog 2

heard, sick, okay / went to, feel better / Good to, By the way, to talk / should meet, make it / Let's meet, at / early, sleep late / How about / sounds

Communicate: Listen - Listen More

wrong with / keeps scratching, lost / have the problem / About, ago / Let, see, has a virus, you some medicine / neet to, Can make, it / fine with / See you

Communicate: Listen - All Ears

make it / wrong with

Communicate: Speak 2 - Talk in pairs

What's, with / have, sore throat / too bad, should drink / I will

Communicate: Speak 2 - Talk in group

Let's play / why not / make it at / fine with, should, meet / Let's, meet / See, there

Wrap Up - Listening ❺

don't feel / seems to be / have a fever / Let me see, have a fever, get, medicine / Thank you

Wrap Up - Listening ❻

thinking of going, come with / want to go / Can, make / fine with / Let's meet at

Communicate: Listen - Listen and Answer Dialog 1

B: Can I go home early, Ms. Song? I don't feel so good.

W: What seems to be the problem?

B: I have a terrible stomachache. It really hurts.

W: Why don't you get some medicine at the nurse's office.

B: I already did. But it didn't help.

W: Okay. You can go. Go see a doctor, okay?

B: Sure. Thanks.

Communicate: Listen - Listen and Answer Dialog 2

B: Hello, Sora.

G: Hi, Jongha. I heard you were sick. Are you okay now?

B: Yes, I went to the doctor, and I feel better now.

G: Good to hear that. By the way, I called you to talk about our science project.

B: Yeah, we should meet. Can you make it tomorrow?

G: Okay. Let's meet at Simpson's Donuts at nine.

B: At nine? That's too early. I sleep late on the weekend.

G: How about 10 then?

B: That sounds fine.

Communicate: Listen - Listen More

M: Hi, Minsol. What's wrong with your dog?

G: She keeps scratching herself. Actually, she lost some hair.

M: When did she first have the problem?

G: About three days ago.

M: Let me see. (pause) She has a virus on her skin. I'll give you some medicine.

G: Thank you.

M: I need to check your dog again. Can you make it next Monday?

G: That's fine with me.

M: Okay. See you.

Communicate: Listen - All Ears

M: 1 Can you make it next Friday?

   2 What's wrong with your cat?

Communicate: Speak 2 - Talk in pairs

A: What's wrong with you?

B: I have a sore throat.

A: That's too bad. You should drink some water.

B: Okay, I will.

Communicate: Speak 2 - Talk in group

A: Let's play basketball this Saturday.

B: Sure, why not?

A: Can you make it at ten?

B: That's fine with me. Where should we meet?

A: Let's meet at the school gym.

B: Okay. See you there.

Wrap Up - Listening ❺

B: Mom, I don't feel well.

W: What seems to be the problem?

B: I think I have a fever.

W: Really? Let me see. Umm, you do have a fever. I'll get you some medicine.

B: Thank you, Mom.

35

G: I'm thinking of going to the Comics Museum tomorrow. Will you come with me?
B: I really want to go.
G: Can you make it at 11?
B: That's fine with me.
G: Okay. Let's meet at the subway station.

본문 TEST Step 1   p.47~48

01 everywhere, it, with
02 are, kinds, bacteria
03 Bacteria, creatures   04 Some, good
05 can, digest, that   06 Others, make
07 that, inside, living   08 cause, such
09 enter, through, skin
10 happens, invade   11 multiply, body
12 becomes, zone   13 feel, weak
14 body, defense   15 sound alarm
16 arrive, germs with
17 macrophage, up, eat
18 Together, called, cells   19 goes, fight
20 In, few, feel   21 invader, copies, itself
22 smart, too   23 change, trick
24 several, protect, from
25 wash, with, warm
26 diet, keep, healthy
27 It, exercise, plenty   28 Finally, shots
29 defense, germs
30 follow, steps, victim   31 Make, copies
32 my, defend   33 was, meal   34 there, eat
35 Next, send   36 see, another   37 What can
38 ready, any   39 give up   40 make, sick

본문 TEST Step 2   p.49~50

01 everywhere, impossible to see
02 major kinds, bacteria, viruses   03 are, creatures
04 Some, good   05 help you digest
06 Others, make, sick
07 germs, inside, other living bodies
08 cause, such as
09 can enter, through, skin mouth
10 happens, invade   11 multiply, body
12 becomes, zone
13 feel, tired, weak

---

14 Luckily, army of defense   15 sound, alarm
16 to fight, germs, antibodies
17 macrophage, show up
18 white blood cells   19 goes well, win
20 few days, feel better
21 invader, cannot make, copies
22 But, smart, too   23 change form
24 several ways to protect
25 wash, with soap
26 keep, strong, healthy
27 important to exercise, plenty of
28 Finally, necessary shots
29 defense against
30 steps, be a victim
31 Make, copies of   32 job to defend
33 nice meal   34 more germs to eat
35 send in   36 for another fight
37 What, do   38 I'm ready to   39 give up
40 make you sick

본문 TEST Step 3   p.51~52

1 세균은 어디에나 있지만 눈으로 세균을 보는 것은 불가능하다.
2 세균에는 두 가지 주요한 종류가 있다: 박테리아와 바이러스이다.
3 박테리아는 매우 작은 생물이다.
4 어떤 것들은 좋다.
5 그것들은 당신이 먹는 음식을 소화하는 데 도움을 줄 수 있다.
6 다른 것들은 나쁘고 당신을 아프게 할 수 있다.
7 바이러스는 다른 살아있는 몸의 세포 안에서만 살 수 있는 세균이다.
8 그들은 독감과 같은 질병을 일으킨다.
9 '나쁜' 세균은 피부, 입, 코, 눈을 통해 몸에 들어갈 수 있다.
10 그들이 침입하면 어떻게 되는가?
11 세균은 몸속에서 증식한다.
12 당신의 몸은 전쟁 지역이 된다.
13 당신은 피곤하고 약해지기 시작한다.
14 다행히도, 당신의 몸은 방어 군대를 가지고 있다.
15 T세포가 경보를 발한다!
16 B세포는 항체로 세균과 싸우기 위해 도착한다.
17 대식 세포가 나타나서 세균을 먹는다.
18 이 군대는 함께 백혈구라고 부른다.
19 모든 것이 잘되면 싸움에서 이긴다.
20 며칠 후면 당신은 회복되기 시작한다.
21 몸은 침입자를 기억하므로 다시 복제할 수 없다.
22 하지만 세균들도 영리하다.
23 그들은 형태를 바꿀 수 있고 몸을 속일 수 있다.

24 세균으로부터 당신 자신을 보호하는 몇 가지 방법이 있다.

25 먼저 비누와 따뜻한 물로 손을 씻어라.

26 균형 잡힌 식단은 당신의 몸을 튼튼하고 건강하게 해줄 것이다.

27 규칙적으로 운동하고 충분한 잠을 자는 것도 중요하다.

28 마지막으로 필요한 주사를 맞아라.

29 그것들은 세균을 막는 최고의 방어이다.

30 만약 당신이 이 단계를 따른다면, 당신은 "나쁜" 세균의 희생자가 되지 않을 것이다.

31 나를 더 복제해 주세요.

32 몸을 지키는 게 내 일이야.

33 정말 맛있는 식사였어!

34 먹을 세균이 더 있니?

35 내년에는 내 사촌을 보낼게.

36 그때 그가 또 싸우려고 널 보게 될 거야!

37 나는 어떤 세균과도 싸울 준비가 되어 있어.

38 우리는 널 아프게 할 수 없어.

본문 TEST Step 4~Step 5 p.53~56

1 Germs are everywhere, but it is impossible to see them with your eyes.

2 There are two major kinds of germs: bacteria and viruses.

3 Bacteria are very small creatures.

4 Some are good.

5 They can help you digest the food that you eat.

6 Others are bad and can make you sick.

7 Viruses are germs that can only live inside the cells of other living bodies.

8 They cause diseases such as the flu.

9 "Bad" germs can enter your body through your skin, mouth, nose, and eyes.

10 What happens when they invade?

11 The germs multiply in the body.

12 Your body becomes a war zone.

13 You start to feel tired and weak.

14 Luckily, your body has an army of defense.

15 The T cells sound the alarm!

16 The B cells arrive to fight the germs with antibodies.

17 The macrophage cells show up and eat the germs.

18 Together, this army is called the white blood cells.

19 If all goes well, they win the fight.

20 In a few days, you start to feel better.

21 The body remembers the invader, so it cannot make copies of itself again.

22 But the germs are smart, too.

23 They can change form and trick the body.

24 There are several ways to protect yourself from germs.

25 First, wash your hands with soap and warm water.

26 A balanced diet will keep your body strong and healthy.

27 It is also important to exercise regularly and get plenty of sleep.

28 Finally, get the necessary shots.

29 They are the best defense against germs.

30 If you follow these steps, you will not be a victim of "bad" germs.

31 Make more copies of me.

32 It's my job to defend the body.

33 That was a nice meal!

34 Are there any more germs to eat?

35 Next year, I'll send in my cousin.

36 He'll see you then for another fight!

37 What can I do now?

38 I'm ready to fight any germs.

39 We give up.

40 We can't make you sick.

구석구석지문 TEST Step 1 p.57

My Speaking Portfolio - Step 1

1. Less, More
2. dangerous, play
3. to out
4. Healthy
5. Eating, good
6. important, enough

Around the World

1. Mexican painter
2. famous, unique
3. cartoonist, character
4. great, writer
5. spent, writing
6. director
7. inventor, created

Think and Write

1. use, to touch
2. touch
3. close, with, too

4. are, that

5. with, get into

6. what should

7. Wash, with

My Speaking Portfolio - Step 1

1. Sit Less, Move More

2. It is dangerous to play online games too much.

3. It is time to go out and exercise.

4. Stay Healthy

5. Eating too many snacks is not good for your health.

6. It is important to eat enough fruit and vegetables.

Around the World

1. Frida Kahlo was a Mexican painter[artist].

2. She is famous for her unique paintings.

3. Charles Schulz was a cartoonist who created the famous character Charlie Brown.

4. Park Gyeongri was a great Korean writer.

5. She spent 25 years writing Toji.

6. James Cameron is the director of the movie, Avatar .

7. Jang Yeongsil was a(n) inventor[scientist] who created water clocks.

Think and Write

1. Every day you use your hands to touch different things.

2. You touch your phone and computer.

3. You open and close doors with your hands, too.

4. There are germs on everything that you touch.

5. If you eat snacks with your hands, the germs on your hands can get into your body.

6. Then what should you do?

7. Wash your hands with soap!

MEMO

MEMO

적중100

영어 기출 문제집

정답 및 해설

천재 | 이재영